FIBER OPTICS HANDBOOK

An Introduction and Reference Guide to
Fiber Optic Technology and Measurement Techniques

3. Edition

Christian Hentschel

Hewlett-Packard GmbH
Boeblingen Instruments Division
Federal Republic of Germany

March 1989

TABLE OF CONTENTS

1. INTRODUCTION

HP's first FIBER OPTIC HANDBOOK was published in 1983. The second edition, 1988, was much more ambitious both in volume and quality. The present third edition only corrects errors of the second edition. The increased size pays tribute to the tremendous technical progress in fiber optics during the past six years, and also devotes more attention to thorough analysis. Part of the progress is that fiber optics research moved from optical **power** engineering to optical **wave** engineering: examples are coherent systems, DFB lasers, integrated optics and interferometric measurements.

The purpose of the book, however, is unchanged: basic information about fiber optic components and systems shall be given, and methods for evaluating their performance shall be discussed. Special emphasis is on first-order mathematical descriptions of both the components and the measurement techniques. The book cannot replace the literature on specific subjects. It should only be considered as a quick reference which lists and illustrates the most important characteristics. In this sense, the book is intended to help answering many questions in a comprehensive and easy-to-read way.

The book is divided into two parts. The first part has been substantially reduced in size. It now contains only an overview article on measurement techniques and a listing of HP's fiber optic measurement instruments. The "old" chapters on fiber characteristics, systems design and laser product safety have all been worked into the second part.

The second and main part is the the "Fiber Optic Reference Guide", which is subdivided into chapters in alphabetical order. Emphasis is not so much on an explanation of technical terms, but on a helping to understand the concept: what is it, how does it work, what are the typical characteristics and tradeoffs, why is it important ? In this sense, the technical terms have been connected to actual communication systems.

In 1983, there was still substantial interest on comparisons of fibers against other transmission media, in particular coaxial cables. Today, fiber optic transmission has been generally accepted, and it has become a major industrial factor. Therefore, we want to shorten this comparison into 3 sentences:
1. Fibers are lightweight and free from electromagnetic interference.
2. Fibers offer high security against intrusion.
3. Today, 1989, routinely available transmission capacity in fibers is 30 Gbit/s x km, versus 0.2 Gbit/s in coaxial cables. These numbers reflect the product of maximum bit rate and repeater spacing.

Especially due to the enormous transmission capacity, virtually all new longhaul-telecommunication systems around the world are realized in fiber technology. Today, fiber optics are also penetrating local-area (computer) networks. And in the new wave of Integrated Services Digital Network (ISDN), fiber optics will offer high-bandwidth data (including television channels) to the private subscriber. These perspectives have triggered an equally enormous research activity. Therefore, we hope that this book will find its way into many fiber optics laboratories around the world.

2. FIBER OPTIC MEASUREMENTS

Fiber optic measurement techniques basically address 2 major areas: the first area is **functional** testing; an example is the measurement of fiber continuity with the help of an optical time-domain reflectometer. The second area is **performance** testing, specifically performance in terms of transmission capacity. Examples for the latter are loss measurements, dispersion measurements and linewidth measurements.

This paragraph is intended to give you an overview over the most important measurements and measurement techniques. Like in many other technical fields, a measurement technique is as good as its international acknowledgment. Therefore, let us first review the major efforts in fiber-optic measurement standardization. Note that many of the published standards are listed in section [1] of the literature index.

A number of national and international organizations are involved in standardizing fiber optic measurements. In the United States, the Electronic Industries Association (EIA) is most active. The EIA's proposals were first published as Fiber Optic Test Procedures (FOTPs); now most of the FOTPs are part of the Recommended Standards RS 455. Although the EIA is a US organization only, it has certainly influenced the standardization efforts in many other countries.

Other important groups in the USA are the National Institute of Standards and Technology (NIST, formerly NBS) and the Department of Defense (DOD).

The International Electrotechnical Commission (**IEC**) tries to set worldwide standards. All major industrial countries, including those of the communist block, are members of the IEC. Major portions of the IEC's stardardization efforts have been published under the publication numbers 793-1 (Optical Fibers) and 874-1 (Connectors). The telephone companies' and post offices' requirements are independently standardized by the International Telegraph and Telephone Consultive Committee (**CCITT**). The CCITT has published their recommendations under the publication numbers G.651 (Multimode Fiber) and G.652 (Single-Mode Fiber).

Generally, measurement standardization did not keep up with the enormous progress in fiber optics. Careful analysis of the current literature on this subject is therefore recommended.

The measurement techniques in this article shall be segmented by the objects of the measurement: fibers, connectors, sources, detectors and systems. Please note that the description below is a summary only; specific details should be extracted from the **Reference Guide**. For a better orientation, arrows (→) indicate the appropriate chapter in the Reference Guide.

2.1 Fiber Measurements

Main Tests: **Multimode Fiber:**   **Single-Mode Fiber:**
Attenuation   Attenuation
Multimode Dispersion   Chromatic Dispersion
Chromatic Dispersion   Cutoff Wavelength
Numerical Aperture   Spot Size
Core Diameter

Multimode Fiber:

As can be expected, the most important fiber parameter is →**attenuation**. Attenuation testing of multimode fibers is complicated by the propagation of many →modes, each of which has its own propagation characteristic. Therefore, the fiber optic community decided that, for testing attenuation, the fiber should be excited with an →equilibrium mode distribution (EMD), which is the modal distribution after a long length of fiber. An optical source and a power meter are the basis for the measurement. A non-destructive measurement can be made by comparing the →insertion loss of a short reference fiber with the loss of the long test fiber. Care should be taken to accomplish the same coupling efficiency in both cases.

The analysis of the fiber's backscatter signal with an optical time-domain reflectometer will additionally provide information on the **uniformity** of the attenuation along the length of the fiber.

→**Multimode dispersion** is the technical term for pulse broadening (reduced bandwidth) due to the different velocities of different modes: the basic measurement concept is to excite the fiber with a short pulse, in which the modal distribution is the EMD, and to measure the pulse width at the end of a fiber. A narrow spectral width must be used for the measurement, such as the one from a laser diode (see below). →**Chromatic dispersion** is pulse broadening due to the different velocities of different colours contained in the spectrum of the source: the pulse broadening depends directly on the spectral width of the source. Chromatic dispersion is basically a material property; it also contributes to the reduction of the bandwidth of the multimode fiber. Chromatic dispersion cannot be measured directly: instead, multimode dispersion adds quadratically to the measurement result.

The →**numerical aperture** (NA) and the core diameter determine how much power can be launched into the multimode fiber. The NA defines the maximum angle of guided rays in the fiber: it is always measured at the output of the fiber (in the far field), because the maximum angle observed at the output is approximately equal to the maximum angle at the input. To do this, a short fiber is fully excited at the input, which means that all modes (rays) are excited. The **core diameter** is measured in the →near field of the fiber output. This means that the power density at the fiber end is observed with a microscope, again with a fully excited input.

Single-Mode Fiber:

If the measurement wavelength is longer than the cutoff wavelength (see below) of the single-mode fiber, then only one mode will propagate. With this condition, attenuation measurements of single-mode fibers are less complicated than those of multimode fibers. In order to maintain a constant input excitation of the fiber, the measurement should be done in 2 steps: first, the output power at the far end should be measured. Then the fiber is cut near the input end, the power is measured again. The difference in power levels, in units of optical dB, is the attenuation. This is the →cutback-method. OTDR analyis will again provide information on the uniformity of the attenuation, which could not be tested otherwise.

The bandwidth of single-mode fiber is only dependent on the →**chromatic dispersion**; multimode dispersion is negligible. The basic idea of a chromatic dispersion measurement is launching narrow pulses of different wavelengths (colours) into the fiber, and then to measure their different arrival times.

The →**cutoff-wavelength** of a single-mode fiber defines the lowest wavelength which should be used if high bandwidth is important. Below the cutoff-wavelength, more modes will propagate. The cutoff-wavelength is measured by launching a wide spectrum (e.g. from a tungsten lamp) into a short fiber. Then the attenuation of each spectral component is measured. The cutoff-wavelength will be visible as a discontinuity of the attenuation curve: the existence of more →modes allows more of the excited power to reach the end of the fiber. Another measurement method is based on the observation that higher-order modes are much more sensitive to fiber bending than the fundamental →mode.

More important than the core diameter of a single-mode fiber is its →**spot size**. The reason is that the fundamental mode of the single-mode fiber can be approximated by a →Gaussian beam, both inside and outside the fiber. The Gaussian beam is fully defined by only 2 numbers: the spot radius and the wavelength. The radiation characteristics (i.e. the far field) of the end of a fiber can directly be calculated from these numbers. Other important characteristics of the single-mode fiber, e.g. the waveguide dispersion, can also be deduced from the spot radius.

2.2 Connector Measurements

Main Tests: Insertion Loss
                         Repeatibility
                         Return Loss

Optical →connectors can considerably degrade the performance of transmission systems and of fiber-optic measurements. The →**insertion loss** is the most important characteristic of the joint of 2 connectors. The measurement setup consists of an LED source, 2 short fibers with the 2 connectors under test, and a power meter. The first step is the measurement of optical power which is radiated from the end of the first cable and the first connector. Then the connection is made, and the power at the end of the second cable is measured. The difference between the 2 measured powers (in units of optical dB) is the insertion loss. In the case of multimode connectors, the test result should record the type of excitation, be it fully-excited or equilibrium. In the case of single-mode connectors, the propagation of only the fundamental mode must be verified.

In measurement-type applications, the **repeatibility** of the insertion loss is particularly important. It can be tested by repetitively joining the connectors and measuring the insertion loss each time.

The →**return loss** of single-mode connectors has gained substantial interest. The reason is the laser's sensitivity to →backreflection, which causes additional noise and changes of the emitted spectrum. Another reason is that marginal return loss is always accompanied by interference in the connector pair; this causes non-reproducibity in measurement applications. The return loss is defined as the ratio of the incident optical power to the reflected optical power, in units of optical dB. It can be measured with a high-resolution OTDR. A less expensive measurement is based on a laser source and a power meter, by splitting the reflection from the connector pair under test with the help of a fiber →coupler.

2.3 Source Measurements

Main Tests:	LEDs:	Laser Diodes:
	Output Power	Output Power
	Modulation Bandwidth	Modulation Bandwidth
	Center Wavelength	Center Wavelength, Number of Modes
	Spectral Width	Chirp, Linewidth
	Source Size	Mode Field of the Gaussian beam
	Far-Field Pattern	

Light-Emitting Diodes (LEDs):

LEDs exhibit a nearly linear dependence of the **output power** on the drive current. The power from the usual pigtail can be measured with a power meter. The actual measurement curve yields the conversion gain and the non-linearity. Because of the wide spectral width of the emitted radiation, the accuracy of the measurement depends on the wavelength-dependence of the power meter's detector, on the details of the spectrum and on how well these factors are taken into consideration.

In the measurement of the **modulation bandwidth**, the LED is intensity-modulated with a sweeper-generator and a PIN diode is used to reconvert the modulated optical signal back to the electrical domain. An oscilloscope will display the frequency response. More elegant is a network analyzer with an optical-to-electrical conversion before the receiver section.

The **center wavelength** and the **spectral width** can both be measured with an optical spectrum analyzer. This measurement is important because its result will influence the pulse broadening on the fiber.

The **size** of the radiating area and the emitted →**far field** should be measured directly at the LED chip, i.e. without the fiber. The size can be measured by analyzing its microscopic image (near field), whereas the measurement of the angular power-distribution in some distance from the source will yield the far-field. Narrow near- and far-fields are desirable for a good →coupling efficiency to the fiber.

Laser Diodes (LDs):

The dependence of the output **power** on the driving current can be measured with a variable current source and a power meter. The threshold current is the current which defines the onset of the stimulated emission, i.e. the desired lasing function. Another important measurement result is the conversion gain, in units of watt/ampere. More advisable than DC-excitation of the LD may be pulse excitation, because of the elevated temperature of the chip during the DC drive.

The modulation **bandwidth** of LDs can be measured in the same way as described above for LEDs. The main difference is the much higher bandwidth of LDs, which requires measurement equipment with higher bandwidth.

The center **wavelength** and the number of **modes** should both be measured with an optical spectrum analyzer. These measurements will usually be sufficient for the use of LDs in (conventional) intensity-modulated, direct-detection systems. The measurement of the →**chirp**, i.e. the undesired wavelength shift caused by intensity modulation, may be important for highest performance in direct-detection. For →coherent applications, laser diodes which emit a single wavelength (longitudinal mode) are required. In this case, the measurement of the spectral →**linewidth** is most important. Interferometric methods are capable of measuring both the chirp and the linewidth; see the reference guide and start with the chapter →optical spectrum analysis.

The radiation characteristics of a laser diodes can be approximated by an elliptic version of the →Gaussian beam. The elliticity is due to the fact that the emitting area is a long stripe, instead of the ideal circle. A **far field** measurement, i.e. the analysis of the power density at some distance from the radiating area, will deliver the parameters of the Gaussian beam. These parameters will then allow the computation of the →coupling efficiency, especially the coupling efficiency to single-mode fiber.

2.4 Detector Measurements

Main Tests:	PIN-Detectors:	APD-Detectors:
	Diameter	Diameter
	Spectral Responsivity	Spectral Responsivity
		Multiplication Factor
	Bandwidth	Bandwidth
	Dark Current, NEP	Dark Current, NEP, Excess Noise

Optical detectors are made for two purposes: signal detection in receivers and optical power measurement. In the first case, the smallest possible **diameter** is desirable, because the noise-equivalent power (NEP) is proportional to the active diameter and the bandwidth is inversely proportional to the active area. In the power-measurement case, a large area is desirable because of the achievable measurement accuracy.

The **responsivity** of a photodetector is the ratio of the generated current to the incident optical power. The responsivity of →PIN-diodes and avalanche photodiodes (APDs) is strongly dependent on the wavelength: a constant quantum efficiency (generated electrons per photon) would ideally result in a responsivity which is proportional to the wavelength. The actual responsivity may be quite different. The measurement is normally made with a wavelength-calibrated combination of a tungsten-lamp and a (tunable) monochromator. In →APDs, the application of a high voltage leads to a multiplication of the number of generated carriers; the **multiplication factor** can also be measured with the above method.

The (demodulation-) **bandwidth** of a photodetector can be tested by exciting it with a sinewave-modulated laser source. A network analyzer, this time with an electrical-to-optical conversion of the generator signal, is most elegant. More difficult is the measurement of detectors with bandwidths of several gigahertz, because of the limited modulation bandwidths of laser diodes. One possible solution is external modulation of the LD with a →modulator. Also possible is mixing the beams of 2 narrow-linewidth →laser diodes with the help of the non-linear electric field - to - current conversion of the detector under test. In this case, the frequency of the generated photocurrent is the difference between the 2 optical frequencies involved; see the chapter on →coherent detection.

A very important characteristic of a photodetector is its →noise-equivalent power (**NEP**), because of its influence on the achievable sensitivity of the receiver. Ideally, the NEP is proportional to the square root of the **dark current**: this allows an estimation of the NEP. More accurate is a measurement with an (electrical) spectrum analyzer, in order to characterize the spectral density of the NEP. In →APDs, the **excess noise** factor is an additional noise contribution which is caused by the multiplication process. It can be measured with the same spectrum analyzer.

2.5 System Measurements

Main Tests: Fiber Continuity (OTDR)
                         Bit Error Rate
                         Sensitivity
                         Eye Pattern

Engineers who are responsible for the proper function of a fiber-based communication →system are rarely interested in device characteristics. Their main concern is functionality. In this field, the optical time-domain reflectometer is an important tool, because it is capable of detecting the fact and the location of an interruption of the cable.

The second important information on the function of a system is the →bit error rate (**BER**), which is defined as the number of (received) false bits divided by the total number of transmitted bits. A typical requirement is a BER of 10^{-9}; any larger number will indicate a degradation of the system. The BER can be tested by modulating the source with a well-defined long bit-sequence (pseudo-random bit sequence, PRBS) and comparing the received sequence with the transmitted one.

More detailed measurements are made during the design and installation of the system. The →**sensitivity** is the lowest power level that leads to the desired BER. It can also be tested with a BER tester; in this case, an optical →attenuator will be used to reduce the transmitted power level until the error rate exceeds the predefined value. Even more specific is the measurement of the →**eye diagram**. To do this, the transmitter is modulated with a PRBS sequence and the received (analog) signal is displayed on a storage-type oscilloscope, using the system's clock to trigger the oscilloscope. This way, many different bit traces appear on the screen, which allows an approximate quantization of the jitter, the signal-to-noise ratio and the intersymbol interference.

3. HP'S FIBER OPTIC INSTRUMENTS

For details of HP's complete range of fiber optic instruments, please refer to the 1994 Lightwave Test and Measurement Catalog, publication number 5962-6832E.

4. FIBER OPTICS REFERENCE GUIDE

Note that all terms refer to **optical** fiber systems and measurements. They may be used differently in other disciplines. Often, the word "optical" is omitted.

Whenever an arrow (→) appears in the text, it refers the reader to another key word of the reference guide.

Acceptance Angle

In conjunction with an optical fiber, the acceptance angle defines the largest angle of a guided ray in the fiber. See →numerical aperture.

Accessible Emission Limits (AEL)

This term is used in order to specify the maximum emission of the various laser product classes. See →safety (laser products-).

Acousto-Optic Modulator

Acousto-Optic (AO-) Modulators are popular devices because of 3 capabilities:
a) Switching between 2 beam directions,
b) Intensity modulation of an optical beam,
c) Frequency-shifting of the optical frequency.

An AO-modulator is based on a transparent crystal with a refractive index which is dependent on external pressure. TeO_2 (tellurium dioxide), $LiNbO_3$ (lithium niobate) and $PbMoO_4$ (lead molybdate) are such materials. In the practical use of the modulator, the pressure is generated by acoustic waves from a piezoelectric transducer. The sound waves form a set of horizontally oriented lines of equal refractive index (a Bragg-diffraction grating), which is moving at the acoustic velocity v_{ac}. The grating is capable of partially reflecting an incoming beam.

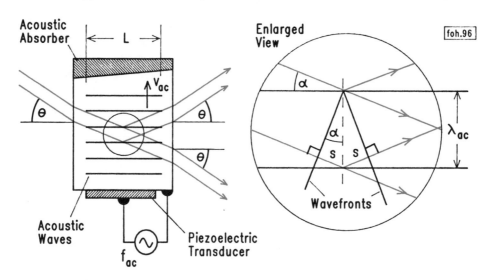

ACOUSTO-OPTIC MODULATOR

Input and output beams form the same angle Θ with the normal to the surface. However, only certain angles (the Bragg angles) will form a new beam direction: constructive interference of all partial waves is obtained when the length 2s is a multiple of one optical wavelength in the material:

$$2s = 2 \lambda_{ac} \sin \alpha \overset{!}{=} \frac{m\lambda}{n}$$

with $\qquad \lambda_{ac} = \dfrac{v_{ac}}{f_{ac}}$

λ_{ac} - acoustic wavelength
v_{ac} - acoustic velocity (3630 m/s for PbMoO$_4$, 4260 m/s for TeO$_2$)
f_{ac} - frequency of the acoustic wave = generator frequency, typically 80 MHz
α - Bragg angle inside the crystal
m - order of the refracted ray
λ - optical wavelength in air
n - refractive index of the crystal (2.38 for PbMoO$_4$, 2.26 for TeO$_2$)

Most interesting is the **first-order Bragg-angle** Θ (outside the crystal). It can be calculated from the above equations with the help of Snell's law (see →reflection and refraction) applied to the interface between the crystal and air:

$$\sin \Theta = n \sin \alpha$$

$$\sin \Theta = \frac{\lambda f_{ac}}{2 v_{ac}}$$

Note that the refractive index n is eliminated. With the fixed acoustic velocity, the Bragg-angle turns out to be dependent on the drive frequency and the optical wavelength only. Typical Bragg angles are on the order of 1°, so that horizontal spacing is required in order to separate the beams.

Typically, a **deflection efficiency** η of 80 % is achieved, with a $\sin^2$ - dependence on the electric drive power:

$$\eta = \frac{P_1}{P_0} = \sin^2 \frac{K}{\lambda} P_{RF}$$

η - deflection efficiency
P_1 - optical power in the deflected beam
P_0 - optical power in the non-deflected beam with no drive power
K - device-typical constant
λ - optical wavelength in air
P_{RF} - electric drive power

Typical drive powers for an η = 80 % are on the order of hundreds of milliwatt. For an intensity modulation of the deflected beam, the RF-power must be amplitude-modulated. Switching is obtained from switching the RF source on and off.

The optical frequency of the deflected beam is higher or lower than the frequency of the input beam:

$$f_{out} = f_{in} \pm f_{ac}$$

The cause is the moving grating. This creates a Doppler-shift of the optical frequency, similar to the Doppler-shift of sound waves. If the beam is directed **against** the direction of acoustic propagation, then the output frequency is **higher** than the input frequency (and vice-versa).

Activation Energy

This parameter is a measure of the reliability of a semiconductor component, e.g. a laser diode. See →reliability.

Antireflection (AR) Coating

An air-to-glass transition at normal (vertical) incidence causes 4% of the incident optical power to be reflected, be it internal or external →reflection. To avoid this, the glass can be coated with a quarter-wavelength optical layer, predominantly Magnesium Fluoride (MgF_2). This material has a refractive index of 1.38 at 550 nm and is quite durable. This way a total reflection of about 1.5% is achieved. For oblique incidence, the thickness of the layer can be specifically adjusted. The coating effect is wavelength-dependent, because the quarter-wavelength condition holds for one colour only. Multilayer coatings are used to reduce the wavelength dependence **and** the reflection.

To understand quarter-wavelength AR coating, the transmission-line concept can be applied (see →**reflection** and refraction).

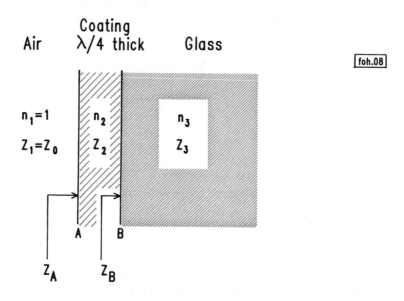

THE EFFECT OF AR-COATING

The three materials in the figure are characterized by their refractive indices n_1, n_2, n_3 and the correspondent →characteristic impedances Z_1, Z_2, Z_3. The glass has a characteristic impedance

$$Z_3 = Z_0 / n_3$$

Z_0 - characteristic impedance of air (377 Ω)

The wave propagating in the coating layer is partially reflected at the B-boundary. This way, the impedance $Z_B = Z_3$ is transformed (via $\lambda/4$-line transformation) into the impedance Z_A at the A-boundary. The following formula was taken from transmission-line theory:

$$Z_A = Z_2 \frac{Z_B + jZ_2 \tan 2\pi L/\lambda}{Z_2 + jZ_B \tan 2\pi L/\lambda}$$

L is the thickness of the coating. Setting $L = \lambda/4$ results in:

$$Z_A = Z_2^2/Z_B = Z_0\, n_3/n_2^2$$

Impedance matching at the coating-to-air boundary means $Z_A = Z_0$, which requires the coating index to be $n_2 = \sqrt{n_3}$. For glass with $n_3 = 1.5$, the ideal coating index would be $n_2 = 1.22$.

APD

Due to their inherent gain, APDs have higher effective responsivities than PIN-diodes, which makes them very attractive for communication receivers. The function of an APD is similar to that of a →PIN-diode, in which incident photons are absorbed and converted to electron-hole pairs. The main difference is operation near reverse breakdown, which causes carrier multiplication.

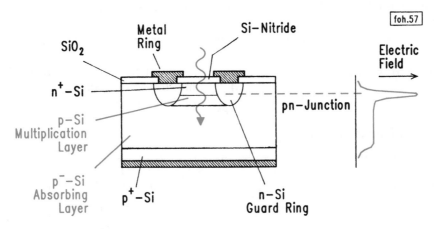

SHORT-WAVELENGTH SILICON APD

In a silicon APD, the sequence of layers is typically $n^+ p\, p^-\, p^+$. The highly doped n^+ and p^+ layers are the contact layers, and the nearly intrinsic p^- zone forms the absorbing layer. The peak of the electric field is observed near the n^+/p junction. This defines the multiplication zone. Guard rings prevent lateral breakthrough. The top layer of silicon-nitride (Si_3N_4) serves as passivation and antireflection coating.

Indium-Gallium-Arsenide (InGaAs) APDs [5.2] usually employ the double-heterostructure, in which the absorption takes place only in the layer with the lowest bandgap, i.e. the InGaAs layer. The enclosing Indium-Phosphide (InP) layers have higher bandgaps and therefore appear transparent to the incident photons. An intermediate-bandgap layer (InGaAsP) provides quick removal of positive carriers (holes) and therefore increases the bandwidth. Again, guard rings stop lateral breakthrough. This structure has been termed **SAM**, for "separate absorption and multiplication".

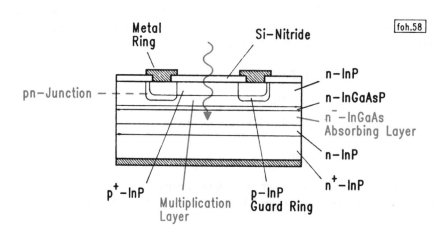

LONG-WAVELENGTH InGaAs APD

Let us assume a photon enters the p⁻ zone from the top (or the bottom) of the diode. There, the photon's energy is absorbed and an electron-hole pair is created, by raising an electron from the low-energy valence band to the higher-energy conduction band. The electron drifts towards the positively charged ring contact. When it reaches the strong electric field zone near the pn-junction, additional electron-hole pairs are generated by impact ionization. An avalanche process is initiated, the result of which is carrier multiplication.

Each of the electrons statistically generates M new electrons. The total photocurrent is

$$I = r \, M \, P_{opt} , \quad \text{with:}$$

r	→ responsivity, $r = 0.8 \, \eta \, \lambda/\mu m$ [A/W]
M	- multiplication factor
P_{opt}	- optical power

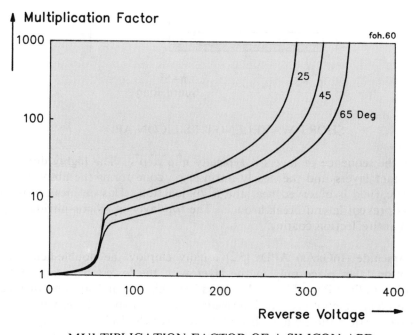

MULTIPLICATION FACTOR OF A SILICON APD

Data sheets either give r x M directly in [A/W], or r and M, or quantum efficiency η and M. Near the breakdown voltage, M(V) can be expressed by:

$$M(V) = \frac{1}{1 - (V/V_{br})^n}$$

V — applied reverse voltage
V_{br} — breakdown voltage
n — device-typical exponent, n < 1

Because of the strong dependence of M on the applied voltage, it is difficult to achieve a stable gain. In addition, M decreases with temperature. A typical compromise between gain and stability is a bias voltage of 0.95 x breakdown voltage. Even then, temperature and voltage stabilization is essential.

Another problem is **non-linearity** due to voltage drop across the load resistor, together with the steep M(V) curves. A second non-linear effect is observed even with a zero load resistor: beyond a certain photocurrent the multiplication factor drops as the current increases. This is caused by local heating of the junction.

Current is also generated with no light present. The usual **dark current** of a PIN-diode appears multiplied with M. Additional surface (leakage) currents are caused by the high bias voltage. These currents give rise to additional noise and limit the lowest detection level; see →noise (photodiode-).

APD	Bias Voltage	Multiplication Factor M	Reverse Current	Maximum attainable M
Silicon	300 V	100	1-10 nA	100
Germanium	30 V	20	1 μA	40
InGaAs	80 V	15	100 nA	40

TYPICAL CHARACTERISTICS OF APDs
(operating point: 0.95 x breakdown voltage, reverse currents scaled to 0.1 mm active diameter)

The **wavelength dependence** of APDs corresponds to the one observed in simple →PIN-diodes. Therefore, silicon APDs are the proper choice for all wavelength below 900 nm. Germanium or InGaAs APDs should be used at 1300 and 1550 nm. Because of the lower dark current, InGaAs APDs offer much better noise performance than germanium APDs.

Typical 3-dB **bandwidths** go up to 1 GHz. Very often, APD bandwidths are specified in terms of the gain-bandwidth product, i.e. the frequency at which M drops to unity. Of course, the gain-bandwidth product can reach many gigahertz.

Also see →noise (photodiode-).

Astigmatism

This term is normally used to describe a lens error: an object point at some distance away from the optical axis cannot be imaged to another small point if the lens shows astigmatism. Instead, the image consists of two short lines, which are perpendicular to each other and separated by a longitudinal distance: the **astigmatic distance**. In between the two lines there is a blurred spot called the circle of least confusion.

A similar phenomenon can be observed when imaging a laser facet through the optical axis of a perfect lens: when changing the distance between laser facet and lens, the image varies from an ellipse parallel to the junction to one perpendicular to it. The object distance between the two ellipses has also been called astigmatism.

Typically double-heterostructure lasers have astigmatisms between 0 and 40 µm. The astigmatism constitutes a basic problem of imaging a laser facet to a fiber core: it causes two separate focus ellipses along the fiber axis, none of which will transfer all the light power. Cylindrical lenses can be used to solve this problem.

Attenuation (Fiber-)

The attenuation of optical power in a silica fiber is caused by these three effects: Raleigh scattering, absorption, and bending. The attenuation of the modulation **amplitude** at high modulation frequencies should be considered as part of the bandwidth characteristics of the fiber; see →bandwidth (fiber-), →multimode dispersion, →chromatic dispersion.

Raleigh scattering is caused by the microscopic non-uniformity of the refractive index of glass. A ray of light is partially scattered into many directions, thus some light energy is lost. An important precondition for this phenomenon is that the structure of the glass is not much finer than the wavelengths of interest. Therefore, the attenuation coefficient α decreases as the wavelength increases: α is proportional to $1/\lambda^4$. Raleigh scattering represents by far the strongest attenuation mechanism in modern silica fibers; it may be responsible for 90 % of the total attenuation.

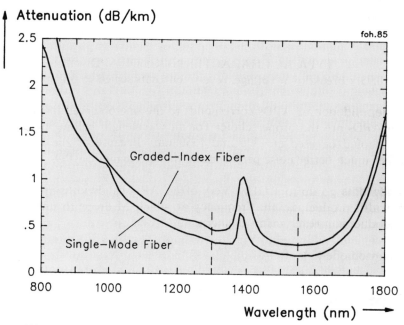

WAVELENGTH DEPENDENCE OF FIBER ATTENUATION

Absorption is caused on unwanted material in the fiber. Water (OH-ions) is the dominant absorber in most fibers, causing the peaks in optical loss at 1.25 and 1.39 μm. Modern manufacturing methods are capable of reducing these effects to almost zero. Above 1.7 μm, glass starts absorbing light energy due to the molecular resonance of SiO_2. The attenuation curve clearly shows why communication link designers prefer the 1.3 μm and the 1.55 μm wavelengths.

The third effect is bending. Two types can be distinguished: **microbending** is due to microscopic imperfections in the geometry of the fiber (rotational asymmetry, changes of the core diameter, "rough" boundaries between core and cladding) caused by either the manufacturing process or by mechanical stress, such as pressure, tension and twist.

Fiber curvatures with diameters on the order of centimeters are called **macrobending**. In this case, the loss of optical power is due to less-than-total reflection at the core-to-cladding boundary. In a single mode fiber, the fundamental mode is partially converted to a radiating mode. Because of the increase of spot diameter with wavelength, single mode →fibers are much more sensitive to bending at longer wavelengths. See the diagram in the chapter →cutoff-wavelength. Bending loss is usually unnoticeable if the diameter of the bend is larger than 10 cm.

An interesting application of the fiber's sensitivity to bending is a non-reflecting termination of the fiber: with one or two knots of 1 cm diameter, the usual reflection of 4 % (-14 dB_{opt}) can be reduced to less than -40 dB_{opt}.

Attenuation causes an exponential decay of the optical power along the fiber:

$$P(x) = P_0 \exp(-\alpha' z)$$

$P(z)$ - optical power at distance z from input
P_0 - optical power at fiber input
α' - attenuation coefficient, [1/km]

Engineers are used to thinking in dB; therefore, the equation may be rewritten (using $\alpha = 4.35$ α', from conversion of base e to base 10):

$$P(z) = P_0 \cdot 10^{-\alpha z/10\,dB}$$

$$\log P(z) = -\alpha z/10dB + \log P_0 \qquad [\,dB_{optical}\,]$$

$$\alpha = \alpha_{scattering} + \alpha_{absorption} + \alpha_{bending}$$

α - attenuation coefficient, [dB/km]

Two methods are commonly used to perform attenuation measurements. The **cutback method** is the most accurate. After measuring the power at the far end, the fiber is cut near the input end without changing the launching conditions. The only problem of this method is its destructive nature. The **substitution method** is non-destructive: the attenuation of a short reference fiber is compared with the attenuation of the fiber under test (DUT). In the latter case, the coupling losses of the DUT and the reference fiber may be different, and a measurement uncertainty is the result.

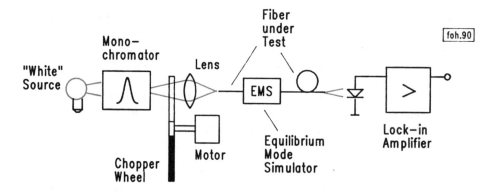

SPECTRAL ATTENUATION MEASUREMENT

Different modes are differently attenuated in a fiber. This effect is called **differential mode attenuation**.

In **multimode** fibers, a large number of modes is always present. "Differential mode attenuation" describes the different attenuation characteristics of different modes. However, a mode-selective measurements is difficult to perform. To achieve interlab reproducibility of attenuation measurements, an →equilibrium mode distribution should be generated at the fiber input. Measurement variations of 1 dB/km on the same fiber have been found where no great effort was made to control this parameter.

In **single-mode** fibers, one should take care that only the fundamental mode propagates. Therefore, the measurement wavelength should be larger than the →cutoff-wavelength. At a smaller-than-cutoff wavelength, higher-order modes also propagate. These modes have much stronger attenuation, which will result in length-dependent attenuation numbers.

In a reflective measurement, the →backscattering mechanism also delivers fiber attenuation numbers. In this case, only one input of the fiber must be accessible. However, attenuation numbers obtained from backscattering measurements are not identical with those obtained by two-port measurements. See →optical time domain reflectometer.

Fiber Type	Attenuation at 850 nm	Attenuation at 1300 nm	Attenuation at 1550 nm
Step-Index	5 - 12 dB/km	/	/
Graded-Index	3 - 5 dB/km	0.5 - 0.7 dB/km	/
Single-Mode	/	0.4 - 0.6 dB/km	0.2 - 0.3 dB/km

TYPICAL ATTENUATION NUMBERS OF MODERN FIBERS

Attenuator

A number of optical measurements can only be made if variable optical power is available. →Bit error rate (BER) testing is one of the important examples. Controlling the output power of LEDs and laser diodes by changing the drive current does not offer a wide dynamic range wavelength. Therefore, many passive optical attenuators have been proposed; some of their principles are listed below. Performance criteria of variable attenuators are: attenuation range, low insertion loss, freedom of interference and reflections, independence of polarization and wavelength. For the application in multimode systems, the attenuation should be mode-independent. Otherwise additional →modal noise is the result.

A continously variable attenuator can be made from a **grey scale**. In Hewlett Packard's HP 8158B and HP 8157A attenuators, the grey scale is realized by depositing a metallic film of variable thickness on a circular glass disk. The disk is inserted into a →collimated beam, and it can be rotated with a motor. Also based on rotation, an attenuator can be made from two →polarizers. Attenuators based on the dependence of →reflection on the angle of beam incidence have also been proposed.

More attractive is a non-mechanical control of the attenuation. For example, **liquid crystals** rotate the polarization of light depending on the drive voltage applied. By placing the liquid crystal between two polarizers, electronically variable attenuation is possible. Rotation of polarization can also be done magnetically by the →Faraday effect.

Another solution is electrically induced →birefringence, e.g. in lithium-niobate. Generally, changing the state of polarization in conjunction with →polarizers can always be utilized to produce variable attenuation; see the chapter →modulator.

Avalanche Photodiode (APD)

A photodiode in which carrier multiplication is caused by a strong electric field. See →APD.

Backreflection-Sensitivity

Laser diodes are sensitive to optical power reflected back into their resonant cavity. See →noise (laser diode-).

Backscattering

The strongest contributor to →attenuation of fibers is backscattering, also called Raleigh-scattering. The nature of the scattering process is light diffraction at the microscopic non-uniformities of the refractive index of glass. As the effect depends on the size of the discontinuities in relation to wavelength, the backscattering coefficient α_s is proportional to $1/\lambda^4$. The scattered light partially travels back to the transmitter where it can be analysed via a directional coupler and signal processing, see →optical time domain reflectometer (OTDR). In conjunction with reflections at glass-air transitions, backscattering allows characterization of a fiber's attenuation, splice loss, breaks, length and even dispersion.

In the following, the backscatter signal shall be calculated: let us assume a fiber with an attenuation coefficient $\alpha = \alpha_a$ (absorption) + α_s (scattering). A pulse with power P_0 and pulse duration w shall be launched into the fiber. From →attenuation of fibers, we learn that at a distance z from the fiber input the **transmitted** pulse power $P_t(z)$ is attenuated to:

$$P_t(z) = P_0 \; 10^{-\alpha z / 10 \, dB}$$

The pulse duration w corresponds to a geometrical pulse length Δz. The total **scattered** power $P_s(z)$ at the distance z is:

$$P_s(z) = \alpha_s \, \Delta z \, P_t(z)$$

Due to the limited →numerical aperture of the fiber, only the fraction S of the scattered power travels back to the source. The numbers for S (below) were extracted from reference [7.1]. While travelling back the same distance, the backscattered power is attenuated again. At the input, the **backscattered** power $P_{bs}(z)$ which was generated at a distance z is:

$$P_{bs}(z) = S \, \alpha_s \, \Delta z \, P_0 \, 10^{-2\alpha z / 10 \, \text{dB}}$$

with: $\quad z = t \, v_{gr} / 2 \qquad$ and $\qquad \Delta z = w \, v_{gr} = w \, c/n_{gr}$

and: $\quad S = (NA/n)^2 \quad /4 \qquad$ in the case of graded-index fibers
$\qquad\qquad\qquad\qquad /4.55 \quad$ in the case of single mode fibers
$\qquad\qquad\qquad\qquad /2.67 \quad$ in the case of step-index fibers

α - total attenuation coefficient, [dB/km]
α_s - scattering coefficient, [1/km].
     In the case that α_s is given in [dB/km], multiply by 0.23 to get α_s in [1/km].
S   - backscattering factor, dimensionless
P_0 - power launched into the fiber, [Watt]
z   - one-way length parameter
t   - round trip time from fiber input to location z
Δz - pulse length on the fiber, [m]
v_{gr} - →group velocity
c   - speed of light, 3×10^5 km/s
n   - refractive index of the fiber core center, $n \approx 1.5$
n_{gr} - group index, $n_{gr} = c/v_{gr} \approx n$
w   - pulse duration
NA   - the fiber's →numerical aperture

The backscattered signal clearly decays exponentially with length or time. For an estimation of the peak of the backscattered signal (z = 0), let us use a pulse width of w = 100 ns (Δz = 20 m).

Fiber	λ	α	α_s	NA	$P_{bs}(z=0)/P_0$
Grad.-Index	850 nm	2.5 dB/km	2.17 dB/km	0.2	44×10^{-6} (-43.6 dB)
Single Mode	1300 nm	0.5 dB/km	0.43 dB/km	0.1	2×10^{-6} (-57.0 dB)
Single Mode	1550 nm	0.25 dB/km	0.22 dB/km	0.1	1×10^{-6} (-60.0 dB)

MAXIMUM POWER LEVELS OF THE BACKSCATTER SIGNAL
(at a pulse width w = 100 ns)

Averaging techniques (see →boxcar averaging) are necessary to resolve such small signals. See →optical time domain reflectometer.

Bandwidth (Fiber-)

Fiber bandwidth is usually characterized in the time-domain as pulse broadening, or, more technically, as dispersion. Two effects are responsible for the finite dispersion: →multimode dispersion (also called intermode or modal dispersion) and →chromatic dispersion (also called intramode or spectral dispersion). The latter can further be subdivided into →material-, →waveguide- and →profile-dispersion.

Multimode dispersion describes the pulse broadening caused by different propagation velocities of different modes, under the assumption that the light source is purely monochromatic. Chromatic dispersion is pulse broadening because of the finite spectral width of the source, with only one mode travelling in the fiber.

There is a substantial difference between bandwidth data of multimode fibers and those of single mode fibers. Multimode fibers are usually characterized by their multimode dispersion only, in units of [MHz x km] or [ns / km]. The total dispersion can be computed by quadratic addition of the chromatic dispersion (mainly material dispersion), see below. In the case of single mode fibers, multimode dispersion is nearly zero, so that their bandwidth is characterized by chromatic dispersion only, in units of ns / (km x nm) .

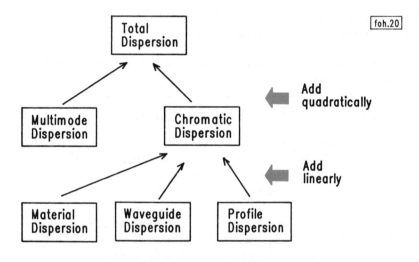

THE DISPERSION HIERARCHY

For a first-order approximation, let us assume that the fiber can be represented by a **Gaussian** low-pass filter, with respect to both multimode- and chromatic dispersion. This means that both the propagation of many modes **and** the finite spectral width of the source cause a Gaussian-type pulse broadening. Most modern fibers can be assumed to be nearly Gaussian. The characteristics of a Gaussian-type network are such that both an impulse (zero-width pulse) and a Gaussian pulse at the input of the fiber will result in a Gaussian output pulse, see →Gaussian pulse.

In the following, the measurement of the **combined** effect of multimode dispersion and chromatic dispersion is discussed. See the chapters on →multimode dispersion and →chromatic dispersion for the separation of these effects and for specific details on the type of mode excitation in the fiber.

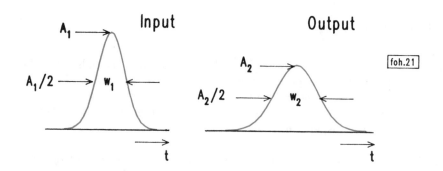

GAUSSIAN PULSES AT THE INPUT AND THE OUTPUT OF THE FIBER

For a bandwidth measurement in the **time domain**, a pulse generator capable of generating very short pulses may be used to drive a large-bandwidth laser diode. At the other end of the fiber, a receiver with the same high bandwidth is necessary to reconvert to the electrical domain. The pulses with and without the fiber are then compared on a sampling oscilloscope. With the help of the 2 pulse widths, the fiber's FWHM impulse response w_{fiber} can be calculated:

$$w_{fiber} = \sqrt{w_2^2 - w_1^2} \quad [ns]$$

w_1 - FWHM pulse width without the fiber
w_2 - FWHM pulse width at the output of the fiber

The cause of the finite width of impulse response is a quadratic addition of multimode dispersion and chromatic dispersion:

$$w_{fiber} = \sqrt{(L\ D_{modal})^2 + (L\ \Delta\lambda\ D_{chromatic})^2}$$

L	- total fiber length
$\Delta\lambda$	- FWHM bandwidth of the (Gaussian) spectrum of the source
D_{modal}	- multimode dispersion [ns/km]
$D_{chromatic}$	- chromatic dispersion [ns/(km x nm)]

In the **frequency domain**, a network analyzer with both an E/O converter (electrical-to-optical) and an O/E converter may be used to determine the system's bandwidth. An example is Hewlett Packard's HP 8702A Lightwave Component Analyzer. Be sure to take the finite bandwidth of the measurement system into account: the bandwidth of the fiber can be extracted (deconvolved) in the following way, if all components of the system behave like Gaussian low-pass filters:

$$B_{fiber}^{-2} = B_2^{-2} - B_1^{-2} \quad [MHz^{-2}]$$

B_1 - bandwidth of the measurement system
B_2 - total system bandwidth, including the fiber

In the field of fibers, bandwidth is most often characterized by the -3 dB$_{opt}$ corner frequency, which corresponds to the -6 dB$_{el}$ frequency. We also use this definition. To convert the impulse response w_{fiber} to the bandwidth B_{fiber}, the following formula may be used if the fiber has a →Gaussian behaviour:

$$B_{fiber} = \frac{0.44}{w_{fiber}} \qquad [ns/km]$$

For other-than-Gaussian systems, the Fourier transform should be used to convert from time domain to frequency domain.

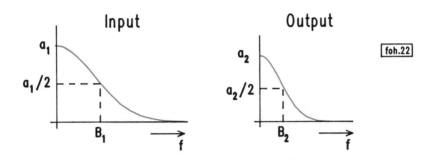

NETWORK ANALYZER PLOTS WITHOUT AND WITH THE FIBER

As an example, let us calculate the bandwidth of a graded-index fiber designed to be driven by an LED. The following data shall be assumed:

LED center wavelength	1300 nm
LED spectral width (FWHM)	100 nm
Graded-index fiber, length	1 km
Multimode dispersion D_{modal}	300 ps/km
Chromatic dispersion $D_{chromatic}$	6 ps/(km nm)
with 100 nm spectral width:	600 ps/km

yields:
	Impulse response w_{fiber}	671 ps
	Fiber bandwidth B_{fiber}	656 MHz

In this case, the LED's modulation bandwidth will limit the total bandwidth. Use a laser diode in order to increase the modulation bandwidth, and in order to eliminate the chromatic dispersion. A single mode fiber will additionally eliminate the multimode dispersion.

Bandwidth (Transmission Systems)

See the paragraphs →systems (direct detection-) and →systems (coherent).

Baseband

The term "baseband" is used in conjunction with "baseband modulation", which, in the field of fiber optics, means modulation of the optical power in contrast to frequency- or phase modulation of the optical carrier.

Beamsplitter

Fiber optic measurements often need beamsplitting: for source monitoring and stabilization, for optical time-domain reflectometry and for interferometric measurements. Here are some desirable features of beamsplitters:

1. Constant beamsplitting ratio, wavelength-independent.
2. Low intrinsic loss.
3. Low level of scattered light.
5. Freedom of →interference effects and ghost images caused by reflections from more than one surface.

Most beamsplitters are dependent on the state of polarization of the incident wave. This effect may be desirable (e.g. when splitting the unpolarized backscatter signal from the polarized front reflex in the case of an →optical time domain reflectometer), or it may be undesirable (when using the beamsplitter for source-monitoring purposes).

A simple beamsplitter based upon →reflection can be made from a **glass plate** oriented at a 45° angle. As this angle is close to Brewster's angle, each surface causes a reflection of 15% of mainly one polarization, while more than 99% of the perpendicular polarization passes. To avoid interference between the two surfaces, one of them should carry an →antireflection coating. This leaves a total reflection of 15%. The polarization-dependence can be strongly reduced by using a much smaller angle, e.g. 5°. This angle reduces the reflection to 4%, once again assuming one surface to be coated.

Pellicle beamsplitters are made from a very thin (5 μm typically) membrane, in order to avoid ghost images. Their disadvantages are dependence on polarization and microphonic effects.

Beamsplitting cubes are made from two cemented prisms with a metal-dielectric film deposited in between the prisms. Their surfaces are antireflection-coated. The film is most often optimized for a 1:1 splitting ratio. Typically, their polarization-dependence is on the order of a few percent, and the total power loss is on the order of 10 %.

Polarizing beamsplitters serve as polarizers and beamsplitters at the same time. Typical applications are in →optical time domain reflectometers and in disk optical recording and reading. The polarizing medium is either multilayer dielectric film (see →polarization) or calcite with its →birefringent nature.

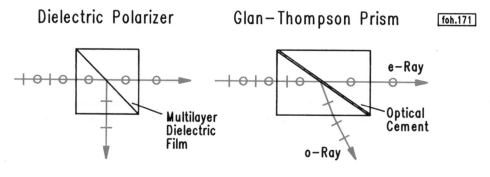

POLARIZING BEAM SPLITTERS

Of all the calcite-based beamsplitters, the Glan-Thompson prism is the most popular. It has the lowest internal loss and the highest purity output polarization. It consists of two cemented prisms, with a finite thickness of the cementing layer. The 2 states of polarization experience different refractive indices; see →birefringence. The ordinary ray (o-ray) "sees" a higher refractive index (n_o = 1.638 at 1300 nm); therefore it is totally reflected at the boundary between calcite and cement. The extraordinary ray (e-ray) "sees" a lower refractive index (n_e = 1.478 at 1300 nm); therefore it basically passes unaffected. Because of the total reflection of the o-ray, the e-ray is highly polarized. The hypotenuse angle is optimized for best splitting performance.

Beat Length

Depending on cross-sectional nonuniformities, different states of polarization of the fundamental mode in a single-mode fiber will experience different propagation velocities. The beat length is a measure for these differences. See the chapter on →birefringence (in fibers).

Bending (Fiber-)

Fiber attenuation is sensitive to bending. See →attenuation (fiber-) and →cutoff-wavelength.

BER

See →bit error rate.

Birefringence (in Bulk Material)

Polarizing →beam splitters and optical →modulators are based on the effect of birefringence. This effect, also called double refraction, is observed in many crystals such as quartz and calcite (calcium carbonate). Birefringence generally means that a single light beam is split into two beams inside a crystal. Only in one direction, called the optic axis, the beam is not manipulated. Crystals with only one optic axis are called uniaxial. We will only discuss those.

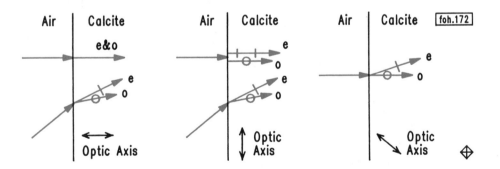

BIREFRINGENCE IN CALCITE

If a light ray enters the crystal at an angle to the optic axis, then it is split into two rays. The polarization of one ray is perpendicular to the optic axis, it is called **ordinary** (o) ray. The polarization of the other ray is orthogonal to the polarization of the o-ray, it is called **extraodinary** (e). If the surface and the optic axis form an angle and the light is at normal incidence to the surface, then the e-ray violates Snell's law by being refracted at an "extraordinary" angle.

In calcite the o-ray experiences a refractive index of n = 1.66. The e-ray's index depends on the angle to the optic axis, ranging from 1.49 (if vertical to the axis) to 1.66 (if parallel to the axis). Thus another result is different travel speeds, which is indicated by the different lengths of the vectors in the figure. →Retardation plates and →modulators are based on this effect.

The birefringence of some materials (e.g. lithium-niobate) depends on the strength of an applied electric field. It is then called **electro-optic effect**. The magneto-optic effect, more specifically the →**Faraday effect**, causes a rotation of the electric field vector. **Optical activity** is the name for a length-dependent rotation of the plane of polarization, even if the light is parallel to the optic axis. The classic material is crystalline quartz. For further information on birefringence, optical activity, electro-optics and magneto-optics consult the classical optical literature like [0.1] and [0.2].

Birefringence (in Fibers)

Many modern optical components, particularly those used in →coherent optical communications, rely on a fixed state of polarization. However, unstable birefringence in standard single-mode fibers cause the state of polarization to change in an unpredictable way. In all single-mode fibers, there are 2 perpendicular orientations of the (transverse) electric field which lead to a maximum difference in phase velocity: the fiber exhibits **linear birefringence**. Let us name the above orientations **fast and slow axes**. Coupling linear-polarized light into one of the axes yields linear-polarized polarized light at the output of the fiber.

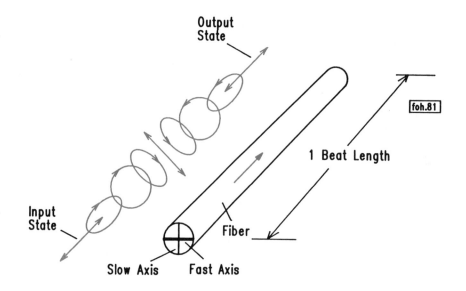

PURE LINEAR BIREFRINGENCE IN A SINGLE-MODE FIBER
(Fiber length = 1 beat length, linear input polarization coupled at 45° relative to axes)

The output state of **multimode fibers** is usually entirely depolarized, because the optical power is transported over many waveguide modes which all have different polarization characteristics. Therefore, birefringence in multimode fibers is not discussed here.

If you are not familiar with polarization ellipses, read the chapter on →polarization first. Let us now discuss the characteristics of a single-mode fiber with **pure linear** birefringence, with no rotation of the axes along the length of the fiber. As stated above, a linear state of polarization coupled into one of the main fiber axes remains linear. If the linear state is coupled at an angle of 45° against the main axes, then the polarization gradually changes from linear to elliptical to circular and so on, as illustrated in the figure. After **1 beat length**, the wave has returned to its original state. The beat length is the length of fiber after which the wave in the slow axis is delayed by exactly one optical wavelength.

For an analytical description of linear birefringence, let us assume a single mode fiber with the fast axis oriented in x-direction and the slow axis in y-direction. Then any state of polarization in that fiber can be described with the following electric fields:

$$E_x = A \cos (\omega t - \beta_x z)$$
$$E_y = B \cos (\omega t - \beta_y z - \phi)$$

with: $\qquad \beta_x = \dfrac{2\pi n_x}{\lambda}$, $\qquad\qquad \beta_y = \dfrac{2\pi n_y}{\lambda}$ $\qquad$ [rad/m]

A,B - electric field amplitudes in x,y-direction
ω - 2π x optical frequency
$\beta_{x,y}$ - propagation constants
ϕ - phase delay of E_y against E_x at the fiber input (z = 0)
$n_{x,y}$ - effective refractive indices in x,y-direction
λ - optical wavelength in air

With this, **linear birefringence** of a fiber with length L can be characterized in one of the following ways:

Linear index difference: $\qquad\qquad \Delta n = n_x - n_y \qquad\qquad$ [dimensionless]

Linear retardation
per unit length: $\qquad\qquad \Delta \beta = \dfrac{2\pi}{\lambda} \Delta n \qquad\qquad$ [rad/m]

Linear retardation: $\qquad\qquad R = \Delta \beta \times L \qquad\qquad$ [rad]

Linear beat length: $\qquad\qquad \Lambda = \dfrac{2\pi}{\Delta \beta} = \dfrac{\lambda}{\Delta n} \qquad\qquad$ [m]

Linear birefringence: $\qquad\qquad B = \dfrac{\lambda}{\Lambda} = \dfrac{\lambda}{2\pi} \dfrac{\Delta \beta}{2\pi} = \Delta n \qquad\qquad$ [dimensionless]

The beat length Λ (capital lambda) of modern single-mode fibers is usually several meters if the fiber is straight. Winding the fiber on a cylinder drastically reduces the beat length, see the chapter on →polarization control.

Even if a linear-polarized wave is coupled into one of the main axes, the field orientation at the output may be rotated against the input: this can be described by an additional **circular**

birefringence. Circular birefringence produces a pure rotation* of any input state of polarization. In contrast, the **definition** of circular retardance is usually based on the difference in propagation constants between counter-clockwise circular polarization and clockwise circular polarization.

* Note: It can be shown that a circular (phase-) retardation of R_c results in a (geometric) **rotation** of the state of polarization of $R_c/2$. If you want to verify this, realize that a linear-polarized wave is equivalent with 2 counterrotating circular-polarized waves.

The mathematical description of circular birefringence is analogous to the description of linear birefringence. Instead of listing the full set of equations, we only want to provide a starting point by giving the index difference:

Circular index difference: $\Delta n_c = n_{ccw} - n_{cw}$ (= circular birefingence)

Circular birefringence can be generated by **twisting** the fiber. Measurements at Hewlett-Packard showed rotations on the order of 16° per 360°-twist of a standard single-mode fiber of 1 m length. The sense of rotation is identical with the sense of the twist.

Another cause for circular birefringence is this: a series connection of two or more linear retarders which are oriented at different angles can always be replaced by a series connection of **one** linear retarder and **one** circular retarder. In this case, there are 2 (perpendicular) linear-polarized input waves which will result in linear, but rotated output states. This situation applies to most single-mode fibers, because the orientation of the main axes usually changes along the length of the fiber. Note that the elements of the model will be changed by moving the fiber.

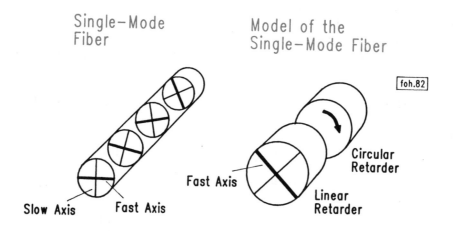

SINGLE-MODE FIBER MODEL
(Consecutive sections of linear birefringence create an element of circular birefringence)

The polarization-characteristics of any length of single-mode fiber can **always** be described by 1 linear retarder and 1 circular retarder. The problem is, that the slightest movements of the fiber cause these elements to change. This, in turn, changes the output state of polarization.

Here is a suggestion for the **measurement** of the model parameters of a fiber of length L. In order to avoid ambiguities, we want to limit ourselves to retardations of less than π (180°). Therefore, L should be sufficiently short, typically less than 1 m:

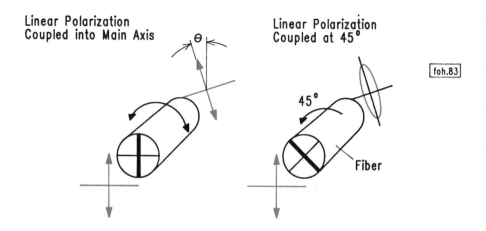

Linear Polarization
Coupled into Main Axis

Linear Polarization
Coupled at 45°

foh.83

45°

Fiber

PRINCIPLE OF THE MEASUREMENT OF FIBER BIREFRINGENCE

1. Apply linear-polarized light to the fiber. Find the **fiber axes** by rotating the entire fiber (or the input state) and by analyzing the output state with a polarizer. As stated above, linear polarization coupled into one of the axes is always transformed into linear polarization.

    Let us assume that a fiber position was found in which linear polarization is observed at the output, and that the electric field is oriented at an angle θ against the field at the input. Then the model's **circular retardation** is $R_c = 2\theta$, as explained above.

2. Rotate the fiber by 45° against the above position. Then maximum inflation of the ellipse should be observed at the output. Calculate the **linear retardation** R by inversing the following formula:

$$A_{max} = \tan \frac{R}{2}$$

A_{max} - the ratio of the short and long axes of the ellipse (electric field amplitudes)

Note that the linear and circular retardations are ambiguous by multiples of 2π. Another problem occurs when R equals a multiple of π. This corresponds to multiples of half-wave plates, in which case the main axes cannot be determined because the fiber will then always produce a linear output state upon a linear input state.

Strong linear birefringence causes linear polarization to be preserved; see the chapter on →polarization-maintaining fibers. More on the polarization characteristics of single mode fibers in [3.7].

Birefringence Noise

This effect is caused by the 2 possible orientations of the fundamental mode in single mode fibers. See →modal noise.

Bit Error Rate

The number of erroneous bits at the output of an optical receiver divided by the total number of received bits is called bit error rate (BER). The BER is the main quality criterium for a transmission system. Many systems require a bit error rate of 10^{-9}, but local area network requirements can go as low as 10^{-14}. The BER can be **measured** by repetitively transmitting and receiving a suitable length of a pseudorandom bit sequence (PRBS). With the help of the attenuator, the dependence of the BER on the received power level can be tested. The oscilloscope will display the →eye pattern.

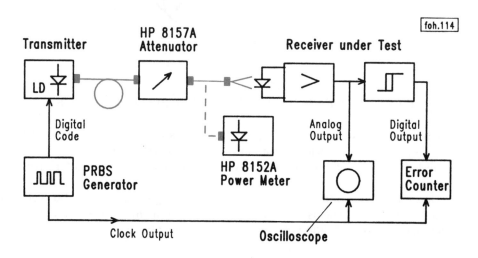

MEASUREMENT SETUP FOR BIT ERROR RATE

Theses are the sources of bit errors in a transmission system:
1. generator intensity noise; see →noise (laser diode-),
2. fiber noise: mode partition noise, as described in →noise (laser diode-), and →modal noise,
3. →receiver noise,
4. timing jitter and intersymbol interference; see →eye pattern.

The dominant noise source is usually the receiver, particularly the photodiode; see →noise (photodiode-). Assuming a Gaussian distribution of noise amplitudes and identical noise power at the "1" and "0" levels, the BER can be calculated from the signal-to-noise ratio, reference [0.8]. The result is shown in the diagram below. It is based on zero intersymbol interference, zero jitter and no sampling errors.

With the assumption that the entire noise of the system can be expressed in terms of a noise equivalent power at the photodiode, the signal-to-noise ratio SNR shall be defined as:

$$SNR = 10 \log (\Delta P_{opt} / NEP) \qquad [dB_{opt}]$$

ΔP_{opt} - difference between the high level and the low level
NEP - noise equivalent power of the photodiode, [W]

We find an SNR of 10.8 dB_{opt} to be sufficient for a BER of 10^{-9}. A slight deviation from this SNR drastically influences the BER, which makes a prediction difficult. Note that the 10.8 dB_{opt} are equivalent to 21.6 dB_{el}. Compare the latter number with a typical 50 dB_{el} requirement for analog systems.

The necessary optical power to achieve a given signal-to-noise ratio, respectively BER, is called the receiver's sensitivity. With direct-detection receivers, a sensitivity of -50 dBm can be achieved at 100 Mbit/s, based on a BER of 10^{-9}. For further information, see →sensitivity.

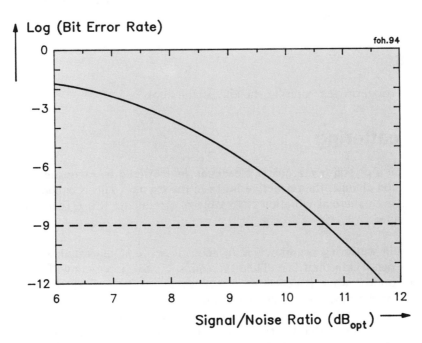

BIT ERROR RATE DEPENDENCE ON SIGNAL-TO-NOISE RATIO

Boltzmann's Constant (k)

$k = 1.38 \times 10^{-23}$ Ws/Kelvin. Also see →constants at the end of the book.

Boxcar Averaging

→Backscattering signals in an →optical time-domain reflectometer are normally buried in noise because of their tiny amplitudes. Boxcar averaging is the common method to improve the signal-to-noise ratio. It is done by repetitively sampling the signal at a fixed time slot, starting at the time t = 0. An arithmetic average of the samples is generated either with a low-pass filter or numerically. Then a variable delay is used to move to the next time slot. This way the boxcar averager scans the entire signal. The larger the number of samples at a fixed time, n, the smaller the effective →noise equivalent power NEP_{eff}:

$$NEP_{eff} = NEP / \sqrt{n}$$

Thus the noise amplitude is reduced with the square root of n. The noise amplitude is 6 to 10 times this value, assuming Gaussian distribution.

Bragg Cell

See →acousto-optic modulator.

Brewster´s Angle

In a situation where a light beam intersects a boundary between 2 dielectric media, Brewster's angle is the angle of incidence at which total transmission (zero reflection) of one state of polarization occurs. See →reflection and refraction.

Brightness

Obsolete photometric term, see →units at the end of the book.

Brillouin Scattering

An optical wave in a crystal (e.g. a quartz fiber) can be scattered by (acoustic) lattice vibration, because the vibration changes the refractive index in the crystal. This is called Brillouin scattering. In principle, even thermal vibration is capable of producing this effect. However, it can normally be neglected.

Stimulated Brillouin scattering occurs when an acoustic wave is generated by a strong electric field (high power density) in the fiber. Then the acoustic wave interacts with the optical wave, such that a new optical wave is generated. This wave travels back to the transmitter. The optical frequency of the new wave is shifted against the generating frequency by approximately 11 GHz, which is the frequency of the acoustic vibration. Two conditions are important to obtain stimulated Brillouin scattering: first, a long interaction length between the acoustic and the optical wave (i.e. a long pulse width), and second, a narrow laser →linewidth on the order of 100 MHz or less. Under these preconditions, the effect can be observed in single-mode fibers at power levels as low as 3 mW.

Stimulated Brillouin scattering (SBS) is the strongest nonlinear effect in fibers: the required power levels are much lower than e.g. for stimulated →Raman scattering. The most obvious effect of SBS is increased attenuation, due to stronger backreflection. In coherent →systems with wavelength-division multiplexing, the new frequency-shifted wave is capable of interacting with other channels. Altogether, SBS sets the highest useful power level in narrow-linewidth communication systems. For further information on this subject, see [3.13] and [3.14].

Buffer

Material surrounding the fiber (core, cladding and coating) in order to protect it from physical damage. Sometimes the buffer is in close contact with the fiber (tight buffer), sometimes a buffer tube allows limited movement of the fiber (loose-tube buffer).

Burrus-Diode

A special construction of a light emitting diode of the surface-emitting type in order to achieve better efficiency in coupling a fiber to the diode. This type of diode was invented by Burrus [4.1] in 1971. See →LED.

Bus

See →network.

Characteristic Impedance

The characteristic impedance Z of an →isotropic dielectric material is the ratio of the electric field amplitude to the magnetic field amplitude, with the assumption that the wave is a TEM wave (transverse electro-magnetic). The characteristic impedance can be used in order to calculate single or multiple reflections from dielectric boundaries.

$$Z = \frac{1}{n} \sqrt{\mu_0/\epsilon_0} = \frac{1}{n} \; 376.7 \; \Omega$$

μ_0 - permeability of vacuum, see →constants at the end of this book
ϵ_0 - dielectric constant of vacuum, see →constants
n - refractive index of the material, n = 1 for vacuum or air, n ≈ 1.5 for glass

Characteristic Temperature

With the help of this variable, the temperature-dependence of the threshold current of laser diodes can be described. See →laser diode.

Chirping

When pulsed between 2 different optical power levels, the optical frequency of typical laser diodes changes, too. Mostly studied in single-line (such as →DFB-) lasers, this effect is called chirping. At low modulation frequencies, increasing the drive current causes a higher temperature, which increases the wavelength due to a higher refractive index and due to an expansion of the laser's resonant cavity (red shift). At high frequencies, this effect is inversed by carrier-induced changes of the refractive index (blue shift). Chirping effectively broadens the laser's spectral bandwidth, often causing increased chromatic dispersion.

On the other hand, the chirp mechanism is utilized for frequency modulation (FM) of the optical carrier in **coherent** transmission: laser diodes generate parasitic FM when intensity-modulated. See →spectrum (laser diode-). Chirp can be measured by demodulation on the slope of a narrow-band wavelength-selective filter; also read →self-heterodyning/homodyning.

Chromatic Dispersion

The velocity at which an optical pulse travels on a fiber depends on its wavelength. This way, the different "colours" contained in a light pulse propagate at different speeds. Depending on the spectral width, this effect results in pulse broadening called chromatic dispersion or intramodal dispersion. The following effects contribute to chromatic dispersion:

1. →Material dispersion, which is caused by the wavelength-dependence of the fiber's refractive index, thereby creating a wavelength dependence of →phase velocity and →group velocity. This effect should be taken into account in both multimode- and single mode fibers.

2. →Waveguide dispersion, which is caused by the wavelength-dependence of the modal characteristics of a fiber. In multimode fibers, this effect can be neglected because it is washed out by the presence of many modes. In a single mode fiber, waveguide dispersion can be explained this way: in a typical operating condition, the light spot extends into the cladding. This yields an effective refractive index somewhere in between the index of the core and that of the cladding. A longer wavelength causes an increased spot diameter (even if the refractive indices were constant), which, changes the effective refractive index.

3. →Profile dispersion, which is due to the different wavelength-dependences of the refractive indices of core and cladding (expressed as wavelength-dependence of the **contrast** or the **profile**). In high-performance graded-index (multimode) fibers, this is an important design parameter. In single mode fibers, profile dispersion is often treated as being part of the waveguide dispersion.

Chromatic dispersion is defined as **minus** the change of group travel time per unit length of fiber per change of wavelength. Accordingly, chromatic dispersion is always given in units of ps / (km x nm).

The propagation in a single mode fiber is determined by an **effective** refractive index n_{eff}, because the indices of both core and cladding influence the propagation.

$$n_{eff} = n_2 + b(\lambda)\,(n_1 - n_2),$$

n_1 - refractive index of the core
n_2 - refractive index of the cladding

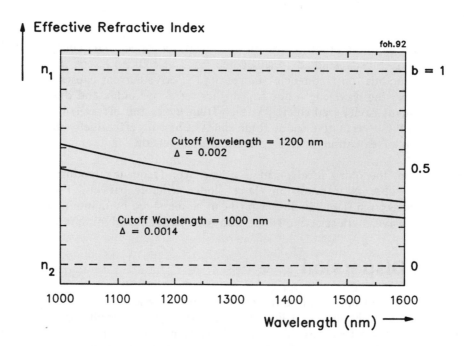

WAVELENGTH-DEPENDENCE OF THE EFFECTIVE REFRACTIVE INDEX
Refractive index: n_1 = 1.46, Core radius = 5 μm,
Refractive index contrasts: Δ = 0.0014 and 0.002.

The variable $b(\lambda)$ describes the effect of the wavelength-dependent spot diameter on the propagation. In reference [0.5], the dependence of b on the →normalized frequency, V, is shown in graphical form. From this the wavelength-dependence of of n_{eff} as a function of the wavelength was calculated. The curves directly represent the parameter b as a function of the wavelength.

Let us now build a model for the chromatic dispersion of single mode fibers. Similar to the procedure in the chapter on →group velocity, we obtain:

$$v_{gr} = d\omega/d\beta$$

$$\omega = 2\pi c/\lambda$$

$$\beta = 2\pi n_{eff}/\lambda$$

v_{gr} - group velocity
ω - 2π x optical frequency
β - propagation constant along the fiber axis
c - speed of light in vacuum, see →constants at the end of the book
λ - wavelength in vacuum

$$t_{gr} = \frac{L}{v_{gr}} = L\frac{d\beta}{d\omega} \qquad [\text{ ps }]$$

$$t_{gr} = \frac{L}{c}[n_{2gr} + (n_{1gr} - n_{2gr})(b - \lambda)\frac{db}{d\lambda}]$$

with $\quad n_{1gr} = n_1 - \lambda\frac{dn_1}{d\lambda}, \qquad n_{2gr} = n_2 - \lambda\frac{dn_2}{d\lambda}$

In the above expression for group travel time, the following approximation was used: $n_1 - n_2 = n_{1gr} - n_{2gr}$. We now assume a change of wavelength $(d\lambda)$ to cause a change of group travel time. Following the IEEE-definition in [1.7], this leads to the **chromatic dispersion** D_{chr}:

$$D_{chr} = -\frac{dt_{gr}}{L\,d\lambda} \qquad [\frac{ps}{km\,nm}]$$

$$D_{chr} \simeq \frac{\lambda}{c}\frac{d^2n_2}{d\lambda^2} + \frac{\lambda}{c}(n_1 - n_2)\frac{d^2b}{d\lambda^2}$$

Material   Waveguide
Dispersion   Dispersion

The material dispersion curve was adopted from the chapter on →material dispersion. The waveguide dispersion was calculated by extracting the parameter $d^2b/d\lambda^2$ from reference [0.5]. In the case of pure quartz, zero chromatic dispersion is obtained at 1280 nm. Doping the core with GeO_2 shifts the zero-point to 1300 nm or higher. Obviously, the waveguide dispersion has little effect on the total chromatic dispersion. In →dispersion-shifted fibers, a much larger waveguide dispersion is created by segmenting the core of the fiber. This way, a cancellation of the material dispersion can be accomplished at one or more wavelengths.

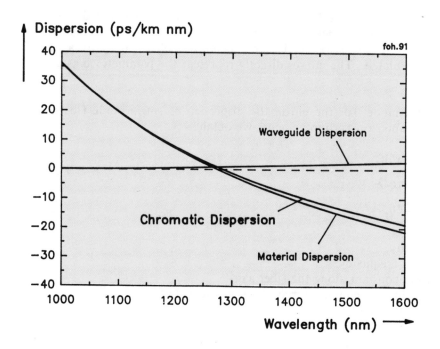

CHROMATIC DISPERSION OF A STANDARD SINGLE MODE FIBER
Refractive index = 1.46, Core radius = 5 μm,
Cutoff wavelength = 1200 nm, Refractive index contrast Δ = 0.002

With the assumption of negligible multimode dispersion, the 3 dB_{opt} fiber bandwidth due to chromatic dispersion, B_{chr}, is given by:

$$B_{chr} = \frac{0.44}{L \Delta\lambda \, |D_{chr}|} \qquad [\,MHz\,]$$

L   - total length of fiber
Δλ - spectral bandwidth (FWHM) of the source

This equation is based on the following: the fiber's response on an optical impulse (zero-width pulse) with a Gaussian spectrum (spectral FWHM width = Δλ) is a →Gaussian pulse, with a FWHM pulse width equal to the denominator of the above equation. The classic setup for the **measurement** of chromatic dispersion employs of a number of different lasers each of which is driven by a narrow pulse, typically on the order of 100 ps. The optical pulses are launched into the single-mode* fiber under test. At the output, the differences in pulse travel time are detected, e.g. with a sampling oscilloscope. Replacement of the lasers by a Raman laser, which emits a number of spectral lines in parallel, is another common method. In this case, a monochromator can be used for the selection of the wavelength, see →Raman dispersion measurement.
*   Multimode fibers will additionally generate →multimode dispersion.

An example for the measurement of the chromatic dispersion, as extracted from [15]:

Laser no. 1, wavelength	803	nm
Laser no. 2, wavelength	824	nm

A group-delay difference of $\Delta t = 2.4$ ns was measured after a fiber length of $L = 1$ km. With $\Delta\lambda = 21$ nm, the resulting chromatic dispersion is:

$$D_{chr} = \frac{\Delta t}{\Delta\lambda\, L} = 114 \, \frac{ps}{nm\ km} \quad \text{at the (average) wavelength of 814 nm}$$

Today, measurement in the frequency domain is more popular. In this case, the laser diodes are driven with a sine wave of fixed frequency, e.g. $f_0 = 30$ MHz. The sine wave $a(t)$ at the fiber output may be expressed by:

$$a(t) = A\cos[\,2\pi\, f_0\,(t - t_{gr})\,]$$

The change of phase $\Delta\phi$ due to the change of wavelength $\Delta\lambda$ can be measured with a vector voltmeter. From the obvious relation between $\Delta\phi$ and the change of group travel time Δt_{gr}, the chromatic dispersion can be calculated:

$$\Delta\phi = 2\pi f_0\, \Delta t_{gr}$$

$$D_{chr} = \frac{\Delta t_{gr}}{L\,\Delta\lambda} = \frac{\Delta\phi}{2\pi f_0\, L\Delta\lambda}$$

Most elegantly, this type of measurement is done with a single LED utilizing its large spectral width, together with a monochromator for selection of the wavelength [23]. Very low power levels are launched in this case. However, the necessary sensitivity does not seem to be prohibitive.

Cladding

The layer of material surrounding the core of a fiber is called cladding. See →fiber.

Cladding Mode

See →modes (fiber-).

Cladding Mode Stripper

See →mode stripper.

Classification (Laser Products-)

According to international rules, all laser products must be classified. See the paragraph →safety.

Coating (Antireflection-)

See →antireflection coating.

Coating (Fiber-)

The material surrounding the cladding of a →fiber is called coating. Mostly made from plastic, it protects the fiber from damage. The coating's refractive index may be smaller than the cladding index, or larger, in which case the coating acts like a →mode stripper for cladding modes.

Coherence

Let us assume that 2 wavetrains, which are separated in time, are cut out from the **same** optical wave. If the comparison of the trains shows a stable phase difference, then the wave is called **coherent**. Increasing the time-difference between the 2 trains always reduces the degree of coherence (i.e. the phase stability), until it is entirely lost. The critical time-difference is called **coherence time**. The coherence time depends on the spectral bandwidth of the source; an ideal monochromatic source has an infinite coherence time. Temporal coherence should be distinguished from spatial coherence, which is the stability of the phase in a wavefront. This chapter is about temporal coherence only.

The →Michelson interferometer was proposed for the measurement of the coherence time [0.9]. In this measurement, the radiation is split into two light beams. One of the beams travels a fixed distance. The path length of the other beam is variable. Then the beams are recombined. If the two path lengths are equal or similar, then one observes interference. Alternating constructive and destructive interference results from changing one path length with respect to the other. If one makes the difference larger, then phase noise (i.e. the finite spectral width) makes the interference less pronounced, until the optical power on the detector remains constant.

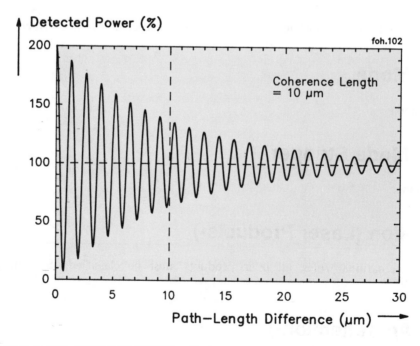

CALCULATED OUTPUT POWER FROM A MICHELSON INTERFEROMETER
(Note that the coherence time of a laser is usually more than 1000 x longer !)

- 30 -

For a detailed analysis of the Michelson interferometer, see the chapter on →Michelson interferometer. Here, we only want to provide engineering-type information.

The difference in path-length, after which the amplitude falls to the 1/e (e = 2.718) of the original value, is called coherence length. The coherence time is the time which the light needs to travel the coherence length.

$$l_c = ct_c = \lambda^2/\Delta\lambda = c/\Delta f$$

l_c - coherence length
t_c - coherence time
c - speed of light, $c = 3 \times 10^8$ m/s
λ - laser center wavelength
$\Delta\lambda$ - line width of a single longitudinal line
Δf - bandwidth of a single longitudinal line

source	$\Delta\lambda$	Δf	l_c	t_c
LED:	100 nm	18 THz	17 μm	0.57 ps
Laser:	0.01 nm	1.8 GHz	0.17 m	570 ps
	0.001 nm	180 MHz	1.7 m	5.7 ns
	0.0001 nm	18 MHz	17 m	57 ns

COHERENCE RELATIONS AT 1.3 μm

Most practical laser diodes generate several longitudinal modes. However, the coherence length is mainly determined by the width of just **one** longitudinal mode. The coherence length only slightly decreases as the number of longitudinal modes increases [4.6].

The table below lists typical coherence properties of today's lasers. Note that the spectral bandwidth usually increases when the laser is modulated.

Source	Coherence Length	Spectral Bandwidth
850 nm multimode laser:	0.05 m	6 GHz
1300 nm multimode laser:	0.3 to 2 m	1 GHz - 150 MHz
1300 nm DFB laser:	15 m	20 MHz

COHERENCE PROPERTIES OF TYPICAL LASER DIODES

For the measurement of today's narrow-linewidth lasers (e.g. DFB- and C³-lasers, see →laser diode), the Michelson interferometer must be modified to cope with the necessary length difference of the 2 arms: single-mode fibers with reflecting ends should be used instead of the open beams, and the beam splitter should be replaced by a →coupler.

→Mach-Zehnder interferometers can be used for the same type of measurement. However, the necessary change of path length is more difficult to accomplish. A small change (several wavelengths) can be realized by stretching the fiber on a piezoelectric ring.

Coherent light in a **single-mode fiber** will remain coherent even after travelling a long distance. The reason is that the beam is not split. In a **multimode fiber**, the optical power is split into many waveguide modes. This way, the degree of coherence depends on the length of fiber. After a short length, one observes speckle patterns (see →modal noise) at the fiber end. After a longer length, →multimode dispersion causes different path lengths, which are equivalent to the different path lengths in the Michelson interferometer. This destroys the possibility of →interference, and a speckle pattern cannot be observed any more.

Coherent Detection

In conventional fiber optic transmission systems, the information is contained in the fluctuation of the optical **power**. The photodiode converts these fluctuations to an equivalent electrical current. This is mostly termed "direct detection". In contrast, "coherent detection" analyzes the characteristics of the received **electric field**, with respect to either its amplitude, frequency or phase. This is done by mixing the received signal and the optical power from a laser diode which operates as local oscillator.

The name "coherent" indicates the need for an optical carrier with pure spectral characteristics. Coherent detection offers big advantages in terms of improved receiver sensitivity and, in the case of wavelength-division multiplexing, narrower channel spacing. Therefore, many laboratories around the world are involved in the research and development of coherent systems.

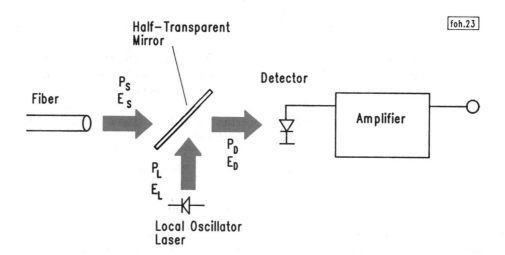

RECEIVER BASED ON COHERENT DETECTION

Let us assume a situation as outlined in the diagram. The electric fields and the optical powers shall be characterized by the following equations. Time-average is indicated by bracketing <> :

$$E_s = A \cos (\omega_s t + \phi_s), \qquad P_s = k < E_s^2 > \quad = k A^2 /2$$
$$E_L = B \cos (\omega_L t), \qquad P_L = k < E_L^2 > \quad = k B^2 /2$$

E_s - electrical field of the received signal
A - amplitude of the received signal, may be time-dependent
ω_s - 2π x optical frequency of the received signal, may be time-dependent
$\emptyset_s$ - phase of the signal, may be time-dependent
P_s - average optical power of the signal
k - constant
E_L - electric field as generated by the local oscillator
B - amplitude of the electric field of the local oscillator
ω_L - 2π x optical frequency of the local oscillator
P_L - average optical power of the local oscillator

These signals are added with the help of a half-transparent mirror. Somewhat arbitrarily, the mirror shall introduce a power-loss of 50 % for both the signal and the local oscillator. Both electric fields shall be oriented in the same direction. The photodiode acts as a low-pass filter, which rejects any spectral components at the optical frequencies. The photodiode current is therefore :

$$i_{ph} = rk < (E_s + E_L)^2 > / 2$$
$$= r(P_s + P_L)/2 + r\sqrt{P_sP_L}\cos[(\omega_s - \omega_L)t + \emptyset_s]$$

r - the photodiode's responsivity [A/W]

The current consists of a DC term and a term at an intermediate frequency (IF), $f_s - f_L$. Two cases can be distinguished, both of which fall into the category "coherent detection". **Heterodyne detection** is based on a fixed IF, e.g. 1 GHz. **Homodyne detection** is based on forcing the oscillator to produce an IF of $f_s - f_L = 0$.

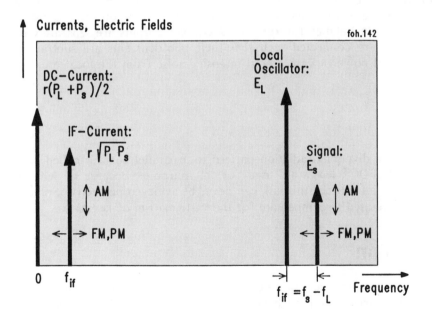

FREQUENCY-DOMAIN REPRESENTATION OF COHERENT DETECTION

Now, let us compare direct detection with coherent detection :

Direct detection: Amplitude $= r\,P_s$

Coherent Detection: Amplitude $= r\sqrt{P_L\,P_s}$,   Gain $= \sqrt{P_L/P_s}$

The power of the local oscillator can easily be a factor of 10 000 larger than the signal power. Therefore, the typical gain in signal current is 100 or more. Most interesting, however, is the gain in signal-to-noise ratio (SNR). Neglecting the contribution of the signal current, the high DC current ($rP_L/2$) creates a larger amount of **shot noise** ; see the chapter on →noise (photodiode-). Accordingly, the mean square noise current of the PIN diode is:

$$\langle i_n^2 \rangle \simeq 2e\,B_n\,r\,P_L/2$$

e -   electron charge $= 1.6 \times 10^{-19}$ As
B_n - →noise-equivalent bandwidth
r -   responsivity of the PIN diode

Relating the 2 electric signals leads to the **signal-to-noise ratio** :

$$SNR = \frac{i_s^2}{\langle i_n^2 \rangle} = \frac{r^2\,P_s\,P_L}{2e\,B_n\,r\,P_L/2} = \frac{r\,P_s}{e\,B_n}$$

With a necessary signal-to-noise ratio on the order of 20 dB$_{el}$ ($= 10$ dB$_{opt}$), this equation defines the minimum optical power P_s in order to obtain a →bit error rate of 10^{-9}. In practical coherent systems, the SNR is also affected by the **linewidth** (i.e. the spectral width) of the both the signal and the local oscillator ; see the paragraph on →**systems (coherent-)**. The net result is, that coherent detection allows an improvement of the sensitivity of 10 to 15 dB$_{opt}$, depending on the type of receiver.

A practical realization of the beam splitter is a single-mode fiber →coupler. An improvement of the system outlined here is possible when both outputs of the coupler are processed. This circuit is called a **double balanced mixer**: the 2 coupler outputs are separately detected with 2 photodiodes which are connected such that their photocurrents are subtracted. This way a factor of 2 in signal power is gained, and intensity noise from the local oscillator is cancelled [9.6].

Collimation

The conversion of a diverging radiation pattern to a parallel beam is called collimation. Conventional and →SELFOC® lenses are used for this purpose. Because of lens errors and light sources not being point sources, this task can never be achieved perfectly. Sometimes additional cylindrical lenses are used to compensate for the →astigmatism of lasers.

Concatenation

The process of connecting pieces of fiber to a link, either by →splicing or by →connectors. For the effect of concatenation on fiber bandwidth, see →multimode dispersion.

Connector (Multimode-)

A large variety of optical connectors has been invented. Most connectors were originally designed for multimode fiber applications; today, single-mode versions are also available. Unfortunately, the fiber optic community could not agree upon a common connector standard. As a consequence, most of the (too many) connectors below are candidates for IEC standards. Among the most popular connectors are:

USA: BICONIC, ST, SMA
Japan: FC, D4, PC
Europe: DIN/IEC, RADIALL, STRATOS

For measurement applications, Hewlett-Packard favours a derivative of the DIN/IEC connector: DIAMOND® HMS10/HP, which was developed in cooperation with the DIAMOND company.

The only possible standardization seems to be in ferrule diameters: 2.5 mm is a popular diameter. A fixed ferrule diameter allows at least a loose mating of connectors of different manufacturers.

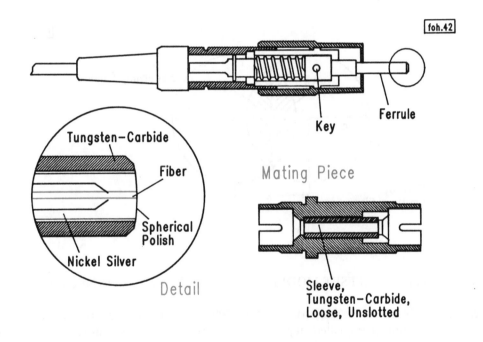

DIAMOND® HMS10/HP OPTICAL CONNECTOR

Today, most connectors are based on physical contact of two well-cleaved fibers in order to allow direct transition of optical power from one core to another. A typical manufacturing process consists of:

1. Stripping the jacket and coating until only core and cladding are left.
2. Centering and fixing the uncoated fiber in the ferrule.
3. Grinding and polishing the ends of fiber and ferrule.
4. Assembly of the connector housing.

The actual connection is made by inserting the two ferrules into a precisely guiding cylindrical sleeve.

In the following, the insertion loss mechanisms in the connection of two multimode fibers shall be discussed.

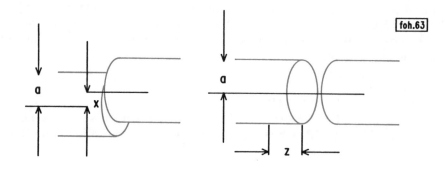

LATERAL AND LONGITUDINAL OFFSET IN A CONNECTOR PAIR
(only fiber cores shown)

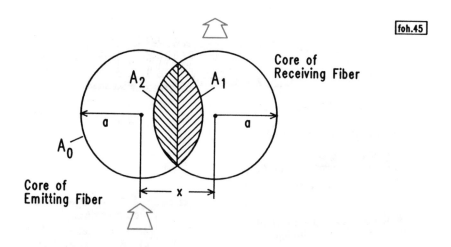

LATERAL OFFSET MODEL FOR A MULTIMODE CONNECTOR

Step-index fiber: In any connector pair, **lateral offset** is the largest contributor to the insertion loss. In the case of uniformly filled step-index fibers, the relative transmitted power is identical to the ratio of the common area, $A_1 + A_2$, divided by the area of one core, A_0. The insertion loss L_{lat} is:

$$L_{lat} = -10 \log \frac{A_1 + A_2}{A_0} \qquad [\, dB_{opt} \,]$$

$$L_{lat} \simeq -10 \log \left(1 - \frac{2x}{\pi a} \cdot \right) \qquad \text{for small offsets d}$$

x - lateral offset
a - core radius

The insertion loss for **longitudinal offset** is caused by the diverging light cone from the emitting fiber. It was suggested that this insertion loss can be calculated by only considering **area mismatch**, i.e. the ratio of illuminated area to core area of the second fiber. This leads to much larger losses than observed in reality.

The reason for this discrepancy is the following: the usual assumption for a step-index fiber is a constant irradiance [W/m^2] in both the near - and the far field. However, the irradiance shows a peak on the central axis in a short distance from the emitting surface. Therefore, calculation of the coupling efficiency cannot be based on area mismatch alone. Careful analysis [2.7] leads to the following insertion loss for small separations:

$$L_{long} = -10 \log \left(1 - \frac{4}{3\pi} \frac{z}{a} \frac{NA}{n'} \right) \qquad [\, dB_{opt} \,]$$

NA - numerical aperture
z - longitudinal offset
a - core radius
n' - refractive index of the medium between the fiber ends

Note that a typical loss of 0.3 dB must be added if the fiber ends are separated by air, because of the reflections at both glass/air interfaces. This is explained in the chapter →connector (single mode-).

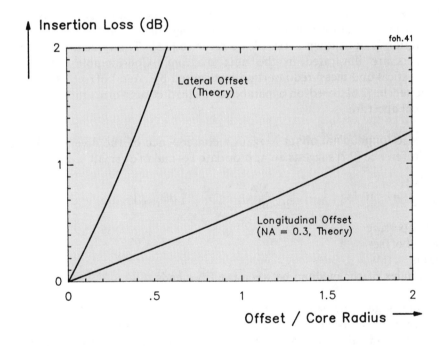

CONNECTOR LOSS MECHANISMS FOR STEP-INDEX FIBERS

Graded-index fiber: The loss mechanism in the connection of graded-index fibers is more complex. First of all, it depends on the **modal distribution** in the fiber. Full excitation of all modes is usually assumed for distances of less than 1 meter from the source. After a long fiber length (typically 1 km ore more), an →equilibrium modal distribution (EMD) is observed. In this case, the modes are more strongly concentrated to the center of the core. The same lateral offset will cause a lower insertion loss. However, the insertion loss will be higher after the EMD is reestablished. Effectively, this is comparable with mating 2 fibers with smaller core diameters.

For simplicity, only the case of **full excitation** shall be considered. This means that the power density at the end of the emitting fiber follows the square of the local numerical aperture (NA_{local}): the density is maximum in the center and falls to zero near the core-to-cladding boundary; see the chapter →near field. All modes of the emitting fiber are accepted in area A_1, because NA_{local} of the emitting fiber is smaller than NA_{local} of the receiving fiber. In area A_2, the situation is reversed. However, the coupled powers in areas A_1 and A_2 are the same. This can be understood intuitively by the following:

Area A_1:   power density small, NA_{local} of receiving fiber large
Area A_2:   power density high, NA_{local} of receiving fiber small

This leads to the insertion loss L_{lat} of a connection of 2 fully excited graded-index fibers:

$$L_{lat} = -10 \log \frac{2 P(A_1)}{P(A_0)} \qquad [\, dB_{opt}\,]$$

$$L_{lat} \simeq -10 \log \left(1 - \frac{8x}{3\pi a} \right) \qquad \text{for small offsets x, from [0.5]}$$

The last approximation is valid for the case of a fiber with **parabolic profile**, see →fiber (multi-mode-). Note that the modal distribution in the receiving fiber is no longer fully excited. The process of integration is not shown here; please refer to [0.5]. The typical loss mechanisms for graded-index fibers are illustrated in the next diagram. Considerable disagreement exists between the theoretical and measured insertion loss caused by lateral offset. Therefore, a better model was suggested in [2.6], based on a parabolic (instead of uniform) radiation pattern from the local numerical aperture.

Insertion loss due to **longitudinal offset** is again a consequence of the diverging beam from the emitting fiber. Reference [2.7] suggests an appropriate formula for small separations z:

$$L_{long} = -10 \log \left(1 - \frac{z}{2a} \frac{NA}{n'} \right) \qquad [\, dB_{opt}\,]$$

NA - numerical aperture
z - longitudinal offset
a - core radius
n' - refractive index of the medium between the fiber ends

Reference [2.7] shows good agreement between theory and measurement. Most often smaller insertion losses are observed because the condition of full excitation is invalid. Again, a typical loss of 0.3 dB must be added if the fiber ends are separated by air. →Index matching liquids can be used to cancel this additional loss.

Measurement standards for connector insertion loss do not specify the type of mode filling. Instead, documentation of the type of mode filling is recommended: equilibrium or fully excitated/overfilled. See the chapter on →insertion loss.

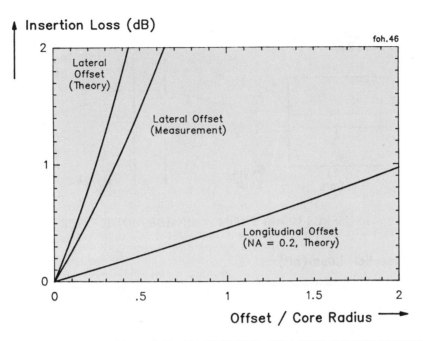

CONNECTOR LOSS MECHANISMS FOR GRADED-INDEX FIBERS

Lensed fiber connections, employing a collimating lens at each connector, have also gained some popularity. These connectors cannot be easily degraded because scratching the lens surface is not as critical as scratching the fiber end. Also, they are not nearly as sensitive to dust as butt-coupled connectors. With good lensed connectors, insertion losses below 1 dB can be achieved. A word of caution concerning laser →safety: due to the collimated beam, lensed connectors are much more dangerous than standard butt-coupled connectors.

Connector (Single Mode-)

Insertion loss is the most critical parameter of optical connectors. In addition, the lowest achievable reflection (return loss) recently became a widely discussed issue. The reason for this discussion is that single mode fibers are mostly driven by laser diodes, and that laser diodes are sensitive to backreflection. This can be most disturbing in measurement situations and in →coherent systems applications. Therefore, the emphasis in this chapter is on insertion loss and return loss.

Insertion Loss: Because of the small core diameter of single mode fibers (typically 9 µm), single mode connectors are most demanding in terms of mechanical alignment. In order to calculate the insertion loss, the →**Gaussian beam** is typically used as a model for the actual light beam inside and outside of the fiber.

As indicated in the figure, the Gaussian beam has a finite beam width which smoothly transits into a light cone of fixed numerical aperture. The beam waist coincides with the end of the fiber. The beam was named "Gaussian" because both the electric field **and** the power density (irradiance) follow a Gaussian error function. Note that the diameter of the beam waist is larger than the core diameter. At a wavelength of 1300 nm and a beam waist diameter of 11 µm, the length of the beam waist is a relatively large 73 µm, as defined by the intersection of the cone and the radius of the beam waist.

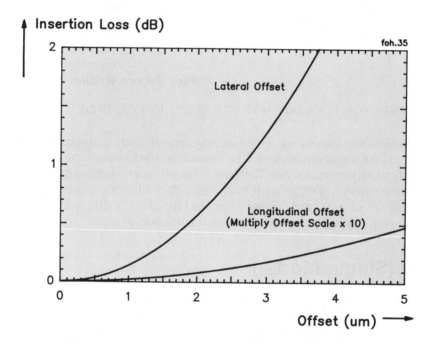

foh.34

GAUSSIAN BEAM FROM A SINGLE MODE FIBER

INSERTION LOSS OF SINGLE MODE CONNECTORS
(Reflection losses are not included)

In the connection of 2 fibers, another Gaussian beam must be excited in the second fiber. Therefore the amount of coupled power is defined by how well the 2 Gaussian fields overlap. The power-coupling coefficient A can be calculated with the help of the so-called **overlap integral**. Solving the integral yields the results below. Note that losses due to reflection are not included in these equations, see the next chapter.

$$A = A_{long} \exp(-A_{long} x^2 / w_0^2), \quad \text{with}$$

$$A_{long} = \frac{4 w_0^4}{4 w_0^4 + \lambda^2 z^2 / \pi^2}$$

A_{long} - power coupling coefficient for pure longitudinal offset
x - lateral offset of the 2 fibers

z — longitudinal offset of the 2 fibers

λ — wavelength in air

w_0 — radius of the beam waist; at this point, the power density is down to $1/e^2$ of maximum. The electric field is down to $1/e$ of maximum. Typical number: $w_0 = 5.5$ μm.

Very clearly, lateral offset is the strongest contributor to insertion loss. The reason is the long length of the beam waist: 73 μm.

See →connector (multimode-) for the most frequent optical connectors. Hewlett Packard's preferred connector, DIAMOND® HMS10/HP, is based on physical contact. Therefore, the influence of reflections on the insertion loss can be neglected. In addition to the usual steps in the manufacturing process, **core alignment** is achieved by pressing an excentric V-groove into the front facet of the ferrule. This way, the lateral offset can be kept below 0.5 μm.

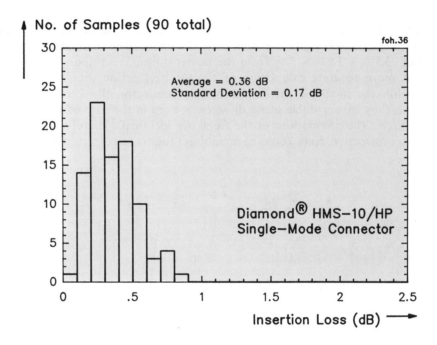

INSERTION LOSSES OF HP's HMS10/HP SINGLE-MODE CONNECTOR

See the chapter →insertion loss for a measurement procedure.

Fiber End Reflection: Because of the different refractive indices (characteristic impedances), the optical power is partially reflected from the input to a fiber. Note that the field-reflection factor r and the power-reflection factor $| r |^2$ should be carefully distinguished. Classical electromagnetic theory yields:

$$r = \frac{Z_0 - Z_1}{Z_0 + Z_1} = \frac{Z_0 - Z_0/n}{Z_0 + Z_0/n} = \frac{n - 1}{n + 1} = 18.7\ \%$$

$$| r |^2 = 3.5\ \%$$

r — reflection factor of the electric field

$| r |^2$ — reflection factor of the optical power

Z_0 -   characteristic impedance of air, $Z_0 = 377 \, \Omega$
Z_1 -   characteristic impedance of glass, $Z_1 = Z_0/n$
n   -   refractive index of silica; $n = 1.46$ at 1300 nm

Also see the figure below for explanation of units. **Return loss** is defined as the logarithm of the ratio of the incident to the reflected optical power.

Summarizing the situation at the input to a fiber:

Impedance	Z_A	$= Z_0$
Field-reflection	r	$= 18.7\ \%$
Power-reflection	$\|r\|^2$	$= 3.5\ \%$
Return Loss	RL	$= 14.5$ dB

Reflection from a connector pair: Let us now consider the reflection from the 2 glass/air interfaces of a connector pair. In this case, the reflections from both interfaces subtract an **average** of $3.5\ \% + 3.5\ \% = 7\ \%$ from the power output, corresponding to an insertion loss of 0.32 dB. A more accurate calculation of the total reflection should be based on the electric fields. Within the small air gap of an optical connector, the 2 reflected electric fields are **coherent**, i.e. they have a stable phase difference, even in the case of the wide spectral width of an LED source. The orientations of the fields are identical. Therefore, the reflected waves can either add (constructive →interference) or subtract (destructive →interference).

foh.37

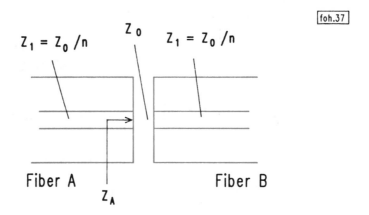

MODEL OF A SINGLE-MODE CONNECTOR PAIR

Using the transmission line theory as outlined in the chapter →**optical interference**, we obtain: a transmission line with a characteristic impedance Z_0, which is terminated with an impedance Z_1, exhibits the following input impedance Z_A. The corresponding field-reflection factor in fiber A is expressed as r :

$$Z_A = Z_0 \frac{Z_1 + jZ_0 \tan \beta z}{Z_0 + jZ_1 \tan \beta z} \qquad r = \frac{Z_A - Z_1}{Z_A + Z_1}$$

β - propagation constant, $\beta = 2\pi/\lambda$
z - length of air gap
λ - wavelength in air

The table below lists the conditions for destructive and constructive interference in the air gap of an optical connector. "m" may be any integer $\geqslant 0$.

	Destructive Interference		Constructive Interference	
Phase	βL	$= 2m\pi$	βL	$= \pi/2 + 2m\pi$
Impedance	Z_A	$= Z_1 = Z_0/n$	Z_A	$= Z_0^2 / Z_1 = n Z_0$
Reflection	r	$= 0\%$	r	$= (n^2 - 1)/(n^2 + 1) = 36\%$
	$\lvert r \rvert^2$	$= 0\%$	$\lvert r \rvert^2$	$= 13\%$
Return Loss	RL	$= \infty$	RL	$= 8.8$ dB
Insertion Loss	IL	$= 0$	IL	$= 0.6$ dB

REFLECTIONS FROM A NON-CONTACTING CONNECTOR PAIR

At a wavelength of 1300 nm, the reflection factor varies periodically with a 0.65 μm - change of separation.

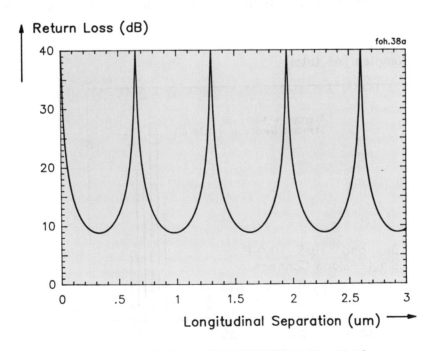

RETURN LOSS IN A CONNECTOR PAIR AT 1.3 μm

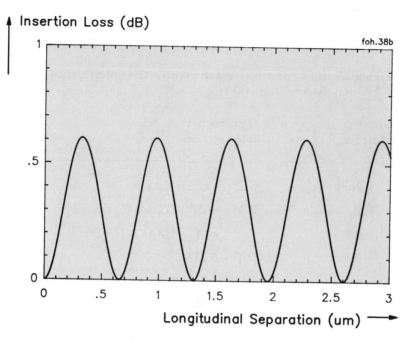

INSERTION LOSS IN A CONNECTOR PAIR AT 1.3 μm

In the diagram, a reflection of 0.01 % (40 dB) was purposely added in order to keep the curves from going to infinity. The strong dependence of the return loss on longitudinal separation explains why it is so difficult to accomplish 40 dB return loss. Often, a practical limit is 30 to 35 dB.

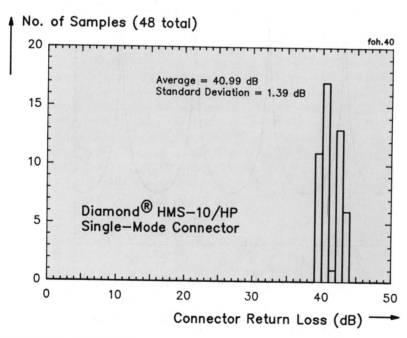

MEASURED RETURN LOSSES OF HP's HMS10/HP CONNECTOR PAIRS

Corresponding to the periodic behaviour of the reflections, the insertion loss also changes periodically, with the same period length of 0.65 µm. The coupled power varies between 100 and 85 %, corresponding to an insertion loss between 0 and 0.6 dB. For a repeatable connection, the separation of the fiber ends would have to be reproduced to within 1/10 of 0.65 µm. As this is impossible, optical interference represents a strong source of non-reproducibility. For measurement applications, non-contacting optical connectors should definitely be avoided.

The key to excellent return losses is a perfectly perpendicular fiber end and the best available polishing process, as demonstrated in the HMS10/HP connector. See the chapter →return loss for the measurement procedure.

Contrast

See →refractive index contrast.

Constants

See →units and constants at the end of the book.

Core

The core is the central cylinder of a fiber, see →fiber. It is characterized by a refractive index which is higher than index of the surrounding cladding. The core diameter is most often determined by measurement of the →near field.

Coupler

Couplers are key devices for local area →networks based on fibers. Other important applications are the measurement of transmitted optical power (monitoring) and the measurement of reflections. Most common is the **evanescent field coupler**. The basic concept is a narrow spacing between 2 adjacent fiber cores. This allows coupling between the cores, because the electromagnetic fields extend beyond the cores.

Different techniques exist for the production of couplers. Most popular is the **fused biconical taper technique**. At a high temperature, the 2 fibers (twisted or straight) are fused together and stretched. The stretching decreases the size of the fibers and their cores. This causes a broadening of the field and a stronger coupling mechanism. In the **polishing technique**, the 2 fibers are first embedded into glass plates and then polished down to the cores. Joining the glass plates brings the cores into close proximity. The freedom of lateral spacing allows a variable coupling ratio in this case. Finally, the evanescent-field principle has been realized with **integrated waveguides**, e.g. similar to the integrated waveguides in Lithium-Niobate →modulators.

Both multi- and single-mode couplers are available. Models for **single-mode** coupler are often based on the 2 fundamental modes of the coupler, i.e. the **even and odd modes**. Let us assume that the electric field vectors are perpendicular to the direction of propagation and that they are oriented vertically, as indicated in the figure. Than the odd mode travels faster because its electric field extends further into the low-index cladding.

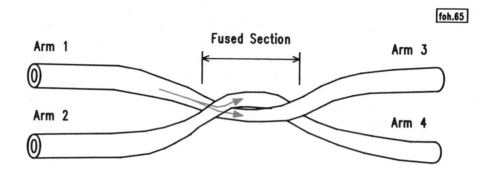

EVANESCENT FIELD COUPLER

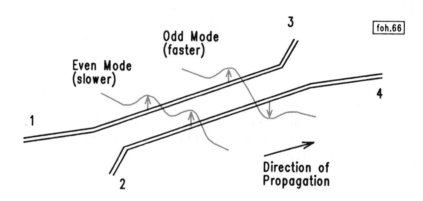

EVEN AND ODD MODES IN A SINGLE-MODE COUPLER
(Input to arm 1, only fiber cores shown)

If optical power is applied to arm 1 only, then the total electric field can be split into an even and an odd mode of equal amplitude. This assumption is valid, because 2 generators, an even-mode generator and an odd-mode generator, would yield the same coupler excitation. The two modes add in arm 1 and cancel in arm 2. After travelling the length L, the odd mode appears advanced against the even mode by an angle ϕ, and the sum of the two modes in arm 4 is no longer zero.

$$\phi = L \left(\beta_{even} - \beta_{odd} \right) = \frac{2\pi L}{\lambda} \left(n_{even} - n_{odd} \right)$$

β - propagation constants
λ - wavelength in vacuum
n - effective refractive indices

The electric field vector at the input of arm 1 shall be assumed to be "E". Then, adding even- and odd-mode vectors at both inputs yields:

$$E_1 = \frac{E}{2} + \frac{E}{2} = E \qquad\qquad E_2 = \frac{E}{2} - \frac{E}{2} = 0$$

In the following, the time-dependences of the electric fields, exp (jωt), are omitted for simplicity. Also omitted are the common phase delays, exp (-jβL), at both outputs:

$$E_3 = \frac{E}{2} + \frac{E}{2} \exp(j\phi) \quad = \frac{E}{\sqrt{2}} \sqrt{1 + \cos\phi} \, \exp(j\phi/2)$$

$$E_4 = \frac{E}{2} - \frac{E}{2} \exp(j\phi) \quad = \frac{E}{\sqrt{2}} \sqrt{1 - \cos\phi} \, \exp(j\phi/2 - j\pi/2)$$

$$= -j \frac{E}{\sqrt{2}} \sqrt{1 - \cos\phi} \, \exp(j\phi/2)$$

PHASE DIAGRAM OF A SINGLE-MODE COUPLER
(The phase shift of both modes due to the length L is neglected)

The result is, that the output of arm 4 is always **delayed** by 90° against arm 3, independent of the coupling length and the strength of the coupling mechanism. This is indicated at the output of arm 4, by the exp (-jπ/2) and the -j.

Another result is that ϕ determines the coupling ratio. $\phi = 0$ means no coupling. A coupler with a 50 % split ratio (3 dB coupler) is based on $\phi = 90°$. If $\phi = 180°$, then no output power is observed in arm 3, and 100 % of the input power appears in arm 4. Altogether a periodic shift of the output power between arms 3 and 4 as a function of the coupling lenght L (and the inverse of the wavelength) is observed.

With an arbitrary input excitation, E_1 and E_2, and by omitting the common phase shift at both outputs, exp (jϕ/2), the following coupler model can be established:

$$E_3 = \quad a \, E_1 - \quad jb \, E_2$$
$$E_4 = -jb \, E_1 + \quad a \, E_2 ,$$

$$\text{with } a^2 + b^2 = 1 \quad \text{(ideally)}$$

a^2 - power coupling coefficient between connected arms
b^2 - power coupling coefficient between coupled arms

All couplers are predominantly characterized by two types of numbers. The **coupling ratio** is the optical power of a single output divided by the total output power. The **excess loss** is the ratio of the total input power divided by the total output power. Both are usually expressed in units of $dB_{optical}$. The excess loss is often less than 0.5 dB in modern couplers. Another figure of merit is the coupler's independence on fiber modes or state of polarization.

The **isolation** of a directional coupler is a measure of the reflected power of arm 2. It is defined by the following equation, under the condition that both output arms 3 and 4 are ideally terminated:

$$\text{Isolation} = 10 \log (P_{in,arm1} / P_{out,arm\ 2})$$

Evanescent field couplers exhibit high isolation; usually more than 50 dB_{opt} is observed. This makes them attractive for the measurement of reflections, e.g. in a →return loss measurement or in an →optical time-domain reflectometer (OTDR).

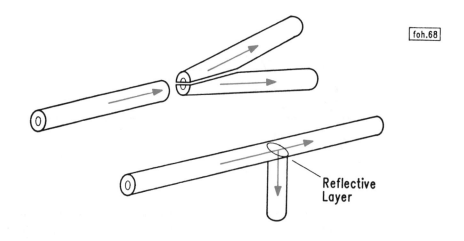

foh.68

COUPLER ALTERNATIVES

A number of other coupler principles have also been realized. One is a joint of an input fiber with two side-by-side output fibers. Another alternative is cutting a fiber at a 45° angle, depositing a partially reflective layer, rejoining the 2 fibers and adding a third fiber. Also possible are combinations of →beam splitters with collimating lenses (or →graded-index lenses). Most of these techniques are more suitable for multimode fibers.

Multiport couplers can be made by fusion of many fibers. One example is the **transmissive star** coupler which is the key device in a star-type →network. It connects each input with all outputs, whereas there is isolation between different inputs. Typically, the inputs are connected to the terminals' transmitters and the outputs are connected to the receivers. Another type of network can be realized with a **reflective star** coupler. In contrast to the transmissive star, its ports are bidirectional, so they are used as inputs and outputs at the same time. Again, each port feeds each other port. Excess losses of less than 2 dB have been realized in couplers with 20 fibers.

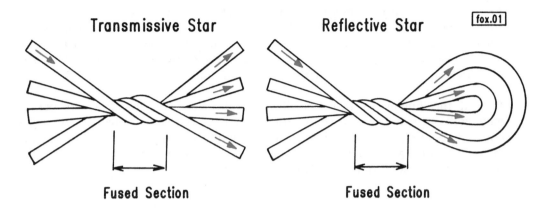

DIFFERENT STAR COUPLERS

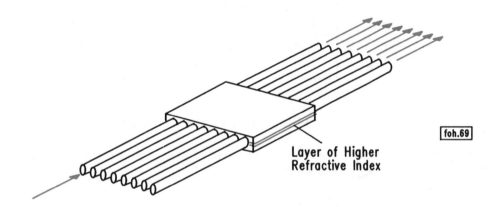

TRANSMISSIVE STAR BASED ON A MIXING PLATE

Another possibility is transmissive and reflective stars based on **mixing plates**. These devices utilize waveguiding in a layer of quartz which is embedded into layers of lower refractive index. The height of the quartz layer is equal to the core diameter of the fibers. Due to the lack of lateral guiding, each input is evenly distributed to all output fibers.

Coupling (Fiber to Fiber)

See the paragraphs →connector (multimode-) and →connector (single mode-).

Coupling (Source to Fiber)

The physics of coupling a source to a multimode fiber may be treated by simple geometrical optics, whereas coupling to single mode fibers should be analyzed by wave optics.

Multimode fiber: mainly two sorts of losses occur when coupling a source to a multimode fiber. These are losses due to area mismatch and losses due to numerical aperture.

Area mismatch occurs when the area illuminated by the source is larger than the core of the fiber. This problem can be solved by using the smallest possible distance between source and fiber (butt coupling), provided the source is smaller than the core. If spacing is unavoidable, a lens can be used for imaging. Trying to reduce the size of the source with a lens will cause numerical aperture problems, see the chapter on →radiance.

Even if the illuminated area is smaller than the fiber core, losses due to **numerical aperture mismatch** occur because the source usually emits into a larger cone than the fiber's acceptance cone. Step-index and graded-index fibers have different acceptance characteristics. The acceptance angle of a graded-index fiber depends on the distance from the core center, in contrast to the constant angle of step-index fibers.

Step−Index Fiber   Graded−Index Fiber

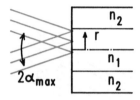 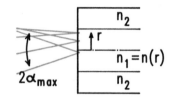

foh.47

FIBER ACCEPTANCE ANGLES

In **step-index fibers**, the linear angle of acceptance, α_{max}, and the →solid angle of acceptance, Ω_{max}, are (assuming α_{max} to be small):

$$\sin \alpha_{max} = NA = (n_1^2 - n_2^2)^{1/2},$$
$$\Omega_{max} = \pi NA^2$$

n_1 - refractive index of the fiber core
n_2 - cladding index
NA → numerical aperture

For the case of **graded-index fibers**, we extract the linear angle α_{max} from the chapter →fiber (multimode-):

$$\sin \alpha_{max} = NA_{local} = [n^2(r) - n_2^2]^{1/2}$$
$$\Omega = \pi (n(r)^2 - n_2^2) \qquad \text{from →solid angle}$$

with $\qquad n(r) \approx \sqrt{ n_1^2 - NA^2 (r/a)^2 } \qquad$ parabolic profile

and $\qquad NA = \sqrt{ n_1^2 - n_2^2 }$

NA_{local} - local numerical aperture

In order to calculate the total coupled power from a surface-emitting LED (SLED), let us first calculate the total **emitted** power P_{total}. An SLED can has the characteristics of a →Lambertian source; the same chapter contains a formula for P_{total}:

$$P_{total} = \pi L_0 A_s = \pi^2 r_s^2 L_0$$

L_0 - (uniform) radiance of the source, normal to the emitting surface
r_s - radius of the source

As a next step, we want to know the **guided** fraction of the power density, M(r), at the input of the fiber. M(r) was computed in the chapter →near field, for the case of an excitation with a Lambertian source:

$$M(r) = \pi L_0 [n(r)^2 - n_2^2] = \pi L_0 NA_{local}^2$$

n(r) - refractive index of the fiber core
n_2 - refractive index of the cladding

Summing all fractions of M(r) yields the total coupled power P_c:

$$P_c = \int_0^{r_{max}} \pi L_0 [n(r)^2 - n_2^2] 2\pi r \, dr$$

r_{max} - core radius a, or source radius r_s, whichever is smaller

Together with the total power P_{total}, the integration delivers the coupling efficiency between a surface-emitting LED (SLED) and multimode fibers. Note that losses due to reflection at the fiber input are not included.

$$\eta = P_c / P_{total}$$

Coupling Efficiency, SLED to step-index fiber:

$$\eta = NA^2 \qquad \text{if source radius} \leqslant \text{core radius}$$

$$\eta = (a / r_s)^2 \, NA^2 \qquad \text{if source radius} > \text{core radius}$$

With a typical NA = 0.3 of step-index fibers, butt-coupling between an SLED and a step-index fiber yields a maximum coupling efficiency of 0.3 x 0.3 = 9 %.

Coupling Efficiency, SLED to graded-index fiber:

$$\eta = NA^2 (1 - \frac{r_s^2}{2a^2}) \qquad \text{if source radius} \leqslant \text{core radius}$$

$$\eta = NA^2 \frac{a^2}{2r_s^2} \qquad \text{if source radius} > \text{core radius}$$

As expected, less power can be coupled to a graded-index fiber: only 50 % of the "step-index" - coupling efficiency is achieved if the source diameter equals the core diameter. It should be noted that a full excitation of all modes is launched into the fiber. Further loss occurs because the fiber will carry an →equilibrium mode distribution a few hundred meters downstream.

Edge-emitting LEDs (ELED) and laser diodes have much smaller beam divergence, resulting in much higher radiance. Following the chapter →Lambertian source, these beam characteristic can be treated by a raised cosine function (parameter m). Fortunately, the source can be assumed to be small in comparison to the fiber core. Therefore, we assume that the source is a point source located at the center of the fiber.

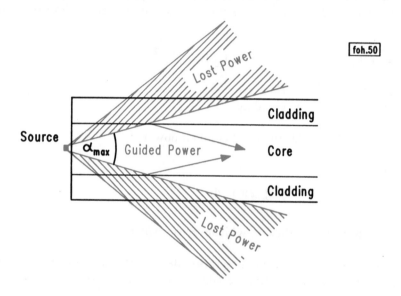

COUPLING A SMALL SOURCE TO A FIBER
(Note that the angle α_{max} is in **front** of the fiber)

The coupled power P_c to both step-index and graded-index fibers is the result of solving the total power-integral for the raised cosine source (see →Lambertian source), except the upper limit is α_{max} instead of $\pi/2$ (= 90°).

Coupled Power: $\quad P_c \quad = 2\pi a^2 H_0 [1 - (\cos\alpha_{max})^{m+1}] / (m + 1)$

Total Power: $\quad P_{total} \quad = 2\pi a^2 H_0 / (m + 1)$

Coupling Efficiency, ELED or laser to step- or graded-index fiber:

$$\eta \quad = 1 - (\cos\alpha_{max})^{m+1} \quad , \quad \text{with} \ \sin \alpha_{max} \ = NA$$

NA - numerical aperture of the fiber
m - parameter defining the source's beam divergence.
    For a Lambertian source use m = 1. The concept of the m-parameter is explained in the chapter →Lambertian source.

Let us construct 2 examples with different numerical apertures of the fiber:

Source divergence (at 50 % power density) ϕ_{HWHM} = 15°
Exponent m calculated from ϕ_{HWHM} m   = 19.9

Numerical apertures NA_1 = 0.2 NA_2 = 0.3
Coupling efficiencies η_1 = 34.7 % η_2 = 62.7 %

Obviously, point-type sources are capable of coupling substantially more power into the fiber.

Further improvement of the coupling efficiency is possible with the help of lenses. The lens produces a larger image of the source, while it reduces its divergence. Of course, this is only useful if the active area of the source is smaller than the core of the fiber.

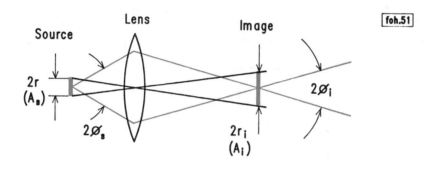

foh.51

EFFECT OF A LENS ON THE CHARACTERISTICS OF A SOURCE

Here, we only want to demonstrate the principal effects of imaging a source to a fiber. Suppose that the diameter of a source is $2r_s$ and the diameter of its image is $2r_i$. Then we have:

Magnification of the system: $m = r_i / r_s$
Reduction of the source's divergence: $\phi_i = \phi_s / m$

The idea is to create an **effective** source from the actual source and the lens, and then to calculate the new coupling efficiency. Possible realizations are bulk lenses, microspheres and domed LEDs.

foh.52

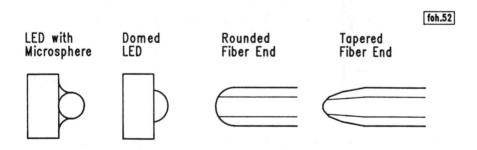

LED with   Domed   Rounded   Tapered
Microsphere   LED   Fiber End   Fiber End

METHODS OF IMPROVING THE COUPLING EFFICIENCY

Another possibility is tapered or rounded fiber ends. The integrated lens increases the fiber's numerical aperture. In the step-index case, the largest aperture, NA_{max}, is observed at the core - cladding boundary. As a first-order approximation, the increased aperture is:

$$NA_{max} = NA + (n-1) a / R$$

NA - numerical aperture of the (flat) step-index fiber
n - refractive index of the fiber core
a - core radius
R - curvature radius of the rounded fiber end

Coupling a source to a **single-mode fiber** should be modeled with the help of wave optics, instead of simple geometric optics. If we assume that both the output of a laser and the input of the fiber can be described by circular symmetric →Gaussian beams, then the coupling efficiency depends on how well the 2 Gaussian beams overlap. An overlap integral can be formulated (not shown here), the result of which was taken from [3.5]:

Coupling efficiency, laser to single-mode fiber:

$$\eta = \eta_{long} \exp \left[-\eta_{long} \frac{x^2}{2} \left(\frac{1}{w_1^2} + \frac{1}{w_0^2} \right) \right] \quad \text{lateral + longitudinal offset}$$

with :
$$\eta_{long} = \frac{4 w_1^2 w_0^2}{(w_1^2 + w_0^2)^2 + \lambda^2 z^2 / \pi^2} \quad \text{longitudinal offset only}$$

x - lateral offset
z - longitudinal offset
w_0 - radius of the fiber's mode field diameter, defined at $1/e^2$ of maximum power density
w_1 - radius of the laser's beam waist, defined at $1/e^2$ of maximum power density

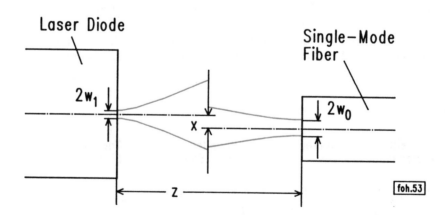

COUPLING A LASER DIODE TO A SINGLE-MODE FIBER

The usual problems of coupling a laser diode to a single-mode fiber are longitudinal spacing and that the laser's beam waist is narrower than the fiber's beam waist. Both problems can be solved with a tapered fiber end, which reduces the fiber's beam waist to w_0* and creates an optimum spacing between the laser and the fiber. In a →Gaussian beam, the beam waist and the beam divergence are related to each other. Therefore, the new beam waist can be evaluated indirectly by measuring the beam divergence $2\alpha_{max}$. To do this, the fiber is excited from the other end.

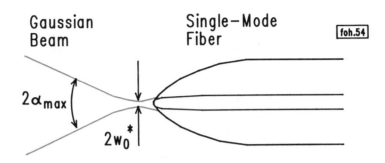

THE EFFECT OF A SINGLE-MODE FIBER TAPER

A typical coupling efficiency between a laser diode and a tapered single-mode fiber is 50%. The taper also reduces the reflection from the fiber end to the laser's resonant cavity, thereby minimizing optical feedback noise. However, any reflections from further downstream couple back to the laser very efficiently.

LED-coupling into single-mode fiber has gained strong commercial interest, particularly for local-area networks and subscriber systems. As expected, the lowest coupling efficiency is accomplished with surface-emitting LEDs, because of their low radiance. Improvement is possible with edge-emitting LEDs, LED doming and fiber tapering. Modeling is again based on wave optics. However, the situation is further complicated by the fact that the LED emission is only **partially coherent** is space, i.e. the wavefront is a statistically changing rough surface. The consequence is destructive interference in the fiber and a reduction of the theoretically coupling efficiency by a factor of 10, depending on the degree of coherence [3.6].

Coupling Length

In multimode fibers, a linear dependence of the pulse broadening is predicted by the theory of →multimode dispersion. Beyond the so-called coupling length the pulse width is only increased with the square root of the length, due to mode mixing. See →multimode dispersion.

Critical Angle

The angle of total reflection, see →reflection and refraction.

Cutback Method

The measurement of fiber characteristics such as →attenuation and →dispersion depends on the input coupling characteristics. As these are hard to control, the cutback idea is to leave this parameter constant for both the item and the reference measurements: First the characteristics of the long fiber are measured, then the fiber is cut back to a length of 1 or 2 meters for the reference measurement. The disadvantage of this method is its destructive nature.

Cutoff Wavelength

A single-mode fiber supports only one mode (the →fundamental mode), if the wavelength is longer than the cutoff wavelength. Below this wavelength more modes may be guided. See →modes (fiber-).

A first definition of the cutoff wavelength can be derived from a solution of Maxwell's equation e.g. for a step-index single mode fiber. One of the results is the "normalized frequency" parameter, V, which can be used to distinguish guided modes from unguided modes:

$$V = \frac{2\pi a}{\lambda} \sqrt{n_1^2 - n_2^2} = \frac{2\pi a}{\lambda} n_1 \sqrt{2\Delta}, \quad \text{with}$$

$$\Delta = (n_1^2 - n_2^2) / 2n_1^2 \simeq (n_1 - n_2) / n_1$$

a - radius of the fiber core
λ - wavelength in vacuum
n_1 - refractive index of the core
n_2 - refractive index of the cladding
Δ - refractive index contrast

The fundamental mode, HE_{11}, is always guided, i.e. for all values of V and all wavelengths. In this sense, it can be compared to the fundamental mode of a coaxial (electrical) cable. The next-order mode, TE_{11} resp. LP_{11}, is only guided if V is larger than 2.405, i.e. if the wavelength is shorter than the cutoff wavelength. For modes of higher order, the critical wavelength is shorter. From this concept, the cutoff wavelength is the minimum wavelength which guarantees the propagation of one mode only. Therefore, the condition for single-mode operation is:

$$V < V_{min} = 2.405$$

$$\lambda > \lambda_{cutoff} = 3.7 \, a \, n_1 \sqrt{\Delta}$$

Practical measurements show that the borderline between guided and unguided modes is not so distinct: the attenuation of the unguided modes beyond the cutoff-wavelength does not increase dramatically. Depending on the wavelength and the curvature of the fiber, higher-order modes can still be detected (e.g. by →near-field measurements) after many meters.

Today's international convention on the measurement of the cutoff wavelength is based on the observation that the attenuation of the higher-order modes strongly increases with the fiber's curvature. In contrast, the effect of bending on the fundamental mode is negligible. The **transmitted power technique** is similar to a spectral attenuation measurement, and the two measurement setups are identical. See the paragraph on →attenuation (fiber-).

Let us use the CCITT-recommendation G.652 as an example: a source of white light is filtered with a tunable monochromator to yield a spectral width of not more than 10 nm (FWHM). It is then launched to a 2 m - piece of single mode fiber, which forms a single loop of 280 mm diameter. At each wavelength point, the power output is recorded. In a second measurement, an additional fiber loop (typical diameter 60 mm or less) is formed behind the first loop. Near the cutoff wavelength, the second loop strongly attenuates any higher-order modes. Effectively, the loop decreases the cutoff wavelength. The power output is recorded again. Now, the two curves are displayed in the form of a **power ratio** R(λ):

$$R(\lambda) = 10 \log [P_{straight}(\lambda) / P_{loop}(\lambda)]$$

The cutoff wavelength was defined as the wavelength at which the power ratio is 0.1 dB larger than the ratio at long wavelengths.

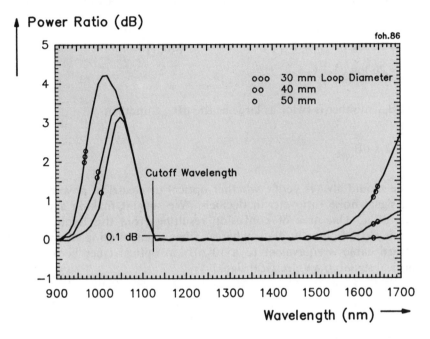

MEASUREMENT OF THE CUTOFF-WAVELENGTH

Another result of this measurement is the strong bending-sensitivity of the fundamental mode at wavelengths beyond 1500 nm.

System designers choose fibers with cutoff-wavelengths near the operating wavelength, e.g. $\lambda_{cutoff} = 1270$ nm at $\lambda_{system} = 1300$ nm. One reason is the optimization of the →spot size and the related →waveguide dispersion. Another reason is bending sensitivity, which depends on the difference between cutoff wavelength and operating wavelength. The latter effect is again caused by the wavelength-dependence of the spot size.

Dark Current

See →PIN-diode and →noise (photodiode-).

dB (electrical), dB (optical)

Using decibels (dB) in conjunction with fiber optics sometimes causes confusion because the same ratio of optical signals may result in different dB numbers. Let us use an example where $P_{opt\ 1}$ and $P_{opt\ 2}$ are the input and output to an optical component with attenuation A. We also assume that the optical powers are measured with a detector: the photocurrent I is proportional to P_{opt}.

$$A_{opt} = 10 \log (P_{opt1} / P_{opt2}) \qquad [dB_{opt}]$$
$$= 10 \log (I_1 / I_2)$$

We now assume P_{el1} and P_{el2} are the electrical powers generated by the currents I_1 and I_2, P_{el} being proportional to the square of I. In terms of electrical power, the attenuation must be calculated as:

$$A_{el} = 10 \log (P_{el1} / P_{el2}) \qquad [dB_{el}]$$
$$= 20 \log (I_1 / I_2)$$

Notice that the dB_{el} number is twice as large as the dB_{opt} number:

$$dB_{el} = 2 \times dB_{opt}$$

In conclusion, one should always verify whether optical or electrical power was used to calculate attenuation, signal/noise ratio etc. in decibels. We suggest making a clear distinction by writing dB_{opt} or dB_{el}. One area of confusion resulting from this is quite common: coaxial cable attenuation is always given in dB_{el}, whereas fiber attenuation is always in dB_{opt}. Thus a 20 dB/km electrical cable is equivalent to a 10 dB/km optical fiber because of the need to reconvert the optical signal to an electrical signal.

dBm

One milliwatt of optical power is used as a reference when specifying an absolute optical power level P_{opt} in terms of dBm:

$$dBm_{opt} = 10 \log (P_{opt} / 1 \text{ mW})$$

System characteristics are often given as a function of the power level in dBm. Most often this parameter refers to the time-average level of the modulated optical power.

Densitiy

See →optical density.

Detectivity

The normalized detectivity D* is used for the description of the sensitivity of photodiodes. The definition of D* below was established in order to make photodetectors with different active areas comparable. It is based on photodetector physics, which require the noise equivalent power (NEP) to be proportional to the square root of the area and the sqare root of the measurement bandwidth.

$$D^* = \frac{\sqrt{A_d \, B}}{NEP} \qquad [\; \frac{\sqrt{cm^2 \; Hz}}{W} \;]$$

A_d - active area of the photodetector [mm^2]
B - measurement bandwidth [Hz]
NEP - noise equivalent power [W]

DFB Laser

Stable single-mode operation of laser diodes is necessary both for high-bandwidth "direct-detection" →systems and for coherent →systems. Several special laser diodes have been invented in order to suppress the usual multimode behaviour, one of which is the C^3-laser [4.7]. Most popular is the buried-heterostructure **distributed-feedback** (DFB) laser in the double-channel form [4.3]. Also, it is the only single-mode laser diode which is commercially available today.

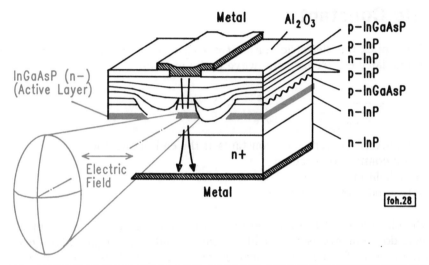

DFB - LASER WITH DOUBLE-CHANNEL BURIED HETEROSTRUCTURE (DC-BH)

Because of the **double-channel (DC)** construction, this diode belongs to the class of index-guided lasers, in which the current flow is additionally channeled by 2 lateral negative-biased pn-junctions. Optical guiding is provided by the lower refractive index of the material that surrounds the active zone. The DC construction is also used for conventional multimode lasers.

Maximum output power	5 mW
Threshold current	40 mA
... temperature coefficient	1.3 mA/K
Characteristic temperature	78 K
Differential gain	70 µW/mA
Modulation bandwidth	600 MHz
Wavelength	1300 nm (1550 nm also available)
... temperature coefficient	0.07 nm/K
Spectral bandwidth	20 MHz (unmodulated)

TYPICAL CHARACTERISTICS OF DFB - DOUBLE CHANNEL LASERS

The additional feature of this laser is the corrugated waveguide adjacent to the active zone. The corrugation creates multiple reflections; stable oscillation is only possible when all reflections interfere constructively. With a desired wavelength of 1300 nm and a refractive index of 3.3, the grating period must be 1300 nm / 3.3 = 390 nm. This mechanism selects one specific mode from the possible laser modes and suppresses all others. One problem remains: two-mode (two-frequency) operation is possible, depending on the location of the facets with respect to the phase of the grating. In order to avoid a competition between the →Fabry-Perot modes of the entire chip and the grating modes, antireflection coating of the main output facet is advisable [4.4].

Dichroic Filter

See →polarizer.

Dielectric Constant

In the field of optics, the dielectric constant $\epsilon = \epsilon_0 \epsilon_r$ of a medium is related to →phase velocity of an unmodulated electromagnetic wave in the medium:

$$V_{ph} = \frac{1}{\sqrt{\mu_0 \epsilon_0 \epsilon_r}} = \frac{c}{\sqrt{\epsilon_r}} = \frac{c}{n}$$

μ_0 - permeability of vacuum, see →constants at the end of the book
ϵ_0 - dielectric constant of vacuum
c - speed of light in vacuum
n - refractive index of the material

Note that the classical electrical method of measuring the dielectric constant, i.e. via measuring a capacitance, does not necessarily yield the same results. A major difference between the 2 methods is the large difference in frequencies involved (optical frequency vs. radio frequency).

Differential Mode Attenuation

See →modes (fiber-) and →attenuation.

Differential Mode Delay

See →multimode dispersion, →modes in a fiber.

Diffraction

This term describes the bending of light rays exiting a narrow opening or passing an edge. The far fields of a →laser diode and that of a single mode fiber is strongly influenced by diffraction.

Diffraction Grating

In the field of fiber optics, diffraction gratings serve 3 main purposes:
1. as wavelength-selective filters in →monochromators;
2. as multiplexers and demultiplexers in →wavelength-division multiplexing (WDM);
3. as wavelength-selective reflectors for the external cavity of tunable lasers.

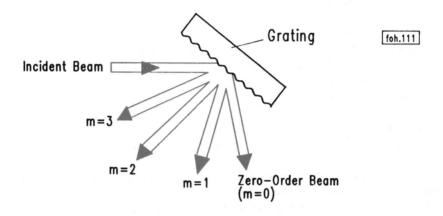

foh.111

DIFFRACTION GRATING
Example for $\lambda/d = 0.4$

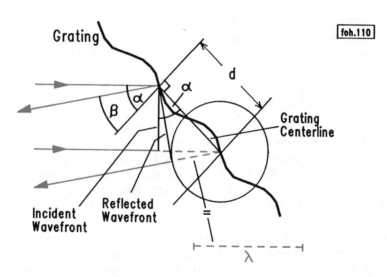

foh.110

DERIVATION OF THE BASIC GRATING EQUATION
Example for $\lambda/d = 1.25$. The radius of the circle is set by:
Total length of the dashed line = wavelength λ

A diffraction grating is basically a mirror into which grooves of extremely narrow spacing are engraved. A typical distance (d) is 0.8 µm (1200 lines per mm). If a parallel light beam of a certain wavelength falls on the grating surface, then each groove produces a cylindrical wave. Depending on the wavelength, these waves form new (discrete) beam directions. The zero-order beam (m = 0) is the one which you would expect from a plane mirror: its incident angle equals the angle of reflection. The first-order beam (m = 1) is generated if the partial waves from neighboring grooves produce a path-length difference of **one** wavelength. The second-order beam (m = 2) is based on a difference of two wavelengths, and so on.

In the illustration, the zero-order beam is omitted. Simple geometric manipulation leads to the **basic grating equation**, which relates the incident and excitant angles:

$$d \left(\sin \alpha + \sin \beta \right) = m \lambda$$

d - distance of the grooves
α - angle of the incident beam against the surface normal
β - angle of the refracted beam against the surface normal
m - order of the refracted beam
λ - wavelength (here in air)

Very often, only the first-order beam is utilized. In fact, if λ is larger than the groove spacing d, then the second order beam does not exist (i.e. there is no solution of the grating equation).

A **special case** is a grating which reflects the first order into the direction of the incident beam. This type of grating is used for the external cavity of tunable lasers and for →wavelength-division multiplexers. In this case, the first-order beam is defined by:

$$\sin \alpha = \sin \beta = \frac{\lambda}{2d}$$

The most important capability of a grating is to diffract different wavelengths into different angles. The **angular dispersion** expresses the change of angle caused by a change of wavelength. This can be obtained by calculating the derivative of β with respect to wavelength. It turns out that the angular dispersion is proportional to the inverse of the spacing d:

$$\frac{\Delta \beta}{\Delta \lambda} = \frac{m}{d \cos \beta}$$

The excitant angles do **not** depend on the microscopic shape of the grooves. However, the power distribution between the zero-order and the first-order beams can be strongly influenced by the shape of the grooves. A **blazed** grating is optimized in such a way that the **microscopic** reflection is into the direction which is set by the grating equation. Note that the exact angle depends on the wavelength. More than 90 % efficiency can be obtained this way (efficiency = power ratio between the first-order beam and the incident beam).

With a parallel input beam of one wavelength only, an ideal diffraction grating would produce a parallel refracted beam (e.g. of the first order). An image formed by an ideal lens would be a spot. However, the superposition of partial waves results in a divergent beam, and the image is a $\sin^2 x / x^2$ function. A formula from reference [0.2] relates the full width (w) of the image to the number of contributing grooves:

$$w = L \Delta \beta = L \frac{\lambda}{N d \cos \beta}$$

$\Delta \beta$ - divergence of the refracted beam (ideally zero)
L - focal length of the lens
N - number of contributing grooves of the grating

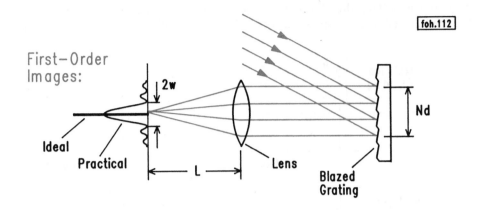

EXPLANATION OF THE SELECTIVITY
In this case: $\beta = 0$, $N = 4$, $\lambda/d = 0.45$

N x d is the beam diameter. For the best separation of different wavelengths, it is therefore advisable to use a grating with large angular dispersion **and** a large beam diameter. For further information on diffraction gratings, see, for example, [0.2].

Dispersion

The technical term for pulse broadening is dispersion, which can be split into →multimode dispersion and →chromatic dispersion. Also, see →bandwidth (fiber-).

Dispersion-Shifted Fiber

Standard single-mode fibers exhibit optimum attenuation-performance at 1550 nm and optimum bandwidth-performance (chromatic dispersion) at 1300 nm. This problem can either be solved with narrow-linewidth lasers or with dispersion-shifted fibers (DSF), using the 1550 nm wavelength. The basic concept of DSF is compensation of the material dispersion and waveguide dispersion, in order to obtain low chromatic dispersion for a wide range of wavelengths (e.g. 1300 to 1550 nm). For a better understanding of this concept, see the chapter on →chromatic dispersion.

Waveguide dispersion is caused by the fact that the (Gaussian) spot in the fiber increases with wavelength. The effect is independent on the wavelength-dependence of the refractive indices of core and cladding. In standard SM fiber with either matched cladding or depressed cladding, waveguide dispersion is very small. In contrast, W-fibers and Quadruple-Cladding (QC) fibers exhibit a much stronger waveguide dispersion. The result is that the material dispersion can be compensated to yield a total chromatic dispersion below 4 ps/km x nm for the wavelength range of 1300 to 1550 nm.

One disadvantage of DS-fibers is their higher sensitivity to bending, which is due to a larger spot size. Bending sensitivity is particularly strong in simple W-fibers; fibers with more complex profiles such as QC-fibers have been invented to reduce this effect. Another disadvantage of DS-fibers is their increased attenuation, which is due to more doping material in the fiber. Therefore, these fibers have not gained strong commercial importance. Instead, the fiber optics industry aims at solving the chromatic dispersion problem with narrow-linewidth sources, which are required for coherent systems anyway. A recent publication on DS-fibers is [3.12].

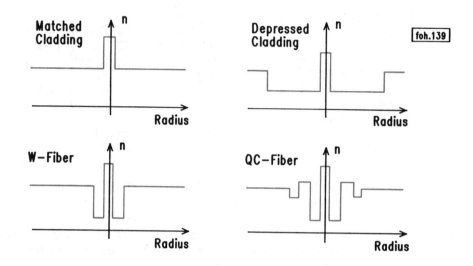

TYPICAL SINGLE-MODE FIBER PROFILES
Standard fiber: Matched Cladding, Depressed Cladding
Dispersion-Shifted Fiber: W-Fiber, QC-Fiber

Distributed-Feedback (DFB) Laser

A semiconductor laser which is capable of producing a single wavelength (frequency). See →DFB laser.

Double Refraction

See →birefringence.

Double-Window Fiber

This term is used in 2 different ways: in conjunction with multimode fibers, it means a compromize in →multimode dispersion for 2 different wavelengths (e.g. 850 and 1300 nm). In conjunction with single mode fibers, it is used for a compromize in →chromatic dispersion performance at 2 different wavelengths (e.g. 1300 nm and 1550 nm).

Effective Mode Volume (EMV)

EMV is one way to describe the distribution of modes (mode filling) in multimode fibers. See →equilibrium mode distribution (EMD).

Electric Field

Optical power is nothing else than electromagnetic radiation. In the most simple case, the power is transported in a TEM-wave, which means that the electric and magnetic fields are perpendicular to the direction of propagation and also perpendicular to each other. Free-wave propagation far from the transmitter **and** bound propagation in a single mode fiber come close to this model.

From the electric field, the local power density (irradiance) can be calculated. Let us assume:

$$E(t) = E_0 \cos \omega_c t \qquad\qquad [\ V/m\ ]$$

E_0 - Amplitude of the electric field
ω_c - 2π x optical frequency

The power density H can be calculated with the help of the →characteristic impedance Z_0. Time-average is indicated by bracketing < > .

$$H = <E(t)^2> / Z_0 = <E_0^2 \ (1 + \cos 2\omega_c t)> / 2Z_0$$
$$H = E_0^2 / 2Z_0$$

The relation between power density and electric field is important for the treatment of →reflections and →interference.

Electro-Optic Effect

This term describes the change of a material's refractive index under the influence of an electric field. Because the change of index is often in one direction only, another name would be "induced birefringence". The classic electro-optic material is Lithium-Niobate ($LiNbO_3$). See the paragraph →birefringence (in bulk material). The effect can be used to build optical →modulators.

Equilibrium Mode Distribution (EMD)

A graded-index fiber with a 50 µm core typically allows around 500 different core modes, each of them having different propagation- and attenuation characteristics. Mode mixing (also called mode coupling) at fiber imperfections such as microbending and ellipticity transfers power from one mode to another one. Additionally, higher-order modes experience higher losses. The result is, that beyond a certain length of fiber a steady-state distribution of fiber modes can be observed to be independent of the launching conditions. This is called EMD and contains fewer modes than the number above. In modern fibers with low mode-mixing, the equilibrium is only observed after many kilometers.

In the measurement of →attenuation or →bandwidth of graded-index fibers, it is important to apply an EMD to the input of the fiber under test. This would imply that the EMD of the fiber under test would have to be characterized first, because the EMD varies from fiber to fiber. This is not very practical; therefore, the fiber optic community decided to use a **fixed EMD**, with the expectation that this EMD is not to far from the ideal EMD.

Accordingly, the EMD of 50/125 μm graded-index fiber was standardized [1.5] with the help of the **effective mode volume** parameter, EMV, which is based on measurements of the →near field and the →far field:

$$EMV = (D_{eff} \, NA_{eff})^2$$

with: $D_{eff} = 26 \, \mu m$ and $NA_{eff} = 0.11$

D_{eff} - FWHM →near field diameter (spot diameter)
NA_{eff} - FWHM numerical aperture in the →far field
Don't confuse NA_{eff} with →NA, which is taken from the 5 % angle.

The question is: how can the EMD be generated ? By definition, a long fiber (2 to 10 km) generates an EMD. This fiber can then be used to drive the fiber under test. More economically, a combination of lenses and apertures can be used to create the so-called **70% - condition** at the input of the test fiber: the fiber is excited with a spot size of 70 ±5% of the core diameter (measured at the points of 5% power density) and with a numerical aperture (again measured at the points of 5 % power density) of 70 ±5% of the fiber's →numerical aperture. Experience shows that this excitation creates a modal distribution which comes close to the EMD as defined above. This can by verified by cutting the fiber near the input end.

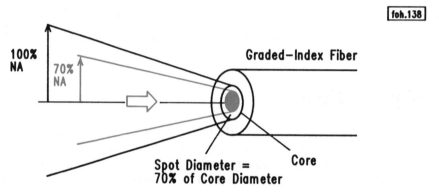

EQUILIBRIUM MODE EXCITATION OF A GRADED-INDEX FIBER

More convenient than launch optics are mode filters in conjunction with mode strippers; see the paragraph on →mode filter.

In **step-index** fibers, the EMD also contains fewer modes than the fully excited state. Again, the main reason is stronger attenuation of the higher-order modes. In a **single-mode fiber**, the equilibrium state is characterized by the propagation of the fundamental mode only. If the operating wavelength is larger than the →cutoff-wavelength, then the equilibrium is accomplished after a few meters of fiber.

Equivalent Step-Index Profile

The equivalent step-index profile is used for single-mode fibers with complex refractive index profiles in order to describe their basic properties with just 2 numbers: the core diameter and the →refractive index contrast. See →normalized frequency and →dispersion-shifted fibers.

Extended-Frequency Fibers

This term is applied to single-mode fibers which are optimized for low chromatic dispersion in a wide range of wavelengths. See the paragraph on →dispersion-shifted fibers.

Extinction Ratio

The ratio of the high-level optical power to the low-level optical power in a transmission system, be it analog or digital, is called extinction ratio. In contrast to electrical systems, the low level in high speed transmission systems cannot become zero, nor can the signal be made symmetrical to zero. This is due to the requirement of operating the laser at or above the threshold level, which is typically 1 mW for a double-heterostructure laser, see →laser diode. Below threshold the laser diode considerably looses speed and linearity. In lower-speed LED-systems the light can be switched on and off, making the extinction ratio virtually infinite.

System designers require the extinction ratio to be larger than 10, because the noise attributed to the low level is small if the low level is close to zero. See →noise (photodiode-).

Eye Pattern

The proper function of a digital system can be quantitatively described by its →bit error rate (BER), or qualitatively by its eye pattern. The eye pattern is obtained by applying the digital data stream to the vertical amplifier of an oscilloscope and triggering the scope with the system's clock. See the measurement setup in the chapter on →bit error rate.

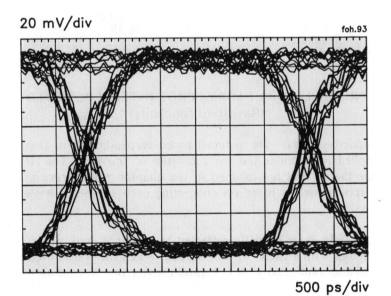

20 mV/div   foh.93

500 ps/div

EYE PATTERN OF A 300 Mbit/s NRZ DATA STREAM

The quality of the eye pattern, critical for achieving a low BER, is influenced by two phenomena. One is noise, which is proportional to the receiver's bandwidth, see →receiver. The other phenomenon is intersymbol interference, which arises from other bits interfering with the bit of interest. The intersymbol interference is inversely proportional to the bandwidth. This way, a bandwidth-compromise has to be made for the best possible eye aperture.

Fabry-Perot Interferometer (FPI)

Interferometers are generally used for narrow-band, high-resolution optical spectrum analysis, i.e. whenever the resolution of grating-type monochromators is not sufficient. The most simple form of an interferometer is the Fabry-Perot interferometer (FPI), which is nothing else than a tunable optical resonator. 2 parallel, partially transparent mirrors is the classical form of the FPI. Generally, these mirrors are highly reflective (up to 99 %), in order to reduce the optical bandwidth. Multilayer dielectric coatings deposited on quartz substrates are commonly used as high-performance mirrors.

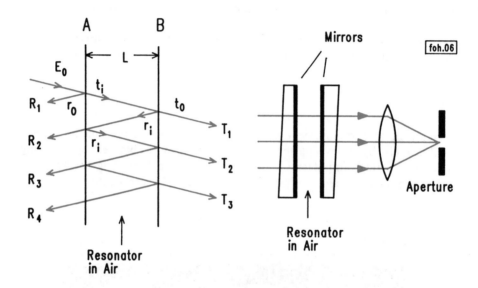

PRINCIPLE OF A FABRY-PEROT INTERFEROMETER
(Rays tilted for clarity)

For reasons of simplicity, all rays are assumed to be perpendicular to the mirror surfaces. 2 methods can be applied to calculate the characteristics of this FPI. The first method is based on transmission line theory and is explained in the chapter →**interference**. Here we want to apply a second method which is based on computing each of the multiple reflections in the cavity.

The incident electric field E_0 is partially reflected at mirror A with a factor r_o (for outside), and partially transmitted with a factor t_i (for inside). When the transmitted field passes mirror B, it appears delayed and multiplied with t_o behind the mirror. Accordingly, the partial electric field T_1 is:

$$T_1 = t_i t_o\, E_0 \exp(-j\beta L) = t\, E_0 \exp(-j\beta L),$$

with
$$t = t_i t_o$$
$$\beta L = 2\pi n L / \lambda = 2\pi n L f / c$$
$$\exp(-j\beta L) = \cos\beta L - j\sin\beta L,\quad j = \sqrt{-1}$$

λ - wavelength in vacuum
L - length of the resonator cavity
n - refractive index of the resonant cavity
f - optical frequency
c - speed of light in vacuum, $c = 3 \times 10^8$ m/s

The partial electric field T_2 results from 2 more reflections (r_i^2) and an additional phase delay ($-2\beta L$) due to twice the length L of the resonator:

$$T_2 = t \, r_i^2 \, E_0 \exp(-j3\beta L) = t \, r \, E_0 \exp(-j3\beta L),$$

with $\qquad r = r_i^2$

Now, the addition of all partial fields is easily accomplished. The total **transmitted** electric field T is:

$$T = T_1 + T_2 + T_3 + + +$$
$$= t \, E_0 \exp(-j\beta L) \left[1 + r \exp(-j2\beta L) + r^2 \exp(-j4\beta L) + + + \right]$$

$$T = t \, E_0 \frac{\exp(-j\beta L)}{1 - r \exp(-j2\beta L)} \qquad \text{(after series summation)}$$

A measurement wiil only yield the **power density** (irradiance, W/m^2), not the electric field. The irradiances can be calculated using :

$$H = E \, E^* / 2Z_0 \quad \text{with} \qquad$$

E - electric field amplitude
E^* - conjugate complex of E
Z_0 - characteristic impedance of air (377 Ω)

The result is the transmitted irradiance H_t. Additionally, the requirement for energy conservation yields the reflected irradiance H_r :

$$H_t = H_0 \frac{(1-r)^2}{(1-r)^2 + 4r \sin^2 \beta L}$$

$$H_r = H_0 \frac{4r \sin^2 \beta L}{(1-r)^2 + 4r \sin^2 \beta L}$$

with $\qquad H_0 = E_0^2 / (2Z_0) \qquad$ (incident power density)

$\qquad r = r_i^2 = r_o^2 \qquad$ (power-reflection coefficient)

The resonant behaviour of both the transmitted and reflected power is obvious. Independent of the actual mirror-reflectivity r, the transmitted power is 100 % and the reflected power is 0 whenever $\sin \beta L = 0$. A physical understanding of this situation may be helpful: at resonance, the electric field in the resonator is much stronger than the incident field. Despite of the high reflectivity of mirror A, the electric field leaking through mirror A (in the backward direction) is therefore strong enough to create complete destructive interference with the field that is directly reflected at mirror A.

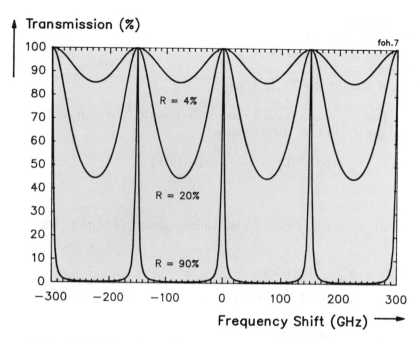

TRANSMISSION OF AN IDEAL FABRY-PEROT RESONATOR
(Resonator Length L = 1 mm, Refractive Index n = 1)

The following equation establishes the resonant frequencies f_m (wavelengths) of the FPI:

$$\sin \beta L = 0$$
$$\beta L = m \pi$$

$$f_m = \frac{m \, c}{2 \, L \, n}$$

m - any integer > 0
c - speed of light in vacuum, $c = 3 \times 10^8$ m/s
L - length of the resonant cavity
n - refractive index of the resonant cavity

More interesting than the absolute resonant frequencies is the spacing between them, called **mode spacing** or **free spectral range FSR**. We obtain from the above equation:

$$\text{FSR (f)} = c \, / \, (\, 2nL) \qquad \text{in terms of frequency}$$
$$\text{FSR } (\lambda) = \lambda^2 \, / \, (2nL) \qquad \text{in terms of wavelength}$$

The example in the diagram was calculated using a resonator length L = 1 mm, with a refractive index n = 1. The result is a free spectral range of FSR (f) = 150 GHz, or FSR (λ) = 0.85 nm. The **reflected** power density is complementary to the displayed curves. The example was chosen such that the FSR is identical to the mode spacing of usual 1300 nm laser diodes.

Somewhat arbitrarily, the bandwidth B of the individual resonance curves is usually defined as the full width at half maximum (FWHM), independent of the actual minimum. With this definition, the bandwidth is:

$$B = \frac{1 - r}{\sqrt{r}} \quad \frac{c}{2\pi nL} \qquad [\text{ Hz }]$$

Relating the bandwidth B to the mode spacing FSR yields the **finesse F**:

$$F = \frac{FSR}{B} = \frac{\pi \sqrt{r}}{1 - r} \qquad [\text{ dimensionless }]$$

With practical resonators, both the 100 % transmission and the ideal bandwidth / finesse cannot be achieved. Reasons are losses in the optical system, finite mirror flatness, non-parallel mirrors and non-parallel beams.

Because of their narrow bandwidth, FPIs are capable of measuring the linewidth of the individual modes. To do this, the FPI must be tuned by changing the resonator length L (**scanning FPI**). The output power is measured for each L; this way, the entire spectrum is sampled. In order to avoid ambiguities, the tuning range should not exceed the free spectral range FSR. In this type of measurement, a monochromator can be used in order to preselect an individual laser mode. One of the problems in this measurement is the reflection back to the laser source: FPIs strongly reflect when not in resonance.

For excercise, we want to construct an FPI for the linewidth measurement of an individual line of a 1300 nm laser diode. Listed below are laser data and FPI design goals as derived from the laser data.

Laser Data / FPI Data	Wavelength		Frequency	
Laser center wavelength	**1300**	**nm**	230	THz
Laser mode spacing	**0.9**	**nm**	160	GHz
Expected laser linewidth	1.12	pm	**200**	**MHz**
Selected FPI mode spacing (FSR)	11.3	pm	**2**	**GHz**
Selected FPI tuning range	11.3	pm	**2**	**GHz**
Selected FPI bandwidth (B)	0.11	pm	**20**	**MHz**

FABRY-PEROT INTERFEROMETER EXAMPLE

"pm" is used for picometers. The following formulas were used to relate frequency (f, Δf) and wavelength (λ, $\Delta\lambda$):

$$\lambda = c / f \quad \text{and} \qquad \Delta\lambda = \lambda^2 \Delta f / c$$

Now, the actual FPI data can be calculated, using the above formulae. As expected, the necessary mechanical movement of the mirror in order to scan 1 FSR, ΔL, is identical to half the wavelength.

Necessary resonator length from FSR :	L = 75 mm
Necessary finesse from bandwidth B :	F = 100
Necessary mirror reflectivity :	r = 97 %
Necessary movement of mirror (1 FSR):	ΔL = 0.65 μm

Mirror movements on the order of one wavelength are usually accomplished with piezoelectric drives. Those small movements indicate the necessity for highest mechanical precision. For further information on Fabry-Perots, see [0.4].

Failure Rate

The failure rate describes the number of failures of a device per unit of time, e.g. per hour. See →reliability.

Faraday Effect

Some materials including quartz and yttrium-iron-garnet (YIG), are capable of rotating the orientation of linearly polarized light under the influence of a magnetic field. The magnetic field orientation must be parallel to the direction of propagation. The angle of rotation is proportional to the field strength and the thickness of the material. This effect can be used to build →modulators and →isolators.

The angle of rotation Θ is expressed by the **Verdet-constant** V:

$$\Theta = V\,d\,H$$

H - (uniform) magnetic field, parallel to the beam
d - optical path length in the material

Magnetically induced rotation is **non-reciprocal**, which means that the orientation of the electric field appears rotated by 2Θ after being reflected behind the crystal. See the illustration in the chapter →isolator. In contrast, the natural circular →birefringence in quartz produces a 0° rotation upon reflection, i.e. the reflected electric field has the same orientation as the incident field.

Far Field

Intuitively, the far field of a light source is the power density measured on the surface of a sphere, with the source located in the center of the sphere. Far-field analysis is important for the measurement of the the →numerical aperture of sources and fibers. The fiber's mode filling (see →equilibrium mode distribution) can also be determined by far-field analysis.

The far field and the →near field of a source are related by the Hankel transform. In this paragraph, we want to follow a more intuitive path. Therefore, we partition the fiber end into a number of concentric rings. Each ring (ring radius r) generates a cone of light with **constant** power density (irradiance). The numerical aperture of the cone equals the "local" numerical aperture at the radius r. Summation (integration) of the irradiances of all cones yields the total far field.

In the case of a **step-index** (multimode) fiber with a mode filling of 100 %, the "local" numerical aperture equals the fiber's numerical aperture NA and does not depend on the (near-field) radius r. Consequently, all rings generate cones of the same shape. The far field is constant, and it decreases to zero at an angle which corresponds to the numerical aperture.

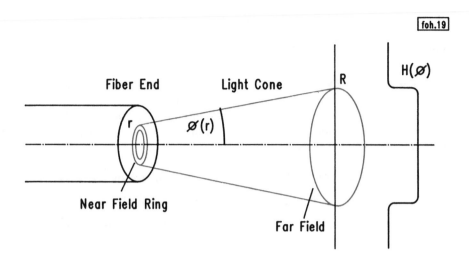

foh.19

MODEL FOR COMPUTING THE FAR FIELD OF A FIBER
Each ring of the fiber end generates a light cone with constant irradiance.

$$H(\phi) = H_0 \qquad \text{for angles } \phi \text{ between 0 and } \phi_{max}$$
$$\quad\ = 0 \qquad\ \text{for angles } \phi > \phi_{max}$$

$$\sin \phi_{max} = NA = \sqrt{n_1^2 - n_2^2}$$

NA - numerical aperture
n_1 - refractive index of the core
n_2 - refractive index of the cladding

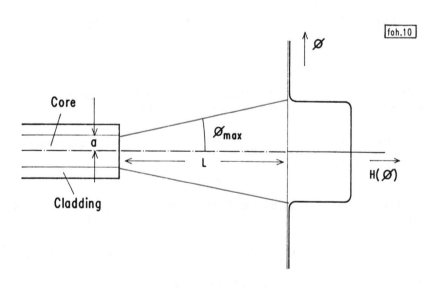

foh.10

IDEAL FAR FIELD OF A STEP-INDEX FIBER
(planar representation)

A relation between the fiber's total power output P_{total} and the far field irradiance H_0 can be found by integration of the far field:

$$P_{total} = \pi H_0 L^2 NA^2 \qquad \text{for the step-index fiber}$$

L - distance between fiber end and illuminated area

In the case of a **graded-index fiber**, the "local" numerical aperture decreases with increasing (near-field) radius r. In the process of summing all far fields at a certain angle $\phi(r)$, it turns out that near-field rings with a radius $r > r_{max}$ don't contribute to the far-field irradiance at that angle. In the case of 100 % mode filling of a graded-index fiber with **parabolic** profile, r_{max} can be calculated from the following equations:

$$NA_{local}^2 = \sin^2 \phi(r) = n(r)^2 - n_2^2 \qquad \text{square of local NA}$$

$$n(r)^2 = n_1^2 - NA^2 r^2 / a^2 \qquad \text{parabolic profile}$$

$$NA^2 = n_1^2 - n_2^2, \qquad \text{from} \rightarrow \text{fiber (multimode)}$$

Therefore:

$$r_{max}^2 = a^2 (1 - NA_{local}^2 / NA^2)$$

r   - radius in the near field
a   - core radius
n(r) - refractive index as a function of the radius r
n_1 - refractive index of the center of the core
n_2 - refractive index of the cladding

We further need the power density (exitance) at the fiber output for the far-field calculation. Therefore we borrow a formula for the uniformly filled fiber from the chapter $\rightarrow$near field:

$$M(r) = M_0 \frac{n(r)^2 - n_2^2}{n_1^2 - n_2^2} \qquad \text{inside the core}$$

$$M(r) = 0 \qquad \text{outside the core}$$

Without further explanation of the integration process, here is the result. The ideal far field of a fully excited graded-index fiber with **parabolic** profile is:

$$H(\phi) = H_0 (1 - NA_{local}^2 / NA^2) \qquad \text{for } \phi \text{ between 0 and } \phi_{max}$$

$$H(\phi) = 0 \qquad \text{for } \phi > \phi_{max}$$

A relation between the total power and maximum irradiance in the far field, H_0, can also be computed:

$$P_{total} = 0.5 \pi H_0 L^2 NA^2 \qquad \text{for the graded-index fiber}$$

Ideally, the irradiance is zero outside of the numerical aperture. A real-life measurement does not give such a clear distinction because of cladding modes and leaky modes. An international agreement defines the numerical aperture as the sine of the angle at which the irradiance has decreased to 5 % of maximum.

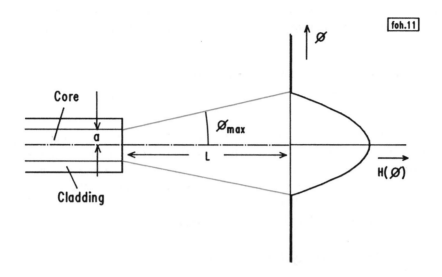

IDEALIZED FAR FIELD FROM A FULLY EXCITED GRADED-INDEX FIBER
(planar representation)

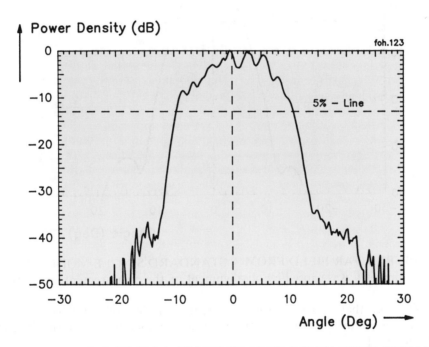

MEASURED FAR FIELD FROM A SHORT GRADED-INDEX FIBER WITH NA = 0.2
(driven by an 850 nm multimode laser diode)

A number of interesting details can be learned from the measured far-field. First, it indicates the mode filling of the fiber. The measured half-angle at 5 % is 10°. A full excitation would result in an angle of 11.5° (= arc sin 0.2). The ripple at the peak of the curve is a representation of the speckle pattern. This pattern is a result from driving the fiber with a laser, see →modal noise. If driven with an LED, a speckle pattern cannot be observed. The existance of cladding modes would indicate itself by a higher power density outside of the numerical aperture. In this case, the cladding modes were absorbed in the coating.

The above-used ray-optics model fails in the case of the **single mode fiber**. Instead, both near- and far fields are often described with the model of the →Gaussian beam. Also see →fiber (single mode).

Like in multimode fibers, the **numerical aperture** NA of single mode fibers is defined as:

$$NA = \sqrt{n_1^2 - n_2^2}$$

The usual 5 % far-field angle is **not** directly related to the NA of single mode fibers. Instead, the far field of a single-mode fiber is influenced by diffraction from the core, which represents a classic aperture. The diffraction causes zeros and sidelobes, which indicates the limited validity of the Gaussian approximation. If one compares the sine of the measured 5 % angle with the NA, a good agreement is obtained anyway:

$$NA_{measured} = 0.104 \quad \text{versus} \quad NA_{ideal} = 0.1 .$$

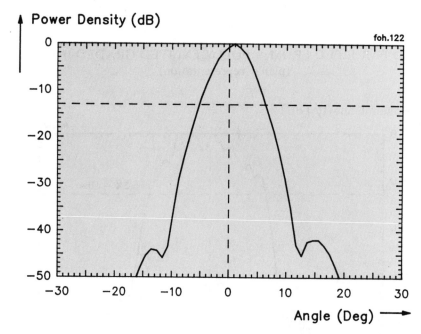

MEASURED FAR FIELD FROM A STANDARD SINGLE-MODE FIBER
(The asymmetry was caused by misalignment of the measurement apparatus)

It should be mentioned that, in a less intuitive way, the far field of any fiber is related to near field by the Fraunhofer diffraction integral, or, in a rotationally symmetric situation, by the Hankel transform [3.11].

A good description of far-field measurements is given in [2.2] . Accordingly, the minimum measurement distance r depends on the source size d and the wavelength λ:

$$r > d^2/\lambda$$

More than 10 r is normally used, which is approximately 10 cm for a 100 μm step-index fiber at 850 nm. This distance suffices for graded-index fibers, lasers, and most LEDs, too. It is convenient for a far-field measurement apparatus in which the spherical scan is realized by placing the detector on a rotating arm.

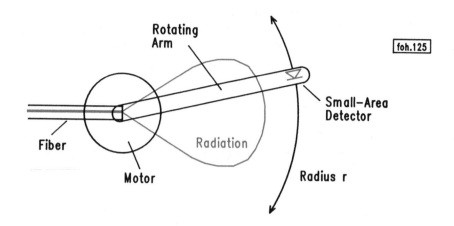

foh.125

FAR FIELD SCANNING APPARATUS

FDHM

Abbreviation for full duration at half maximum. Used to describe the width of a function, identical to full width at half maximum FWHM.

Fiber (Multimode)

Step-index and graded-index fibers belong to the class of multimode fibers. The term "multimode" illustrates the propagation of many →modes.

Depending on the type of fiber, different mechanisms are utilized to keep the light in the core of the fiber. In any case, the core is made from a material with a higher refractive index. The cladding is usually made from quartz (SiO_2), and doping with germanium-dioxide (GeO_2) creates the core's higher refractive index. For mechanical protection, plastic coating surrounds the cladding. Often, the coating removes cladding →modes via its higher-than-glass refractive index.

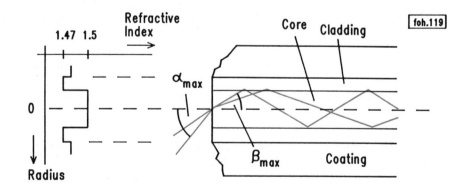

foh.119

STEP-INDEX MULTIMODE FIBER

In a **step-index** multimode fiber, light rays are guided by total reflection at the core-cladding-boundary. Due to the conditions of total reflection (see →reflection and refraction), only those rays are guided, which fulfil the condition of total →reflection:

$$\beta \leqslant \beta_{max} \, , \quad \text{with}$$

$$\cos \beta_{max} \; = \; n_2 \, / \, n_1$$

With Snell's law, β_{max} leads to a maximum coupling angle α_{max} at the entrance to the fiber, the sine of which is the →**numerical aperture NA**. Note, that only meridional rays (rays intersecting the axis) are discussed here.

$$NA = \; \sin \alpha_{max} = n_1 \; \sin \beta_{max}$$
$$= \; \sqrt{n_1^{\,2} - n_2^{\,2}}$$

The difference of the refractive indices thus determines the NA and the →coupling efficiency to a light source. It also determines the fiber's bandwidth and the number of guided modes. In this context, the →**refractive index contrast** Δ is the preferred variable:

$$\Delta \; = \; (n_1^{\,2} - n_2^{\,2}) \, / \, 2 n_1^{\,2} \; \simeq \; (n_1 - n_2) \, / \, n_1 \, , \quad \text{or}$$

$$\Delta \; = NA^2 \, / \, 2 n_1^{\,2}$$

Low bandwidth is the most significant disadvantage of step-index fibers. The main cause for this is that modes with a larger β experience a longer time delay: as indicated in the figure, different modes travel different total path lengths. This mechanism can also be expressed in terms of →multimode dispersion. The NA thus also determines the fiber's bandwidth.

Step-index fibers are mostly used for short-range communications, in conjunction with wavelengths of up to 900 nm. Typical data are listed below. Step-index fiber have also been made completely from →plastic. So far, their application is in short links allowing higher attenuation.

Core Diameter	Cladding Diameter	NA	Δ (Contrast)	Attenuation at 850 nm	Bandwidth (Multimode-)
100 µm	140 µm	0.3	2×10^{-2}	5 - 12 dB/km	20 MHz x km

TYPICAL PARAMETERS OF A STEP-INDEX FIBER

Graded-index fibers represent a compromise in coupling efficiency in order to reach much higher bandwidth. This is done by giving the core a bell-shaped index profile.

The profile causes the light to travel on wavelike tracks. The angle of acceptance depends on the distance from the core center: it is maximum at the center and zero at the core-cladding boundary, in contrast to step-index fibers. At any radius r, a maximum angle $\beta_{max}(r)$ is observed. $\beta_{max}(r)$ can be constructed with the help of Snell's law and the condition that the core-to-cladding boundary is tangential to most extreme ray:

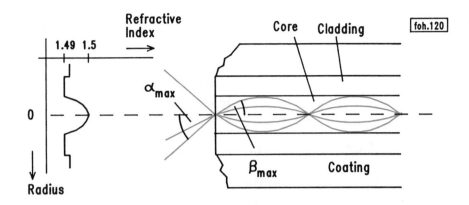

foh.120

GRADED-INDEX FIBER

$$n(r) \cos \beta_{max}(r) = n_2$$

Applying Snell's law to the input of the fiber then yields the maximum angle of acceptance α_{max}:

$$\alpha_{max}(r) = \sqrt{n(r)^2 - n_2^2}$$

The angle of acceptance depends on the radius; it is highest on axis and zero at the core-to-cladding boundary. The numerical aperture NA of graded-index fibers is defined with the angle on the axis, in compliance with the one of step-index fibers:

Numerical Aperture: $\qquad\qquad NA = \sqrt{n_1^2 - n_2^2}$

Refractive Index Contrast: $\qquad \Delta = (n_1^2 - n_2^2) / 2n_1^2 \simeq (n_1 - n_2) / n_1$

The high →bandwidth of graded-index fibers can be attributed to similar effective "speeds" of the different rays (modes). The longer length of the outer rays is compensated by the higher speed v of these rays, due to $v = c/n$. One possible index profile, called power-law profile, is given by:

$$n(r) = [n_1^2 - NA^2 (r/a)^\alpha]^{1/2}, \quad r \leqslant a \text{ (core radius)}$$

$$= n_1 [1 - 2\Delta(r/a)^\alpha]^{1/2}$$

The parameter α determines the effective speed differences of the →modes and thus the bandwidth. The profile is called parabolic if $\alpha = 2$. The optimum α (smaller, but very close to 2) is wavelength-dependent, which makes it difficult to manufacture high-bandwidth graded-index fibers for a wide range of wavelengths. A compromise for both 850 and 1300 nm is called **double-window fiber**.

Typical data of graded-index fibers are listed below. Their main application is in high-performance local-area networks, employing the wavelengths of 850 and 1300 nm. Attenuation is typically 3.5 dB/km at 850 nm and 0.6 dB at 1300 nm. Bandwidths range from a few hundred MHz to more than 1 GHz.

Core Diameter	Cladding Diameter	NA	Contrast Δ	Attenuation	Bandwidth (Multimode-)
50 μm	125 μm	0.2	1×10^{-2}	3 dB/km (850 nm) 0.6 dB/km (1300 nm)	1 GHz x km
62.5 μm	125 μm	0.29	2×10^{-2}	1 dB/km (1300 nm)	400 MHz x km

TYPICAL PARAMETERS OF GRADED-INDEX FIBERS

For the measurement of multimode fibers, see →attenuation (fiber-), →bandwidth (fiber-) and →numerical aperture.

Fiber (Single-Mode)

Today, the fiber enjoying the highest commercial attention is the single mode fiber, also termed monomode fiber. All new installations of long-range cable communications are exclusively realized in single mode fiber, with a growing percentage of single mode fiber used in local area networks. The reason for this popularity is high bandwidth. In the following, only the most important basics and properties of this type of fiber shall be discussed.

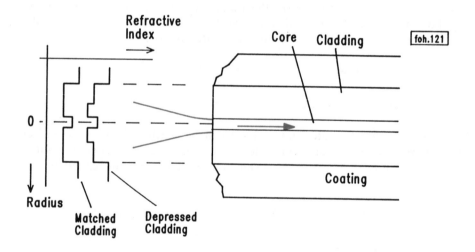

SINGLE-MODE FIBER

The classic version of the single-mode fiber is based on a **matched cladding**: the core is defined by a small step of the refractive index, which is created by appropriated doping (GeO_2). In contrast, the core of a fiber with **depressed-cladding** is formed by 2 types of doping: a ring of 40 μm diameter is doped with a material (fluorine) which **reduces** the refractive index of the cladding. This way, the core only requires very small doping levels, in order to create the same index step. The result is a slight improvement of the attenuation. Also, less bending sensitivity is observed at wavelengths around 1550 nm. Note that the figure indicates a higher refractive index of the plastic coating; this feature is capable of absorbing cladding →modes. More exotic profiles are described in the chapter →dispersion-shifted fibers.

The name of this fiber hints to the propagation of one mode only (the fundamental mode), which is a consequence of core diameters of not more than 5 to 10 μm. Intuitively, the fundamental mode is the mode that propagates in a "straight" fashion, without being reflected at the boundary between core and cladding. Below the cutoff wavelength, higher-order modes may also propagate: in this case, the fiber characteristics will change. See the chapter on →**cutoff-wavelength**. In the following, single-mode propagation will be assumed. The ray-optics model fails to describe the function of the single-mode fiber. Instead, wave optics have to be applied.

The "father" of today's most common model of single mode fibers is A. Snyder [3.1]. His model is based on the propagation of a transversal wave, which means that the electric and magnetic fields have **no** components in the direction of propagation. In single mode fibers, this assumption is valid due to the small difference in refractive index between core and cladding. Except for being bound to a fiber, the wave is identical to a transversal wave in free space.

A further assumption is linear polarization. Let us use an electric field in the x - direction, which necessitates a magnetic field in the y - direction. This way, vectors in space can be treated as scalars (E_x and H_y). In complex notation:

$$E_x = E(r) \exp [j(\omega t - \beta z)] \qquad [V/m]$$

$$H_y = \frac{n(r)\, E(r)}{Z_0} \exp [j(\omega t - \beta z)] \qquad [A/m]$$

E(r) - amplitude of the electric field as a function of the radius
ω - 2π x optical frequency
n(r) - refractive index as a function of the radius
β - propagation constant, see below
Z_0 - see →characteristic impedance

The propagation constant β is defined by a refractive index n_{eff} which must be smaller than n_1 (core) but larger than n_2 (cladding):

$$\beta = 2\pi\, n_{eff} / \lambda, \qquad \text{with: } n_1 > n_{eff} > n_2$$
$$= \omega / v_{ph}$$

v_{ph} - see →phase velocity

The last of Snyder's assumptions is an electromagnetic field which forms a Gaussian error function. Surprisingly, this assumption proves to be acceptable even for more complex profiles than the step-index.

$$E(r) = E_0 \exp [- (r/w)^2] \qquad [V/m]$$
$$M(r) = M_0 \exp [- 2(r/w)^2] \qquad [W/m^2]$$

M(r) - power density in the cross-section of the fiber
w - spot radius, determined by the decrease of the power density to $1/e^2$.

The above definition of spot radius coincides with today's international standards. It should be mentioned that Snyder uses a 1/e - definition.

Maxwell's equations should now be used to solve for the propagation constant β and the spot radius w. Despite of the simplicity of the above assumptions, this method leads to integrals which can only be solved numerically. Solutions are given in the paragraph →spot size.

Let us use a typical example with a = 4.5 µm, n_1 = 1.46 and Δ = 2.5 x 10^{-3}:

$$\lambda = 1.2 \text{ µm} \quad => \quad w/a = 1.08$$
$$\lambda = 1.3 \text{ µm} \quad => \quad w/a = 1.16$$

SPOT RADIUS AS A FUNCTION OF WAVELENGTH

For those wavelength where the fiber allows the propagation of the fundamental mode only, the spot diameter is obviously larger than the core diameter, and it increases with the wavelength. This behaviour explains a number of single-mode fiber characteristics: as the wavelength is increased, the spot extends more and more into the cladding. This causes the following effects:

1.   When increasing the wavelength, the optical wave experiences a lower refractive index, causing n_{eff} and β to decrease;
2.   When increasing the wavelength, the phase velocity increases (because of β);
3.   →Waveguide dispersion is a consequence of the changing phase velocity;
4.   Bending sensitivity is particularly strong at long wavelengths, due to the increased spot size.

Note that no wavelength-dependence of the refractive index is necessary to obtain these effects.

Due to the propagation of one mode only, one might expect a single mode fiber to have infinite **bandwidth**. More accurately, there are actually 2 modes of orthogonal (perpendicular) polarizations. Due to unavoidable imperfections, these modes travel at slightly different speeds. This effect is called "polarization dispersion"; it results in pulse broadening and finite bandwidth (→multimode dispersion) on the order of 10 - 100 GHz x km. See the paragraph →birefringence (in fibers).

A much more severe limitation in bandwidth is caused by the fiber's →**chromatic dispersion**, in conjunction with the finite spectral bandwidth of the driving source. Standard GeO_2-doped, step-index single-mode fibers exhibit zero chromatic dispersion around 1320 nm; at this wavelength, material dispersion and waveguide dispersion cancel each other. →Dispersion-shifted fibers are built for zero chromatic dispersion at 2 or 3 different wavelengths between 1300 nm and 1550 nm.

Unexpectedly, the **attenuation** of single mode fibers is usually lower than the one of multimode fibers, see the chapter on →attenuation. This attitude is due to the lower refractive-index contrast of single mode fibers, which requires a lower concentration of doping material in the core. Typical numbers are 0.45 dB/km at 1300 nm and 0.2 dB/km at 1550 nm.

Accurate attenuation measurements of single-mode fibers are mostly based on the cutback method, due to unacceptable reproducibility of coupling 2 single mode fibers. The measurement wavelength must be larger than the cutoff-wavelength. A fiber loop of 3 cm diameter will effectively reduce the cutoff-wavelength by around 100 nm, without affecting the attenuation of the fundamental mode. Most measurement standards therefore recommend the fiber loop, in order to ensure single-mode operation.

Like in multimode fibers, the **numerical aperture** NA of single mode fibers is defined as:

$$NA = \sqrt{n_1^2 - n_2^2}$$

The usual 5 % far-field angle is **not** directly related to the NA of single mode fibers, . Instead, the far field of a single-mode fiber is influenced by diffraction from the core, which represents a classic aperture. Therefore, the NA must be determined from the measurement of the refractive indices. Note that the →Gaussian beam is a good representation of the far field from a single mode fiber. See →far field.

Core Diameter	Cladding Diameter	NA	Δ (Contrast)	Attenuation 1300 / 1550 nm	Bandwidth* (Multimode-)
9 μm	125 μm	0.1	2.5×10^{-3}	0.5 / 0.25 dB/km	100 GHz x km

TYPICAL PARAMETERS OF A SINGLE-MODE FIBER
* The bandwidth of an SM-fiber is usually limited by →chromatic dispersion

For further information, see →modes (fiber-), →modal noise and →coupling.

Flux

The photometric unit "flux" is analogous to the radiometric unit "power". See →units at the end of the book.

Fresnel Reflection / Refraction

At the transition between 2 dielectric media (e.g. glass and air at the end of a fiber), light rays are partially refracted (bent upon the transition) and partially reflected. This phenomenon is usually treated by Fresnel´s laws of reflection. See →reflection and refraction.

Fundamental Mode

This term is used for the lowest-order fiber →mode. Intuitively, it is the "straight" mode, which is propagates without reflection at the core-to-cladding boundary. For a first order approximation, this mode is usually modeled by a →Gaussian beam. Also see →fiber (single mode).

FWHM

Abbreviation for full width at half maximum. Used to describe the width of a function, identical to full duration at half maximum FDHM.

Gaussian Beam

Different models are used for the description of optical beams, the simplest one being the infinitely thin beam (ray) used in geometric optics. This simple model fails when the beam diameter comes close to the wavelength. For example, the mechanism of diffraction when a light beam passes through a small aperture cannot be described with geometric optics. Other examples are the radiation patterns from a laser diode or from the end of a single mode fiber. The Gaussian beam is the simplest **physical** beam that complies with Maxwell's equations. It therefore comes much closer to real light beams.

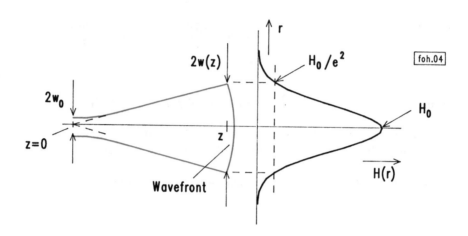

GAUSSIAN BEAM

As indicated in the figure, the Gaussian beam has a finite beam width which smoothly transits into a light cone of fixed numerical aperture. It is rotationally symmetric to the direction of propagation. The beam was named "Gaussian" because both the electric field E and the power density H (irradiance) follow a Gaussian error function. Let us assume linear polarization, with the electric field oriented into the x-direction, perpendicular to the direction of propagation (z). The magnetic field - not listed below - is oriented into the y-direction.

$$E_x(r,z) \quad = \quad E_0(z) \ \exp[\ -r^2 / w^2(z) \ ] \qquad\qquad [\ V/m \ ]$$

$$H(r,z) \quad = \quad H_0(z) \ \exp[\ -2r^2 / w^2(z) \ ] \qquad\qquad [\ W/m^2 \ ]$$

z - distance from the beam waist, into the direction of propagation
$E_0(z)$ - electric field on the z-axis (depends on z)
$H_0(z)$ - power density (irradiance) on the z-axis (depends on z)
r - radial distance from the z-axis
$w(z)$ - beam radius; r is the distance from the z-axis where the power density is down to $1/e^2$ of maximum. At this point, the electric field is down to $1/e$ of maximum.

At any distance z, the beam radius $w(z)$ is usually defined by the $1/e^2$ - power density, which coincides with the $1/e$ - electric field, both related to the maximum:

$$w^2(z) \quad = \quad w_0^2 \ [\ 1 + (\ \lambda z / \pi w_0^2 \ )^2 \ ] \qquad\qquad \text{for all z}$$

$$w(z) = \frac{\lambda z}{\pi w_0} \qquad\qquad \text{for large } z$$

w_0 - radius of the beam waist at the point of the $1/e^2$ - power density

The wavefront is planar at the beam waist. It turns spherical at larger distances. At those distances, the beam can be described by a fixed numerical aperture NA, using the 5 % - power density definition. The Gaussian characteristic yields:

$$NA = 0.39\ \lambda\ /\ w_0$$

Despite of the spherical wavefront, we suggest to assume a power flow (Poynting's vector) into the z-direction only. Of course, this approximation is only valid for small numerical apertures.

A relation between the total power in the beam, P_{total}, and the on-axis irradiance, $H_0(z)$, can be found by integrating the irradiance on a plane at the distance z from the origin. Once again, vertical incidence of the power flow is assumed on the entire plane:

$$P_{total} = \frac{\pi}{2}\ H_0(z)\ w^2(z) \qquad [\ W\ ]$$

There are 2 variables which influence the coupling between Gaussian beams: amplitude and phase of the electric field. An appropriate extension of the model should therefore also describe the phase. By definition, the phase of the electric field is constant on the entire wavefront. With the wavefront's curvature, the phase on a plane perpendicular to the direction of propagation can be calculated. In the formula below, the phase on the z-axis is arbitrarily set to zero. Power flow is still into the z-direction only.

$$E(r,z) = E_0(z)\ \exp\left[\ \frac{r^2}{w^2(z)}\ \right]\ \exp\left[\ -j\ \frac{z\lambda r^2}{\pi w^2(z)w_0^2}\ \right]$$

A unique characteristic of the Gaussian beam is that it is completely determined by just 2 parameters: the radius of the beam waist, w_0, and the wavelength. In particular, the beam divergence (numerical aperture) is fixed this way. With a measurement of the beam diameter at different distances z, this fact can be used to determine the diameter of the beam waist, which may be difficult to measure otherwise; see the paragraph on →**spot size** (of a single-mode fiber). Another consequence is that an ideally collimated (parallel) beam does not exist: the smaller the beam waist, the larger the divergence.

Gaussian Pulse

The Gaussian pulse has the unique feature that it is invariant under Fourier transform. Accordingly, the time-domain representation and the frequency-domain representation have the same appearance. If an impulse (zero-duration pulse) or a Gaussian pulse is applied to a low-pass filter with a Gaussian frequency characteristic, the resulting output pulse is again Gaussian. The frequency response (in the **electrical** domain) of many practical systems such as fibers with well-controlled index profile or laser diodes or detectors can be approximated by the Gaussian shape, although the mathematical function extends to + and - infinity.

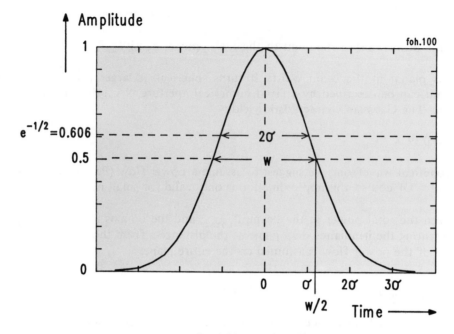

GAUSSIAN PULSE

Based on the usual definition of the Gaussian probability function, the following formula shall define the Gaussian pulse:

$$f(t) = \exp(-t^2/2\sigma^2), \quad \text{or alternatively:}$$
$$= \exp(-2.77\, t^2/w^2)$$

σ - RMS (root mean square) pulse width, $f(\sigma) = \exp(-1/2) = 0.606$.
 Note that in the probability function, σ represents the "standard deviation"
w - FWHM pulse width, $w = 2.355\, \sigma$

From a table of Fourier-transform correspondences, we find the following relations:

$f(t)$, time domain		$F(f)$, frequency domain
$\exp(-\pi t^2)$	=>	$\exp(-\pi f^2)$
$f(t/a)$	=>	$a\, F(af)$

From these correspondences, the Fourier transform (frequency domain) of the above pulse was calculated to be:

$$F(f) = \sigma\sqrt{2\pi}\,\exp(-2\pi^2\sigma^2 f^2), \qquad \text{or alternatively:}$$
$$F(f) = \sigma\sqrt{2\pi}\,\exp(-f^2/2f_s^2), \qquad \text{or alternatively:}$$
$$F(f) = 1.06\, w\,\exp(-3.56\, w^2 f^2).$$

with $\quad f_s = \dfrac{1}{2\pi\sigma}$

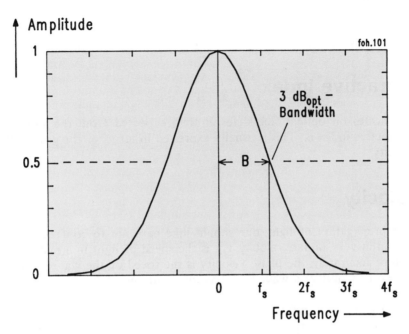

FOURIER TRANSFORM OF THE GAUSSIAN PULSE

The bandwidth of fiber-optic systems is most often defined by the point at which the signal (electrical **or** optical) is reduced to 1/2 of maximum. This bandwidth should then be called the "3 dB$_{opt}$ bandwidth" or the "6 dB$_{el}$ bandwidth". An impulse (zero-width pulse) shall be applied to a fiber with Gaussian characteristic. Then the bandwidth and the duration of the resulting Gaussian pulse are related by:

$$B = 0.187 / \sigma = 0.44 / w = 1.175 \, f_s$$

In a practical measurement of a system's pulse response, w should be determined from the quadratic sum of the individual pulse durations (e.g. laser 1, fiber 2, detector 3).

$$w^2_{system} = w_1^2 + w_2^2 + w_3^2 + \dots \qquad [\, ns^2 \,]$$

The relation between the individual bandwidths is:

$$\frac{1}{B^2_{system}} = \frac{1}{B_1^2} + \frac{1}{B_2^2} + \frac{1}{B_3^2} + \dots \qquad [\, GHz^{-2} \,]$$

Graded-Index Fiber

See →fiber (multimode).

Graded-Index Lens

See →Selfoc lens.

Grating

See →diffraction grating.

Group-Refractive Index

Information propagates on optical fibers slower than expected from the speed of light, c, divided by the refractive index n. This is usually expressed in terms of the group-refractive index. See →group velocity.

Group Velocity

When discussing propagation of light, one should take care not to confuse phase velocity and group velocity. Intuitively, **phase velocity** v_{ph} is the speed of light in a material with a refractive index n. More accurately, the phase velocity is the speed of the wavefront of an unmodulated wave: $v_{ph} = c/n$. Consider a wave traveling in a medium:

$$E = A \exp[\, j(\omega t - \beta z)\,]$$
$$\omega = 2\pi c/\lambda$$
$$\beta = 2\pi n/\lambda$$

E - electric field vector
A - amplitude vector
ω - 2π x optical frequency
β - propagation constant along z; often, the symbol "k" is used instead
z - length dimension on the fiber
c - speed of light in vacuum, see →constants at the end of the book
λ - wavelength in vacuum
n - wavelength-dependent refractive index of the medium; for waves traveling in a fiber, n also depends on both the core- and cladding indices, see →waveguide dispersion

The phase velocity is identical with the usual definition of the speed of light:

$$v_{ph} = \frac{\omega}{\beta} = \frac{c}{n}$$

If the wave carries an information via amplitude modulation, then the information travels at a somewhat lower speed called **group velocity**. The formula below can be obtained by adding two optical sine waves with slightly different angular frequencies (difference $d\omega$) and slightly different propagation constants (difference $d\beta$), this way creating a **modulated** wave with an (angular) **envelope** frequency $d\omega$. The result is a speed v_{gr} of the envelope, i.e. of the modulation, which does not depend on the modulation frequency:

$$v_{gr} = \frac{d\omega}{d\beta} = \frac{c}{n - \lambda \dfrac{dn}{d\lambda}}$$

From this term, the **group refractive index** n_{gr} can be derived:

$$n_{gr} = \frac{c}{v_{gr}} = n - \lambda \frac{dn}{d\lambda}$$

A diagram of the refractive indices of quartz is in the chapter →material dispersion.

Heterodyning, Homodyning

The principle of heterodyning is explained in the paragraph →coherent detection. System design is discussed in →systems (coherent-). For spectral linewidth measurements, see the paragraph →optical spectrum analysis.

Impulse Response

See →bandwidth (fiber-).

Index Matching

Reflections and associated losses from a fiber joint can be avoided by connecting the two fibers with a material whose refractive index is similar to the core index. Immersion oil, which is normally used for microscopic purposes, or optical cement are most often used for index matching. Index matching can also be achieved between media of unequal indices. See →antireflection coating for an example.

Insertion Loss

See the chapters →connector for the loss mechanisms in fiber joints. Here, we only discuss the **measurement** of insertion loss. The insertion loss IL of an optical connector pair or splice is defined as:

$$IL \ = \ 10 \log (\ P_{in} \ / \ P_{out} \ ) \qquad\qquad [dB_{opt}]$$

How should the insertion loss of a connector pair be measured ? The setup basically consists of an LED source and an optical power meter. The connector pair 2/3 is the device under test. In the first step, fiber 1 is connected to the LED source and the power output from connector 2 is measured (P_{in}). In the second step, connectors 2 and 3 are mated and the power output from fiber 2 is measured (P_{out}).

These are the critical points of the measurement:

1. A stable optical source is required.
2. It is important to leave connector 1 in place, in order to maintain a constant power input.
3. For multimode connectors used in local-area networks, full excitation is desirable.
4. For multimode connectors used in telecommunications, an equilibrium mode excitation should be launched into the fiber. This can be accomplished with a →mode filter and a cladding →mode stripper **before** the device under test. In fiber 2, the same type of filtering should be performed.
5. For single-mode connectors, the excitation of only the fundamental mode is desirable.
6. The power meter must be capable of collecting all radiated optical power.

The type of mode filling should be recorded together with the measurement data. A word of caution concerning insertion-loss data of connectors: some manufacturers publish data in which different connectors are mated with a "golden device". In order to obtain reliable data, it is very important to measure each connector against each other connector !

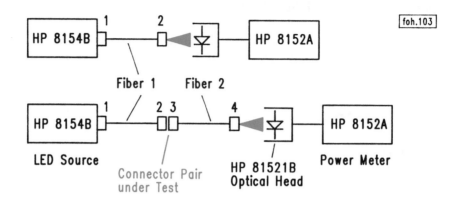

INSERTION-LOSS MEASUREMENT SETUP

For the measurement of **splice loss**, step 1 is as described before. In the second step, fiber 1 is cut in the middle and then re-spliced. For further information on the measurement of insertion loss, see the FOTP-34 [1.3].

Intensity

See →units at the end of this book.

Interference

Adding two optical beams usually causes addition or subtraction of the electric fields. Constructive or destructive interference is created when the wave is monochromatic and →coherent, and when the orientations of the electric fields are identical. The exact conditions of the interference depend on the phase difference between the two waves. Interference is responsible for the speckle patterns at the output of a fiber, see →modal noise. Interference is also created by the 2 glass-air interfaces in an optical connector; see the chapter →connector. Finally, the interference effect can be utilized for spectral bandwidth measurements, see →Fabry-Perot interferometer, →Mach-Zehnder interferometer, →Michelson interferometer.

As an example, let us analyze the reflections from of a simple glass plate. In the first step, the thickness L shall be infinite, so that there is only one transition between air and glass. The incident parallel beam shall be perpendicular to the glass plate, and both the electric field and the magnetic field shall be transversal to the direction of propagation. Linear polarization is assumed. For the analysis of this situation, we use **wave impedances**: the wave impedance Z is the electric field divided by the magnetic field.

The situation of a air-glass interface is comparable with a coaxial cable having a characteristic impedance Z_0 and a terminating resistor $Z_n = Z_0/n$, with n = 1.5, the result is a phase-inverted reflected field of 20 % and a reflected power of 4 %.

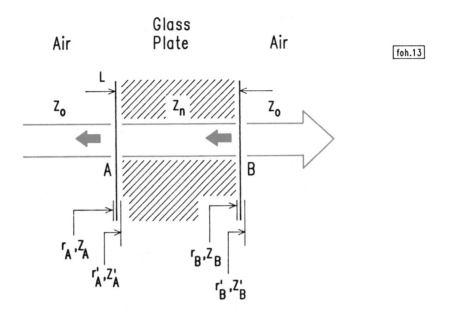

REFLECTION FACTORS AND IMPEDANCES ON A TRANSMISSION LINE

The field-reflection factor at interface A is:

$$r_A = \frac{Z_n - Z_0}{Z_n + Z_0} = \frac{n - 1}{n + 1} = -0.2 \qquad (-20\%)$$

$$|r_A|^2 = 0.04 \qquad (4\%)$$

$|r_A|^2$ - reflection factor of the optical power at interface A
Z_0 - characteristic impedance of air, $Z_0 = 377\ \Omega$
Z_n - characteristic impedance of glass, $Z_n = Z_0 / n$, with $n \simeq 1.5$

For the actual case of **2 transitions**, the reflected electric fields can add or subtract, depending on their relative phase, i.e. the thickness of the glass plate. They cancel each other whenever the phase difference between the reflected fields is 180°. At 0° phase difference, they add up to a strong reflection: instead of an expected 8 % of the incident power, a maximum of 16 % is observed. Here is the reason for the discrepancy: interference is not created by superposition of two optical powers, but by **superposition of two electric fields**:

Added reflections in the case of **destructive** interference:

$$r = -0.2 + 0.2 = 0, \qquad |r|^2 = 0 \ (0\%)$$

Added reflections in the case of **constructive** interference:

$$r = -0.2 - 0.2 = -0.4, \qquad |r|^2 = 0.16 \ (16\%)$$

Note that the above model is a rough approximation only, because it only takes 2 of the multiple reflections into account. A more accurate model would have to use **all** reflections. This problem can be solved very elegantly with the transmission-line theory:

Let us assume that the characteristic impedances of the 3 transmission lines are Z_0, Z_n and Z_0, with $Z_n = Z_0/n$. Looking at both sides of interface B more closely, we obtain:

$$Z_B' = Z_0 , \qquad\qquad r_B' = \frac{Z_B' - Z_0}{Z_B' + Z_0}$$

$$Z_B = Z_B' = Z_0 , \qquad\qquad r_B = \frac{Z_0 - Z_n}{Z_0 + Z_n} = \frac{n - 1}{n + 1}$$

Now, the reflection factor r_A' and the impedance Z_A' at interface A (further upstream) shall be calculated. To do this, we use a relation from electrical transmission lines: the complex reflection factor r_A' appears phase-delayed by an angle which corresponds to **twice** the length L. This yields the impedances and the reflection factors on both sides of interface A:

$$Z_A' = Z_n \frac{Z_0 + jZ_n \tan \beta L}{Z_n + jZ_0 \tan \beta L} , \qquad r_A' = r_B \exp(-j2\beta L)$$

$$Z_A = Z_A' , \qquad\qquad r_A = \frac{Z_A - Z_0}{Z_A + Z_0}$$

β - propagation constant, $\beta = 2\pi n /$ wavelength
L   - length of transmission line between points A and B

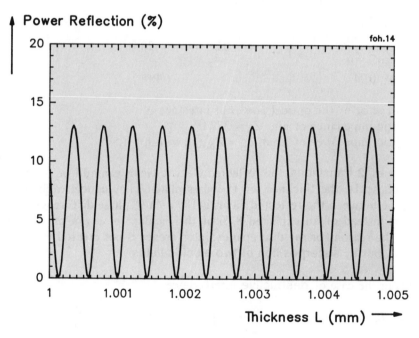

OPTICAL POWER REFLECTED FROM A GLASS PLATE
(Thickness L = 1 mm, wavelength = 1300 nm)

Using these equations, the field-reflection from a glass plate of length L turns out to be:

$$r_A = - \frac{(n^2 - 1) \tan \beta L}{(n^2 + 1) \tan \beta L - j 2n}$$

As before, the power-reflection factor at point A is the $|r_A|^2$. The transmitted power fraction is $1 - |r_A|^2$. The resonant characteristic of the glass plate is obvious: a glass plate is a simple form of a →Fabry-Perot resonator.

In the design of optical components, the resonant behaviour can be very disturbing, because the exact conditions of interference are usually non-reproducible. Antireflection coatings and wedging are the cures to this problem.

Intersymbol Interference

See →eye pattern.

Irradiance

Radiometric term used for power density, see →units at the end of this book. The relation between irradiance and electric field can be found in the chapter →electric field.

Isolator

An isolator is a non-reciprocal optical or electrical network, which means that the device's characteristics change if input and output are interchanged. Here it means, the device is only transporting optical power into one direction. Isolators are commonly used to avoid disturbing reflections back into the laser, which can cause extra noise, see →noise (laser diode-). In particular, reflections from various fiber interfaces may cause this problem.

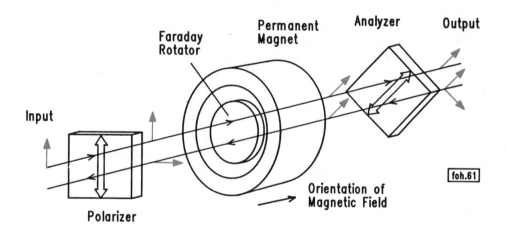

ISOLATOR BASED ON FARADAY ROTATION

Before entering the Faraday rotator, usually an yttrium-iron-garnet (YIG) material, the beam passes through a polarizer, which is oriented in parallel to the incoming state of polarization. The crystal then rotates the polarization by 45°. At the output, the beam passes an analyzer, which is oriented at an angle of 45° against the first polarizer. Of all possible reflected beams, only those with a 45° orientation of the polarization are allowed to pass backwards.

Reciprocity would now demand the polarization of the reflected beam to be rotated back to a state which is identical with the input state of polarization. Instead, the polarization of the reflected beam is rotated by another 45°, which results in a total rotation of 90°. This way, the reflected beam is blocked by the polarizer. In order to not disturb the proper function of the isolator, all its surfaces should be antireflection-coated.

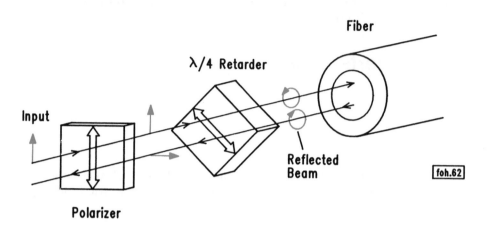

ISOLATOR BASED ON A QUARTER-WAVE RETARDER

A less useful but cheaper version of an isolator is based on polarizer and a quarter-wave retarder: after passing these 2 elements, the light is circularly polarized (see →retardation plate). When reflected from a glass surface, the light is still circularly polarized, but with an opposite sense of rotation. The light then passes the retarder again, which restores linear polarization with an orientation perpendicular to original orientation. This way, the light is curbed by the polarizer. In contrast to the first isolator, this isolator is reciprocal. Its disadvantage: any change in polarization of the reflected light, as it may be caused by the fiber, will cause a leakage of power back to the source. Note that in a practical realization a lens system must be added, in order to image the parallel beam to the fiber input.

Isotropic

A material, e.g. an optical glass, is called isotropic if its physical characteristics, optical and electrical, are not dependent on the direction in which they are measured. See →birefringence as an example for non-isotropic material characteristics.

Jones Calculus

The **Jones vector** is an analytical description of the state of polarization. It supplies geometric, amplitude and phase information. Based on the same idea, the **Jones matrix** is capable of describing the polarization characteristics of an optical component. Jones vectors and Jones matrices allow optical network analysis much in the same way as electric network analysis. This concept was invented in 1941 by R.C. Jones.

Here is the relation between electric fields and Jones vector. Note that the usual time dependence, exp (jωt), is omitted:

Electric fields:
$$E_x(t) = A \cos \omega t$$
$$E_y(t) = B \cos (\omega t - \phi)$$

Jones vector:
$$E = \begin{bmatrix} E_x \\ E_y \end{bmatrix} = \begin{bmatrix} A \\ B \exp(-j\phi) \end{bmatrix}$$

Examples:

Linear polarization:
(E_x and E_y are in phase)

$$E = \begin{bmatrix} A \\ B \end{bmatrix}$$

Circular polarization (CCW):
(E_y is delayed by 90°)

$$E = \begin{bmatrix} A \\ -jA \end{bmatrix}$$

The output of an optical component, E_2, is the multiplication of its **Jones matrix**, J, with a Jones-vector at the input, E_1:

$$E_1 = \begin{bmatrix} E_{1x} \\ E_{1y} \end{bmatrix} \qquad J = \begin{bmatrix} J_{11} & J_{12} \\ J_{21} & J_{22} \end{bmatrix}$$

$$E_2 = J \times E_1 = \begin{bmatrix} J_{11}E_{1x} + J_{12}E_{1y} \\ J_{21}E_{1x} + J_{22}E_{1y} \end{bmatrix}$$

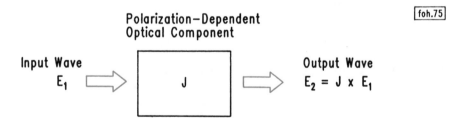

Polarization–Dependent
Optical Component

foh.75

Input Wave
E_1 ⇨

J

Output Wave
$E_2 = J \times E_1$ ⇨

JONES CALCULUS

As an example for a Jones matrix, let us discuss the **quarter-wave plate**, as discussed in the chapter →retardation plate. If the fast axis of the crystal is oriented parallel to the x-direction, then the quarter-wave plate can be described by:

$$J = \begin{bmatrix} 1 & 0 \\ 0 & -j \end{bmatrix}$$

Let us analyze the output states of the quarter wave plate with various input states, E_1. To do this, we multiply J with each of the E_1. First, let us apply **linear polarization oriented in y-direction**. The y-component of E_2 appears phase-delayed by 90°, and the x-component is still 0. This means that E_2 is still linear in y-direction:

$$E_1 = \begin{bmatrix} 0 \\ 1 \end{bmatrix} \qquad \text{yields} \qquad E_2 = \begin{bmatrix} 0 \\ -j \end{bmatrix}$$

Now, let us apply **linear polarization oriented at an angle** $\Theta = 45°$. The x-component of E_2 is still 1, and the y-component is delayed by 90°. This describes a circular state of polarization, in which the sense of rotation is CCW:

$$E_1 = \begin{bmatrix} 1 \\ 1 \end{bmatrix} \qquad \text{yields} \qquad E_2 = \begin{bmatrix} 1 \\ -j \end{bmatrix}$$

Finally, let us apply **circular polarization (CW)**. Both the x- and y-components of E_2 are 1, which describes linear polarization oriented at $\Theta = 45°$:

$$E_1 = \begin{bmatrix} 1 \\ j \end{bmatrix} \qquad \text{yields} \qquad E_2 = \begin{bmatrix} 1 \\ 1 \end{bmatrix}$$

The quarter-wave plate is obviously a very useful component, because it is capable of converting linear polarization into elliptical or circular polarization, and vice-versa. Here is a list of the Jones matrices of the most important optical components:

Quarter-wave plate: this is a special case of the retardation plate, see the next component.

Fast axis in x-direction:

Fast axis in y-direction:

$$J = \begin{bmatrix} 1 & 0 \\ 0 & -j \end{bmatrix} \qquad\qquad J = \begin{bmatrix} -j & 0 \\ 0 & 1 \end{bmatrix}$$

General retardation plate: like the quarter-wave plate, the general retardation plate exhibit a fast axis (oriented in the Θ-direction of the transverse plane) and a slow axis. The phase delay of the slow plane against the fast plane shall be ϕ, with $\phi' = \phi/2$):

$$J = \begin{bmatrix} \cos\phi' + j\sin\phi'\cos 2\Theta & j\sin\phi'\sin 2\Theta \\ j\sin\phi'\sin 2\Theta & \cos\phi' - j\sin\phi'\cos 2\Theta \end{bmatrix}$$

Half-wave plate: this is another special case of the retardation plate. Here, the phase delay is 180°. In the case that the input is linear-polarized, this component is capable of rotating the plane of polarization depending on the angle between the plane of polarization and the fast axis of the plate. See the chapter on →retardation plate. The fast axis shall be in Θ-direction:

$$J = \begin{bmatrix} \cos 2\Theta & \sin 2\Theta \\ \sin 2\Theta & -\cos 2\Theta \end{bmatrix}$$

Rotator: in contrast to the half-wave plate, this component rotates the state of polarization independent on the orientation of the input field. This behaviour is characteristic for circular birefringence, which may result from optical activity (see →birefringence) or from →Faraday rotation. The amount of rotation is given by 2Θ, the sense is clockwise:

$$J = \begin{bmatrix} \cos 2\theta & -\sin 2\theta \\ \sin 2\theta & \cos 2\theta \end{bmatrix}$$

Polarizer: The output of an ideal polarizer only contains electric field components oriented in the direction of the main axis of the polarizer. The main axis shall be oriented in θ-direction:

$$J = \begin{bmatrix} \cos^2 \theta & \cos \theta \sin \theta \\ \cos \theta \sin \theta & \sin^2 \theta \end{bmatrix}$$

$$J = \begin{bmatrix} 1 & 0 \\ 0 & 0 \end{bmatrix} \quad \text{if } \theta = 0$$

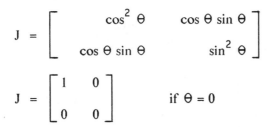

Polarization—Dependent Optical Components

foh.79

Input Wave E_1 → J | K → Output Wave $E_2 = K \times J \times E_1$

Note that the Order is Reversed !

L

SERIES CONNECTION OF 2 POLARIZATION-DEPENDENT COMPONENTS

A series connection of 2 or more components can be modeled with the multiplication of their matrices. Let the Jones matrices be J and K, with a combined matrix L. Then L must be calculated by **reversing** the order:

$$L = K \times J \qquad \textbf{not} \qquad L = J \times K$$

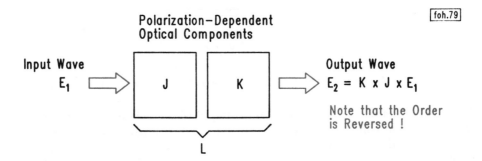

$$K = \begin{bmatrix} K_{11} & K_{12} \\ K_{21} & K_{22} \end{bmatrix} \qquad J = \begin{bmatrix} J_{11} & J_{12} \\ J_{21} & J_{22} \end{bmatrix}$$

$$L = \begin{bmatrix} K_{11}J_{11} + K_{12}J_{21} & K_{11}J_{12} + K_{12}J_{22} \\ K_{21}J_{11} + K_{22}J_{21} & K_{21}J_{12} + K_{22}J_{22} \end{bmatrix}$$

The combined matrix, L, can then be treated as derived above. For further information on the Jones calculus, see e.g. [0.6].

Lambertian Source

Typical light sources in fiber optics are lasers, LEDs and filament lamps (for spectral attenuation measurements). In order to characterize the radiation geometrics of lasers, the model of the →Gaussian beam is very popular. In the case of LEDs and filament lamps, the model of a

Lambertian source is preferred. An extension of the Lambertian source can be used to also describe laser diodes and edge-emitting LEDs.

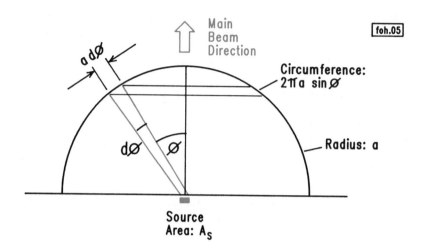

LAMBERTIAN SOURCE, RADIATING INTO A HEMISPHERE

The Lambertian source is defined by a uniformly diffusing, light emitting surface. Let us consider an example, in which the source diameter is small compared to the measurement distance: on an axis perpendicular to the surface, a power density (far-field irradiance) H_0 can be measured. When leaving the axis, all measurements in the far field turn out to follow a cosine-function (the surface of the detector is assumed to move on a sphere, the center of which is the source). Compare with the chapter →radiometric units at the end of the book:

$$\text{Irradiance:} \qquad H(\phi) \ = H_0 \cos \phi \qquad\qquad [W/m^2]$$

$$\text{Radiance:} \qquad L(\phi) \ = \frac{H_0 a^2}{A_s} \cos \phi = L_0 \cos \phi \qquad [W/sr\ m^2]$$

$$\text{Intensity:} \qquad I(\phi) \ = H_0\ a^2 \cos \phi = I_0 \cos \phi \qquad [W/m^2]$$

ϕ - viewing angle
H_0 - on-axis irradiance
a - distance between source and detector (radius of the sphere)

Note that, in the polar representation, the irradiance follows a circle. The total power (or flux) can be calculated by integration over the entire hemisphere (2π steradian):

$$P_{total} \ = \int_{0}^{\pi/2} H(\phi)\ 2\pi a \sin \phi \ a\ d\phi$$

$$P_{total} \ = \pi\ a^2\ H_0 \qquad [watt]\ or\ [lumen]$$

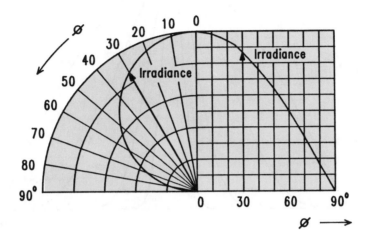

Polar.
Representation

Linear
Representation

IRRADIANCE OF A LAMBERTIAN SOURCE

This relation can be used to estimate the total LED-power P when only the maximum intensity I_0 is given.

Example: I_0 = 1×10^{-3} cd at 555 nm

$= 1 \times 10^{-3}$ lumen/sr

$= 10^{-3} / 683$ watt/sr (from →units at the end of the book)

P_{total} = $\pi \, 10^{-3} / 683$ W = 4 μW

Most fiber optic sources have beam profiles which are narrower than the Lambertian source: examples are laser diodes and edge-emitting LEDs. These sources can be modeled by a raised-cosine function and by selecting an adequate value of m:

$$H = H_0 \, (\cos \alpha)^m$$

A measurement of the far field will deliver the source's half-width at half-maximum (HWHM) angle α_{HWHM}. With this, the parameter m may be calculated:

$$m = \log 0.5 / \log (\cos \alpha_{HWHM}) = -0.3 / \log (\cos \alpha_{HWHM})$$

example: α_{HWHM} = 15° (angle at the 50 % - irradiance point)
m = 19.9

In this case, the integration yields the following total power, which for m = 1 is identical to the total power of the Lambertian source:

$$P_{total} = \frac{2 \pi \, a^2 \, H_0}{m + 1}$$

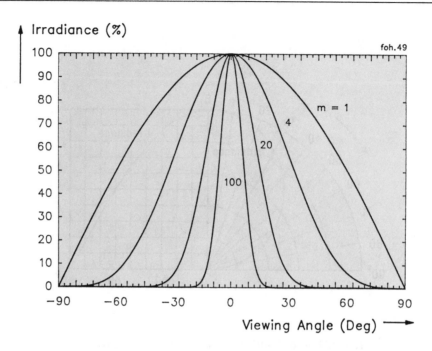

SOURCES WITH DIFFERENT DIVERGENCES

Laser Diode (CW Type)

The term "laser" stands for "light **a**mplification by **s**timulated **e**mission of **r**adiation". More accurately, two mechanisms determine the light-generation in a laser diode. **Spontaneous** emission is the result of recombination of excited electrons in the conduction band and holes in the valence band. This is the main process in an LED. In a laser diode (LD), photons are predominantly generated by **stimulated** (or induced) emission: this means that photons trigger the generation of additional photons by stimulating additional recombinations. In the figure, the generation of one additional photon is illustrated. The stimulated photons are **coherent** with the generating photons, i.e. generating and generated photons have the same wavelength and phase. The result is a narrow →spectrum.

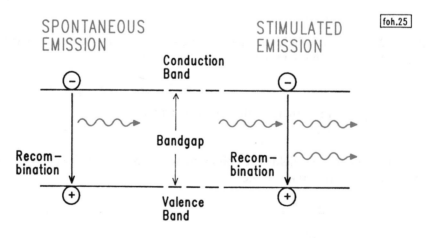

SPONTANEOUS AND STIMULATED EMISSION

Threshold current: An important precondition for the stimulated emission is "population inversion": the number of (excited) electrons in the conduction band must be larger than the ones in the valence band. Generally, this is achieved by **pumping**. In a semiconductor laser, pumping means forcing a high current density into the active layer. The gain of the stimulation process is proportional to the current density. Emission changes from spontaneous to stimulated when the gain exceeds the absorption and radiation losses; the necessary current is the threshold current.

Electrical confinement: In the usual **double-heterostructure**, the active layer is made from the material with the lowest bandgap; the top and bottom layers exhibit larger bandgaps. Therefore, the generation of photons is limited to the active layer only. In addition to the vertical confinement, strong efforts are made for a narrow lateral confinement. One way of creating a narrow current path is a narrow width of the electric contact. In this case, the lateral width of the active zone is determined by the critical current density. This method is therefore termed **gain guiding.** More effectively, a laterally narrow current flow can be accomplished with the help of lateral, negative-biased pn-junctions; this is called **index guiding.** Today, the most popular index-guiding lasers are of the buried heterostructure (BH) type. Another version is the double-channel (DC-BH) structure, which is explained in →DFB laser.

Optical confinement: Most important for the laser characteristic is the optical resonator. In a semiconductor laser, the resonator is formed by embedding it into material with lower refractive index, with the result that the optical power is emitted from the facets only. Fortunately, the material with the lowest bandgap (the active zone) usually exhibits the highest index of refraction. Therefore, vertical optical confinement is a natural consequence. In the case of the gain-guided laser, weak lateral optical guiding exists because the region with high current density has a slightly higher index of refraction. In the case of an index-guided laser, the zones right and left from the active layer exhibit a lower refractive index, and the optical guiding is much stronger.

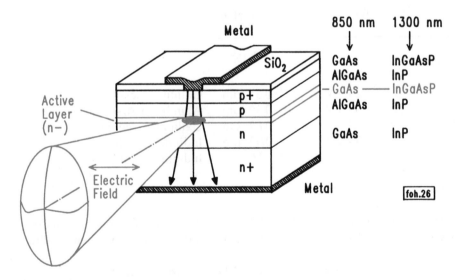

GAIN-GUIDED DOUBLE-HETEROSTRUCTURE LASER

In typical laser diodes, the active zone is 5 - 10 μm wide and 0.1 - 0.2 μm high. The average length is 300 μm. The facets represent semi-transparent mirrors which terminate the resonator cavity. Emission is from both facets, with similar radiation characteristics.

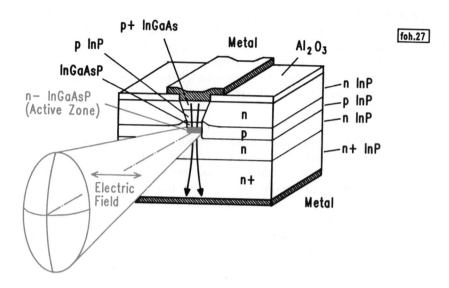

INDEX-GUIDED BURIED HETEROSTRUCTURE (BH) LASER

Spectrum: The generated wavelength λ is defined by the bandgap E_g:

$$\lambda = \frac{h\,c}{E_g} = \frac{1.24\ \mu m}{E_g\,[eV]}$$

h - Planck's constant; $h = 6.62 \times 10^{-34}\ Ws^2$
c - speed of light; $c = 2.998 \times 10^8$ m/s
E_g - bandgap energy of the material of the active layer; usually expressed in units of [eV].

Material	Bandgap	Wavelength	

Binary materials:

GaP	2.24 eV	0.55 μm	Gallium-Phosphide
AlAs	2.09 eV	0.59 μm	Aluminum-Arsenide
GaAs	1.42 eV	0.87 μm	Gallium-Arsenide
InP	1.33 eV	0.93 μm	Indium-Phosphide
InAs	0.34 eV	3.6 μm	Indium-Arsenide

Ternary and quaternary materials:

AlGaAs	1.42-1.61 eV	0.77-0.87 μm	Aluminum-Gallium-Arsenide
InGaAsP	0.74-1.13 eV	1.1-1.67 μm	Indium-Gallium-Arsenide-Phosphide

POPULAR LASER DIODE MATERIALS

Short-wavelength LDs (850 nm) are made from the **ternary** alloy GaAlAs. The ratio of materials used in the active layer sets the wavelength. The GaAlAs alloy offers the benefit of a nearly constant crystalline lattice period, which must be maintained in the entire device. A ternary alloy such as InGaAs would also allow wavelength selection for long-wavelength LDs (1300 and 1550 nm); however, the **quaternary** alloy InGaAsP is generally used because of the lattice matching problem. As a practical consequence, the wavelengths achievable with quaternary materials are more limited than could be expected from the bandgaps of the participating binary materials.

Gain-guided lasers typically generate several longitudinal modes, which correspond to different wavelengths (frequencies). Index-guided lasers produce fewer or only one main frequency. See →**spectrum (laser diode-)**. The best spectral performance can be obtained from distributed-feedback lasers, see →DFB laser.

Temperature strongly affects the characteristics of laser diodes. The threshold current of GaAlAs lasers (850 nm) typically increases by 1 % per °C heatsink temperature. In the case of InGaAs lasers, a higher 2 % per °C is observed. The temperature dependence of the threshold current is often expressed in terms of the "characteristic temperature" T_0:

$$I_{th} = I_{th0} \exp (\Delta T / T_0), \text{ leading to:}$$
$$\Delta I_{th} \simeq I_{th0} \Delta T / T_0 .$$

I_{th} - actual threshold current
I_{th0} - original threshold current
ΔT - change of temperature
ΔI_{th} - change of threshold current

The characteristic temperature T_0 of GaAlAs-lasers (850 nm) is around 150 Kelvin. InGaAsP-lasers (1300 nm) have a T_0 of typically 50 to 70 Kelvin. Because of the laser diode's high differential gain beyond threshold, the temperature-dependence of the threshold current causes a strong negative temperature-coefficient of the output power. Assuming a constant drive current, the power may easily drop 10 % per °C. Maintaining the power often includes the risk of destruction.

The differential gain of both GaAlAs lasers (850 nm) and InGaAs lasers (1300 nm) typically decreases between 0.5 and 1 % per °C. The emitted wavelength is temperature-dependent, too. It increases by typically 1 nm per 3 °C for both 850 nm and 1300 nm lasers.

The junction temperature not only changes due to environmental changes, but also due to the laser's internal power dissipation. This causes a "droop" of the power following the rising edge of a step-function drive pulse. In order to reduce these effects and to improve the reliability, the laser heatsink is often temperature-stabilized using Peltier-type thermoelectric coolers. In addition, electronic feedback via a backfacet PIN-diode corrects the drive current and thus helps stabilizing the output power.

Maximum obtainable optical power depends on the duty cycle: for unmodulated DC-operation the maximum power is between 5 and 20 mW. If driven with a narrow pulse (e.g. 100 ns pulse width), the power can go as high as 500 mW.

Linearity: Modern lasers exhibit good linearity, typically -40 dB$_{el}$ total harmonic distortion for 50% modulation depth can be achieved with gain-guided lasers. Index-guided lasers show a sharper transition between the two regions and an even better linearity. Some care is recommended when dealing with linearity, because different portions of the beam exhibit different linearity characteristics: sometimes integral measurements are made, sometimes only the fraction coupled into a fiber is considered. In practical situations, the good linearity is often useless because of strong noise sources such as →modal noise and optical feedback noise; see →noise (laser diode-).

In older lasers severe distortions of the laser curve can be observed; they are called **kinks**. They are caused by transverse mode jumps inside the laser cavity. This effect can also be provoked by reflections back into the laser and is then called optical feedback noise.

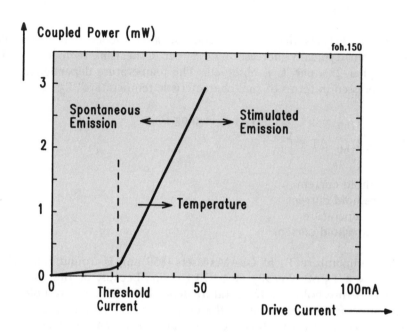

1300 nm LASER DIODE CHARACTERISTIC
(when coupled into single-mode fiber)

Parameter	Typical Data	
Maximum CW Power	10 mW	(total output)
Maximum Pulse Power	500 mW	(at 100 ns pulse width)
Threshold Current	30 mA	
Differential Gain	200 μW/mA	(total output when lasing)
Distortion (THD)	-40 dB$_{el}$	(at 50 % modulation depth)
Threshold Voltage	1.8 V	
Series Resistance	3 Ω	
Modulation Bandwidth	1 GHz	

TYPICAL DATA OF DOUBLE-HETEROSTRUCTURE LASER DIODES

Radiation: Laser diodes produce an elliptical radiation pattern (→far field) with a full width at half maximum between 20° and 40°. The ellipticity stems from different degrees of diffraction at the junction-parallel and the junction-perpendicular cavity boundaries. In contrast to index-guided lasers, gain-guided lasers produce well pronounced peaks in the parallel scan, as indicated in the figure. The →near-field of a laser diode is elliptical too, but with perpendicular orientation as indicated in the figure. Also see →astigmatism. The →Gaussian beam is well suited to describe the emission from a laser diode. A further refinement is possible by changing the circular geometry of the Gaussian beam to an elliptical one.

In contrast to LEDs, lasers generate partially **polarized** light. The orientation of the electric field is **parallel** to the junction. If operated in the stimulated emission region, then the radiation of gain-guided lasers is better than 90 % polarized; index-guided lasers are better than 98 % polarized.

For further information on laser diodes, see →spectrum (laser diode-), →coherence and →coupling.

Laser Diode (Pulse Type)

Pulse lasers are normally used in high-power pulse applications such as in an →optical time-domain reflectometer. The most common pulse laser is of the single-heterostructure type, which is somewhat simpler than the double-heterostructure laser: only one gallium-aluminum-arsenide layer is used for optical guiding. See →laser diode (cw-type) for the construction of the double-heterostructure laser.

Parameter	Typical data, related to a device with 100 µm stripe width	
Maximum pulse power	3	W
Threshold current	2-5	A
Peak current	5-10	A
Threshold voltage	1.8	V
Peak voltage	10	V
Maximum pulse width	200	ns
Maximum duty cycle	0.01-0.1	%
Risetime	1	ns
Spectral width	5-10	nm
No. of lines	30-50	

TYPICAL DATA OF AN 850 nm SINGLE-HETEROSTRUCTURE LASER

Single-heterostructure lasers have large resonant cavities: 100 µm stripe width and 2 µm stripe height are typical numbers. Both these values are in the order of 10 times larger than those of double-heterostructure lasers, resulting in a 100 times larger emitting area. Thus the →coupling efficiency to fibers is drastically reduced. The generation of the maximum power is normally limited to around 200 ns pulse width at a maximum duty cycle between 0.01 nd 0.1%. This is due to the high threshold current which is typically 2-5 amperes for 100 µm stripe width. The current necessary to reach the peak power is 10 to 20 amperes. Accordingly, the peak voltage may reach 10 volts.

This type of laser allows many transversal and longitudinal modes in its large resonant cavity. This leads to a somewhat wider spectral width when compared to double-heterostructure laser: a typical number is 10 nm. The fastest risetimes of single-heterostructure devices is around 0.5 ns.

Lasers of this type are also available as series-connected stacks: such lasers are capable of delivering up to a few hundred watts pulse power. However, an even larger emitting area has to be taken into account.

Pulse operation also seems possible with double-heterostructure, CW-type lasers: although generally non-specified, pulse powers of more than 1 watt at 20 ns pulse duration have been generated in the laboratory. For fiber optic test and measurement the usage of such devices may be more attractive because these are the same devices as used in real communication systems. Thus the good coupling efficiency and other favourable characteristics can be maintained.

Law of Brightness

No lens system is capable of enhancing the brightnesss (radiance) of a light source. See →radiance.

Leaky Mode

See →modes in a fiber.

LED (Light Emitting Diode)

The light generating process of a LED or laser is determined by recombination of electrons and holes inside a pn-junction. Each recombination releases a photon with an energy equal to the bandgap energy of the material. This mechanism is called **spontaneous emission** or, more generally, electroluminescence. See →laser diode. In terms of the generated spectrum, the main difference to lasers is that LEDs generate a wide spectral width, typically 40 to 80 nm FWHM. The bandgap energy E_g of the material combination defines the center wavelength:

$$\lambda = \frac{h\,c}{E_g} = \frac{1.24\ \mu m}{E_g}$$

h - Planck's constant; $h = 6.62 \times 10^{-34}\ Ws^2$
c - speed of light; $c = 2.998 \times 10^8$ m/s
E_g - bandgap energy of the material of the active layer, in units of [eV].

For pure GaAs λ is 870 nm. By adding Al to the alloy, the wavelength can be lowered to 770 nm. For even lower wavelengths in the visible region, GaAsP or GaP is used. For longer wavelengths, InGaAsP is the common material.

With appropriate n- and p-doping (usually Sn or Te for n, Zn for p) the above materials can be used to form a simple pn-diode, which will actually function as an LED. The only constraint is the need for crystalline lattice matching. This requires well-defined material doses in the alloys, see e.g. [0.3]. Today, the **double-heterostructure** is exclusively used for LEDs instead of the simple pn-junction. The double-heterostructure consists of a nearly undoped active zone which is covered by p and n layers of larger bandgap materials. No photon generation takes place in the material with the larger bandgap; this way, the generation is confined to the active zone only. Additonally, the larger bandgap prevents photon absorption (generation of electrons and holes) and makes the embedding layers transparent for the emitted wavelengths.

Material	Bandgap	Wavelength	

Binary materials:

GaP	2.24 eV	0.55 μm	Gallium-Phosphide
AlAs	2.09 eV	0.59 μm	Aluminum-Arsenide
GaAs	1.42 eV	0.87 μm	Gallium-Arsenide
InP	1.33 eV	0.93 μm	Indium-Phosphide
InAs	0.34 eV	3.6 μm	Indium-Arsenide

Ternary and quaternary materials:

AlGaAs	1.42-1.61 eV	0.77-0.87 μm	Aluminum-Gallium-Arsenide
InGaAsP	0.74-1.13 eV	1.1-1.67 μm	Indium-Gallium-Arsenide-Phosphide

POPULAR MATERIALS FOR LEDs AND LASER DIODES

In the case of a **surface emitting LED**, the active layer radiates into all directions, therefore at least half of the optical power is lost. A small fraction of the optical power may be reflected at the base metallization and therefore contribute to the output power. The preferred version of this LED is the Burrus-type LED, named after its inventor [4.1]. An etched well allows a narrow spacing between the active zone and the fiber. Simultaneously, the form of the contacts allows a small light-emitting volume.

Most surface-emitting LEDs generate a nearly →Lambertian emission with a large →numerical aperture of around 0.9. In many cases, some form of lens is applied to reduce the NA down to 0.2. Even though the NA of 0.2 is quite small, the emitting area is large as compared to a laser. The low power density results in coupled power levels which are typically 20 μW into a graded-index fiber or 2 μW into a single-mode fiber. See →coupling efficiency.

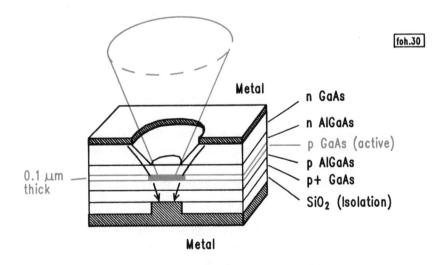

foh.30

SHORT-WAVELENGTH BURRUS LED
(Cross-sectional view)

Edge emitting LEDs offer much better coupling efficiency: typically 50 µW (30 % of the available optical power) can be coupled into a graded-index fiber and 20 µW into a single-mode fiber. The construction of edge-emitting LEDs is similar to that of gain-guided double-heterostructure →laser diodes. One step into this direction is lower current density, usually obtained by a laterally wide active zone (typically 50 µm). The second step is to avoid the Fabry-Perot type optical resonance of the laser diode, with the help of a) short channel lengths, b) antireflection-coated output facets and c) the channel ending in a zone with no current flow.

One example of an edge-emitting LED was extracted from [4.5]. The device utilizes the V-groove technology, which was invented to construct gain-guided laser diodes: the usual double-heterostructure is covered with 2 n-type layers which form a negative-biased pn-junction. Zinc (Zn) is diffused into the V-groove; it forms a conductive p-type stripe. In this case, the V exhibits a flat bottom in order to generate a wider active zone. Finally, the front facet is antireflection-coated and the electric contact is shorter than the length of the chip; this was done in order to prevent stimulated emission.

The emitted beam (far field) from an edge-emitting LED is usually elliptical. The ellipticity is perpendicular to that of a laser diode. Typical far field angles (FWHM) are 50° vertically and 100° horizontally.

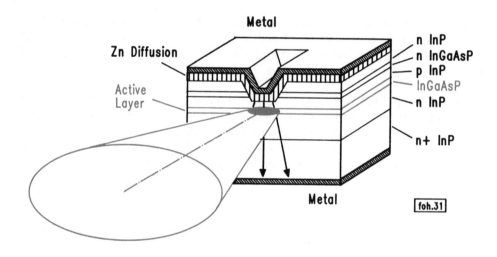

LONG-WAVELENGTH EDGE EMITTING LED

Edge-emitting LEDs belong to the class of **superradiant LEDs**, which hold a position between LEDs and lasers. The current density is strong enough and quality of the optical resonator is good enough to create an emission on the borderline of stimulated emission. The result is narrower spectral width (e.g. 20 nm) and higher output power, but also stronger temperature dependence.

LEDs offer a comparatively low bandwidth. A typical number is 100 MHz, although 1 GHz bandwidth was reported. Laser diodes are at least a factor of 5 faster. In system applications, the large spectral width of around 60 nm may contribute to even lower bandwidth because of →chromatic dispersion. See →spectrum (LED-). In measurement applications, LEDs are more stable and less noisy. The spectral width solves all problems with optical interference. Additional LED advantages are: linearity and low power consumption. High reliability is a benefit from low current density. As LEDs are not very sensitive to overloads, simple drive circuits can be used.

Typical efficiency is 50 μW/mA (related to the total output), with no threshold current required. Surface emitters are more efficient. However, the situation is reversed when the output is coupled to a fiber (as shown in the diagram).

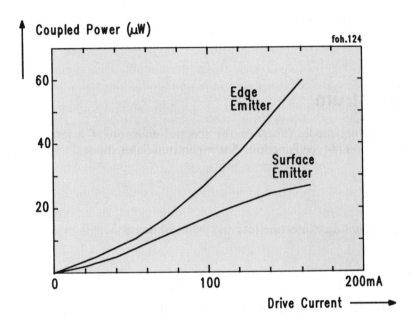

TYPCIAL LEDs COUPLED TO A 50 μm GRADED-INDEX FIBER
(1300 nm InGaAsP: edge emitter and surface emitter)

Similar to laser diodes, light-emitting diodes (LEDs) show a negative temperature coeffient of the output power at constant drive current. Typical numbers are between -0.5 and -1.5 % / °C for both GaAlAs LEDs (850 nm) and InGaAs LEDs (1300 nm). Temperature stabilization, utilizing thermoelectric (Peltier-) coolers, is frequently done in order to stabilize the power and to improve the reliability. Electronic feedback is not necessary for most applications.

In the measurement of the emitted power of an LED, an error on the order of 5 % (in addition to the inaccuracy of the meter) has to be taken into account, if the power meter is based on a photodetector. The reason is that each spectral component is multplied with a different responsivity r(λ). There is no additional error if r(λ) forms a straight line for the wavelengths of interest **and** if the spectral emission is symmetric to the center wavelength. If these conditions do not apply, a mathematical correction can be made which takes the spectral responsivity **and** the spectral emission of the LED into account, see reference [5.4].

There is no threshold current in LEDs. Therefore, the "characteristic temperature" model, which describes the change of the threshold current, does not apply.

Light Emitting Diode

See →LED.

Linewidth

The term "linewidth" is used for the spectral bandwidth of an individual mode (line) of the (usually) several cavity modes of a laser diode; see →spectrum (laser diode). Several methods can be used for the measurement of the linewidth; see →Fabry-Perot interferometer, →ring resonator, →self-heterodyning, →coherence.

Local-Area Network

See →network.

Lorentz Spectrum

Each of the longitudinal modes (lines) of the spectral emission of a laser diode is usually assumed to follow a Lorentz-type function. See →spectrum (laser diode).

Loss

See →attenuation, →coupling, →insertion loss and →optical density.

LP-Mode

Abbreviation for linear polarized mode. See →modes (fiber-).

Luminance

See →units at the end of the book.

Mach-Zehnder Interferometer

In classic optics, Mach-Zehnder Interferometers (MZI) are constructed for collimated (open) beams. They are typically used for the measurement of the refractive index of an unknown material. In fiber optics, MZIs consist of fibers and couplers. In both cases, the principle is the same: optical radiation is split into 2 branches, 1 branch is manipulated and then the 2 branches are recombined. In the process of recombination, the electric fields produce variable optical interference which is then analyzed.

Like in all interferometric devices, it is important to provide identical states of polarization at the coupler, because an addition of the **electric fields** is required. This could be provided with either a →polarization-controller or with a →polarization-maintaining fiber.

Fiber-optic MZIs perform a number of tasks:

1. FM-demodulation; see below.
2. Linewidth-measurement; see →self-heterodyning, self-homodyning.
3. Intensity-modulation; see →modulator.

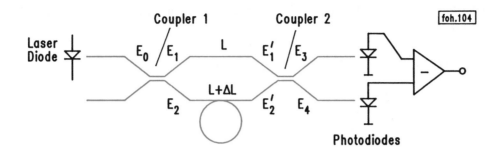

MACH-ZEHNDER INTERFEROMETER BASED ON SINGLE-MODE FIBER
(Here shown in its function as FM-demodulator)

In the following, the interferometer's function as an FM-demodulator shall be analyzed. For simplicity, we assume lossless fibers and couplers. The analysis is based on the coupler model derived in the paragraph on →coupler. If we omit the time-dependences of the electric fields, exp (jωt), then the outputs of coupler 1 are:

$$E_1 = a\,E_0, \qquad E_1' = a\,E_0 \exp[-j\beta L]$$
$$E_2 = -jb\,E_0, \qquad E_2' = -jb\,E_0 \exp[-j\beta(L+\Delta L)]$$

E_0 - electric field at the input
$E_{1,2}$ - electric fields at the output of coupler 1
β - the fiber's propagation constant; $\beta = 2\pi n/\lambda$
n - effective refractive index of the fiber
λ - optical wavlength in air

Now, the outputs of coupler 2 shall be calculated. We omit the common phase shift after the couplers:

$$E_3 = a\,E_1' \quad - jb\,E_2'$$
$$E_4 = -jb\,E_1' \quad + a\,E_2'$$

In order to further simplify the derivation, we assume a 3 dB - coupler, which leads to a = b = 0.707:

$$E_3 = a^2\,E_0 \exp(-j\beta L)[1 - \exp(-j\beta\Delta L)]$$
$$E_4 = -ja^2\,E_0 \exp(-j\beta L)[1 + \exp(-j\beta\Delta L)]$$

The optical powers at the output of the interferometer can be calculated by squaring the absolute values of E_3 and E_4. With k being a constant, the result is:

$$P_3 = k\,E_0^2\,[1 - \cos(\beta\Delta L)]$$
$$P_4 = k\,E_0^2\,[1 + \cos(\beta\Delta L)]$$

$$P_3 - P_4 = -2k\,E_0^2\,\cos(\beta\Delta L) \qquad\qquad \text{(difference signal)}$$

Now, let us apply the so-called **quadrature condition**, which means that ΔL is chosen such that $\cos(\beta \Delta L)$ is zero:

$$\beta \Delta L = \frac{2\pi n \Delta L}{\lambda} = \frac{2\pi n \Delta L\ f}{c} \overset{!}{=} \frac{\pi}{2} + 2m\pi$$

m - all positive integers
n - effective refractive index of the fiber; $n \approx 1.5$
c - speed of light in vacuum

Now, if the optical carrier is **frequency-modulated**, the difference signal can be expressed by:

$$P_4 - P_3 = 2k\ E_0^2\ \sin\ \frac{2\pi n \Delta L\ \Delta f}{c}$$

As a practical example, we want to design a circuit in which the difference signal reaches its peak at a frequency deviation of $\Delta f = 100$ MHz. Setting the argument of the sine equal to $\pi/2$ yields a necessary length difference of $\Delta L = 0.5$ meters.

Taking the difference signal from 2 photodiodes, the output of the circuit is proportional to the frequency-deviation of the optical carrier, if the deviation is not too large. This way, the circuit acts like a **delay-line discriminator**. A possible application the detection of an FM or PM-modulation of the optical carrier. An additional feature of this circuit is that the **sum** of the photodiode signals is proportional to the input power only.

Magneto-Optic Effect

This term denotes different mechanisms in which a magnetic field changes the optical characteristics of a material. The most important effect is described in the chapter →Faraday effect.

Material Dispersion

Material dispersion, →waveguide dispersion and →profile dispersion are the contributors to the →chromatic dispersion, which is inversely proportional to the total →bandwidth of fibers. In both multimode and single mode fibers, material dispersion plays a dominant role.

Material dispersion, which is usually given in units of ps/(nm x km), is caused by the wavelength dependence of the fiber's refractive index n and the associated differences in speed of light. Many practical light sources have a spectral width of at least one nanometer. Different components within this spectrum travel at different speeds. This way, the fiber creates a broader pulse; the broadening is proportional to the spectral width of the pulse.

For simplicity, the fiber shall be characterized by the core's refractive index, n, and by the optical power being bound to the core only. We also limit our discussion to the fundamental →mode only, such that the →multimode dispersion is zero in this case. In order to calculate the material dispersion, let us first repeat some basics from the chapter →group velocity:

$$v_{gr} = d\omega/d\beta$$
$$\omega = 2\pi c/\lambda$$
$$\beta = 2\pi n/\lambda$$

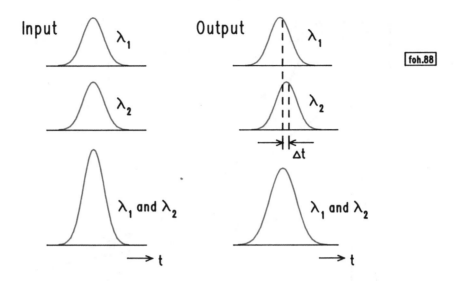

foh.88

PULSE BROADENING DUE TO MATERIAL DISPERSION

This leads to the group travel time t_{gr}:

$$t_{gr} = \frac{L}{v_{gr}} = \frac{L}{c}(n - \lambda\frac{dn}{d\lambda}) = \frac{L}{c}n_{gr} \quad [\,ps\,]$$

ω - 2π x optical frequency
β - propagation constant on the fiber axis
c - speed of light in vacuum, see →constants at the end of the book
λ - wavelength in vacuum
n - refractive index of the fiber core
n_{gr} - group refractive index

We now assume a change of wavelength ($d\lambda$) to cause a change of group travel time (dt_{gr}, see →group velocity). This leads to material dispersion D_{mat}. Following the IEEE-definition in [1.7], we obtain:

$$D_{mat} = -\frac{1}{L}\frac{dt_{gr}}{d\lambda} = -\frac{1}{c}\frac{dn_{gr}}{d\lambda} = \frac{\lambda}{c}\frac{d^2n}{d\lambda^2} \quad [\frac{ps}{km\ nm}]$$

See the paragraph →chromatic dispersion for the influence of the material dispersion on pulse broadening and on bandwidth reduction. The refractive indices n and n_{gr} and the material dispersion of pure quartz (SiO_2) are shown in the diagram. The actual numbers are based on a Sellmayer-model for the refractive index of quartz [0.7]:

$$n(\lambda) = c_1 + c_2\lambda^2 + c_3/\lambda^2 \ ,$$

with $c_1 = 1.45084$
          $c_2 = -3.34 \times 10^{-9} / nm^2$
          $c_3 = 2.92 \times 10^3 \ nm^2$

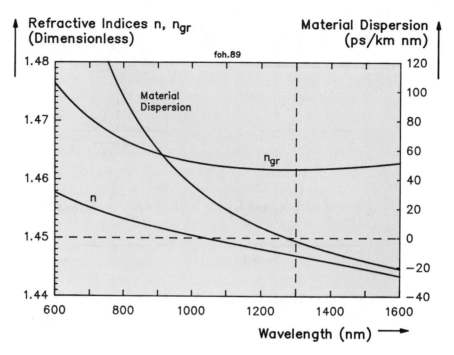

REFRACTIVE INDICES AND MATERIAL DISPERSION OF QUARTZ

Zero dispersion occurs at 1280 nm. This point corresponds to the turning point of the n-curve and to the minimum of the n_{gr}-curve. By adding GeO_2 the zero-point can be shifted rightwise to longer wavelengths. At the classical 850 nm wavelength, material dispersion is around 80 ps/ (km x nm). A source line width of 3 nm causes 240 ps/km material dispersion at 850 nm.

The material dispersion of multimode fibers cannot be measured directly, because →multimode dispersion disturbs the measurement. Quadratic subtraction is possible; see →bandwidth (fiber-). Another possibility is the measurement of the refractive index, in order to solve the above equations. The material dispersion of single-mode fibers cannot easily be separated from →waveguide dispersion; usually only the total →chromatic dispersion is measured.

Meridional Ray

A meridional ray in a fiber repetitively intersects the optical axis (center line) of the fiber, in contrast to skew rays which propagate by forming some sort of spiral around the optical axis. Only meridional rays are considered when determining the →numerical aperture.

Mesial Power

This term describes the mathematical average between high level and low level powers of a modulated light signal, using:

Mesial Power = (High Level + Low Level) / 2

The mesial power level does not depend on the signal's duty cycle and should not be confused with the average power level.

Michelson Interferometer

Michelson interferometers can be used to characterize laser diodes and LEDs in terms of →coherence length or →spectrum.

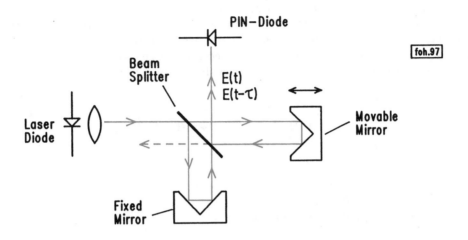

MICHELSON INTERFEROMETER

The radiation from the laser is first collimated and then split into 2 partial beams with a semi-transparent mirror. Normally, plane mirrors are utilized in order to reflect the beams back to the semi-transparent mirror. In our setup, corner-cube mirrors are preferred, because disturbing reflections back to the laser diode can be avoided this way. Finally, the beams are recombined and the total optical power is detected with a photodiode. As indicated in the figure, the 2 electric fields are offset by the delay time τ, which is the difference of path lengths divided by the speed of light. Both beams are assumed to carry equal amounts of power (P_0).

The following integral represents the time-average of the optical power on the detector:

$$P(\tau) = a \lim_{T\to\infty} \frac{1}{2T} \int_{-T}^{T} [\, E(t) + E(t-\tau)\,]^2 \; dt$$

$$P(\tau) = 2a \lim_{T\to\infty} \frac{1}{2T} \int_{-T}^{T} E(t)^2 \; dt + 2a \lim_{T\to\infty} \frac{1}{2T} \int_{-T}^{T} E(t)\, E(t-\tau) \; dt$$

$$P(\tau) = 2\, P_0 + 2\, AKF(\tau)$$

a — constant containing the beam diameter and the characteristic impedance Z_0
E(t) — defines the amplitude, the frequency and the phase of the electric field.
2T — observation time

The first term represents the average optical power of the 2 beams. The second integral is the power resulting from the optical interference of the 2 beams; mathematically, it is the autocorrelation function (AKF) of the 2 electrical fields. Note that the above definition of the AKF includes the constant a. The AKF cannot be calculated directly, because the optical wave E(t) exhibits random phase fluctuations and therefore cannot be expressed in analytical form.

For the calculation of the AKF, we want to use the following statement, without proving it: **the Fourier-transform of the AKF is the spectral power density**, p(f). Thus we can calculate the AKF with the help of the **inverse** Fourier transform of the spectral power density. As an example, we want to calculate the interferometer output for a monochromatic spectrum, for example the spectrum of a (single-longitudinal-mode) →DFB laser. The lineshape is usually assumed to follow a **Lorentz**-function; see →spectrum (laser diode) for an illustration. In the symmetric Fourier-type form, the spectral power density of a Lorentian spectrum is:

$$p(f) = \frac{b}{2} \left(\frac{1}{1 + k\,(f - f_m)^2} + \frac{1}{1 + k\,(f + f_m)^2} \right) \qquad [W/Hz]$$

with $\qquad k = 4 / \Delta f^2$

b - power-proportional constant
f_m - optical center frequency
Δf - FWHM spectral bandwidth of the laser source

We now simply calculate the inverse Fourier transform of p(f) and insert the result, AKF(τ), into the formula for P(τ). The amplitude of the AKF was found from the condition that P(τ) must be $4\,P_0$ for $\tau = 0$. With this, the optical power on the detector is:

$$P(\tau) = 2\,P_0 \left[1 + \exp\left(-\frac{\tau}{\tau_c}\right) \cos(2\pi f_m \tau) \right]$$

with: $\qquad \tau_c = \left(\frac{k}{2\pi}\right)^{1/2} = \frac{0.8}{\Delta f} \simeq \frac{1}{\Delta f}$

τ_c - **coherence time**
P_0 - power of the 2 partial beams

The result is that moving the interferometer's second mirror (changing τ) causes the detector power to follow a **damped cosine** curve. The coherence length ($= \tau_c c$) of the laser emission is defined by the path-length difference at which the amplitude is down to 1/e of maximum. The actual curve is shown in the paragraph →coherence.

In addition to the measurement of the coherence length and -time, the Michelson interferometer is capable of measuring the **spectral power density**. To explain this, let us recall: the Fourier-transform of the AKF is the spectral power density. Therefore, digital computation of the Fourier transform of the interferometer's output waveform will deliver the spectrum. Note that this method is not restricted to special types of spectra; for example, multimode spectra can also be measured this way.

Microbending

Mechanical stress in a fiber may introduce local discontinuities called microbending. This results in unwanted light radiation, extra loss and →mode coupling.

Modal Dispersion

Obsolete term for →multimode dispersion.

Modal Noise

Modal noise occurs whenever the optical power propagates through mode-selective devices. Examples for mode selective devices are connectors and fibers with their mode-dependent attenuation.

When coupled into a multimode fiber, each spectral laser line (longitudinal mode) of a laser output splits up into many fiber waveguide modes. At the end of the fiber the modes interfere and cause a speckle pattern, both in the near and far fields. Adjacent longitudinal laser modes only weakly interfere because of their >50 GHz frequency difference. Graded-index fibers show more pronounced speckle patterns than step-index fibers, due to fewer waveguide modes and lower multimode dispersion.

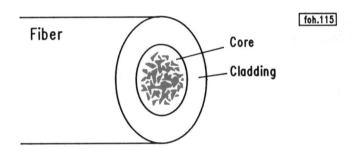

SPECKLE PATTERN AT THE END OF A GRADED-INDEX FIBER

As the **speckle pattern** is based on phase relations, it is sensitive to changes of phase. These changes are already caused by small movements and temperature changes of the fiber. Therefore the speckle pattern is always moving.

If two well cleaved multimode fibers are brought into contact, then no additional noise is observed if the entire power is transmitted. If there is a lateral (axial) offset, then the output speckle pattern of the first fiber core moves statistically across the core boundary of the second fiber, causing modal noise. The same problem arises at the transition of a fiber to a small-area detector.

In the case of single mode fibers, modal noise may occur whenever the operating wavelength is near the cutoff-wavelength and therefore higher order modes are present. Once again, a connector will introduce mode-selective loss and thereby cause modal noise [2.10].

To avoid modal noise, several methods can be applied:

1. Use good connectors or splices.
2. Do not use connectors close to the transmitter. The speckle pattern is more pronounced due to stronger coherence within a certain distance from the source. See →coherence.

3. Use lasers with many longitudinal modes or LEDs. Since each of the laser modes creates its own speckle pattern, the patterns overlap and average. Caution: the total laser line width increases the →chromatic dispersion.
4. Use single mode fibers in conjunction with any source. Single mode fibers don't show speckle patterns, because there is only one waveguide mode and no chance of interference. The operating wavelength should be larger than the cutoff-wavelength.
5. Use large area detectors or good imaging.

Another type of modal noise is **polarization noise** (also called **birefringence noise**) in single-mode fibers. The state of polarization in the fiber changes as a function of mechanical stress such as vibrations. Polarization-selective devices (e.g. beam splitters and diffraction →gratings) will then cause modal noise.

A detailed article about modal noise is reference [2.3].

Mode Competition Noise

See →noise (laser diode-).

Mode Coupling

Exchange of optical power between different waveguide modes is called mode coupling. See →multimode dispersion.

Mode Field

This term is often used to describe the radiating spot at the end of a single-mode fiber. See →spot size.

Mode Filter

Also called mode mixer or mode scrambler. The purpose of this device is to establish an →equilibrium mode distribution (EMD) in a graded-index fiber which is independent of the light-launching conditions. The EMD contains fewer modes than the fully excited state, see the chapter →equilibrium mode distribution.

One approach to generating an EMD is, by definition, a sufficiently long launching fiber of the same type as the fiber under test. Its length depends on the degree of mode mixing (see →multimode dispersion), 1 to 2 km are widely used for graded-index fiber measurements. However, modern fibers with low mode mixing may require lengths of 10 km or more. Therefore, many researchers have been thinking about more convenient ways of generating an EMD. Two principles are commonly used: mandrel-wrap filters and specific launching fibers.

A mandrel wrap filter for a 50 μm graded-index fiber typically consists of a 12.7 mm (0.5 inch) diameter rod with 5 turns of coated fiber. The exact number of turns and the rod diameter have to be determined empirically by comparing the output →far field with the one obtained from a long fiber. At the input of the filter, the fiber is usually overfilled with respect to both the core diameter and the numerical aperture. The filter causes high order modes to be converted to lower order modes, until equilibrium mode distribution is reached. Highest order modes are forced to leave the core and are converted to cladding modes. Therefore, a mandrel-wrap filter should always be followed by a cladding →mode stripper. Due to this effect, a mandrel-wrap filter always introduces a loss of a few dB.

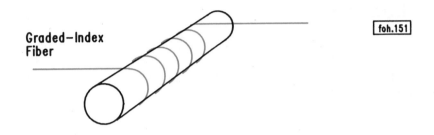

foh.151

MANDREL WRAP FILTER

A similar mode filter can be made by pressing the fiber into a serpentine-shaped surface.

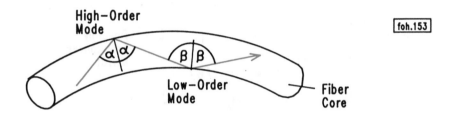

foh.153

EFFECT OF CURVATURE ON FIBER MODES

The figure demonstrates the conversion of a high-order mode to a low-order mode. Reversing the beam direction generates the opposite effect. However, the first effect dominates. For further information on mode filtering in graded-index fibers, see [2.9]. A more precise way of generating an EMD is the combination of special fibers, as illustrated in the diagram.

In the case of **step-index** fibers, mandrel-wrap filters seem to function in a similar way. In the case of **single-mode** fibers, mandrel-wrap filters cause strong attenuation only for higher-order modes; the power of fundamental mode is basically unchanged.

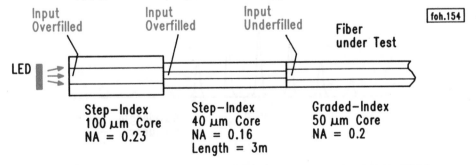

foh.154

MODE FILTER USING A SPECIAL FIBER COMBINATION

It must be mentioned that the exact EMD is different from fiber to fiber. Therefore, mode filters can only come close to the desired EMD. In any case, butt-coupling the fiber under test to the mode filter must be done very precisely in order not to destroy the modal distribution. →Index matching is recommended for best performance.

Mode Locking

Mode locking is typically performed in a gas laser in order to generate **ultrashort** and **repetitive** optical pulses, e.g. for chromatic dispersion measurements. Typical pulse durations are from 100 ps down to 0.1 picoseconds. To understand mode locking, we want to analyze the illustrated external-cavity laser. If we remove the modulator for the moment, then the figure shows a typical gas laser.

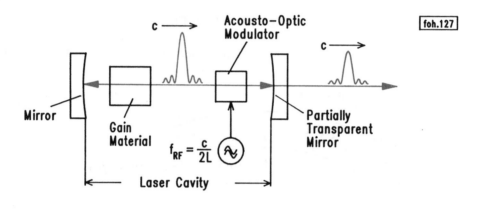

MODE LOCKING IN A GAS LASER

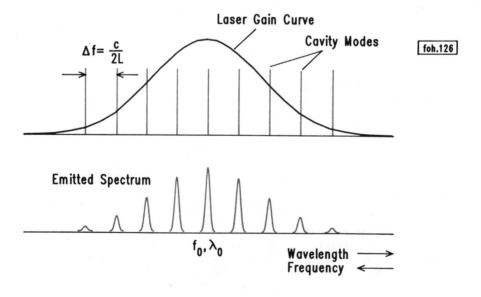

HOW THE EMITTED SPECTRUM IS GENERATED

The **gain curve** of the active material selects the range of possible wavelengths. The resonant conditions inside the cavity define the fine structure of the spectrum: the cavity is nothing else than a →Fabry-Perot resonator. A resonant condition only exists for integer numbers of wave cycles in the cavity. This condition leads to the **mode spacing**:

$$\Delta\lambda = \lambda^2 / 2nL \qquad \text{in terms of wavelength}$$

$$\Delta f = c / 2nL \qquad \text{in terms of frequency}$$

with: $\qquad \Delta f = c \, \Delta\lambda / \lambda^2$

c - speed of light = 3×10^8 m/s
n - refractive index of the cavity medium
L - length of the cavity
λ - wavelength in air

The combination of cavity modes and gain curve leads to the emitted spectrum. To further simplify the analysis, let us assume a **rectangular** comb of spectral modes. Mathematically, the electric field at an arbitrary point in the cavity can then be described by the sum of all electric fields:

$$E(t) = \sum_n \exp[\, j\,(\, 2\pi\,(f_0 + n\Delta f)\, t + \phi_n(t)\,]$$

with: $\qquad f_0 = c / \lambda_0$

f_0 - optical center frequency
λ_0 - center wavelength
n - current number of the individual mode, $1 < n < N$
N - total number of participating modes
Δf - mode spacing in terms of frequency
ϕ_n - phase of the mode no. n

With arbitrary (and time-dependent) phases ϕ_n, the electric fields add up to a continuous optical output, like the one you would expect from a Helium-Neon laser. Now, let us assume that we are capable of fixing all ϕ_n to be constant and zero. In this case, the electric field can be rewritten as:

$$E(t) = \exp(\, j\, 2\pi f_0 t) \; \frac{\sin(N\,\Delta f\, t/2)}{\sin(\Delta f\, t/2)}$$

The first term in this equation represents the oscillation of the electric field at the optical frequency. The second term defines a **low-frequency** amplitude modulation. The optical power is simply the square of the second part. It turns out that the addition of partial waves with a fixed phase results in a comb of narrow pulses, in which the pulse width is strongly dependent on the number of participating modes, N. Careful analysis of this fact yields that the total pulse width is approximately 2 x the inverse of the total width of the gain curve [0.13]

$$\Delta t \approx \frac{2}{B_f} = \frac{2\,\lambda_0^2}{B_\lambda\, c} \qquad \text{with} \quad B_f = c\, B_\lambda / \lambda^2$$

Δt - total pulse width: time between the first zeros
B_f - total width of the gain curve in units of frequency
B_λ - total width of the gain curve in units of wavelength

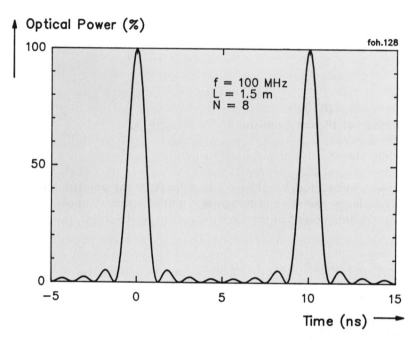

PARTIAL WAVES ADD UP TO A COMB OF NARROW PULSES

The pulse train in the diagram was calculated using N = 8 and a cavity length of 1.5 m. The latter also defines a pulse repetition frequency of 100 MHz.

The remaining question is: how can you arrange a setup which will cause the randomly fluctuating phases ϕ_n to become zero ? There are 2 ways to attack this problem. The first one is called **active mode locking**: as illustrated in the first figure, a loss modulator is inserted into the cavity. The modulator is driven with the frequency $f_{RF} = \Delta f$ (the round-trip frequency), i.e. the modulator is synchronized with the desired pulse frequency. Each time when the pulse peak passes, the modulator is in a low-attenuation state. At other times, the attenuation is high, which causes the pulse tails to be cut off. On subsequent passes through the cavity, the peak will be continuously increased and the tails will be flattened. After many passes, a steady state like the one in the figure will be reached.

There is another way of expressing this: the modulator will only allow certain phases to exist. This was the condition to be accomplished.

Passive mode locking is achieved by placing a saturable absorber into the laser cavity. This type of absorber has the property that its light transmission increases as the light intensity increases. Consequently, the peak of a recirculating pulse experiences a low attenuation, whereas the tails experience a high attenuation. This way the pulse amplitude is increased and the pulse duration is reduced on subsequent passes through the cavity. No drive circuit is required in this case.

The short pulses obtained by mode locking are ideally suited for the test of high-speed fiber optic components: examples are bandwidth testing of photodiodes and dispersion measurement of fibers (see →Raman dispersion measurement). Ultrashort **electrical** pulses can be generated by exciting a fast photodiode with mode-locked optical pulses. Another application is masking the pulse comb by a binary data stream (e.g. with the help of a →modulator); this way, an optical data stream with very narrow pulses can be generated. For further information on mode locking, see [0.13].

Mode Mixer

See →mode filter.

Mode Partitioning Noise

See →noise (laser diode-).

Mode Volume

One way to describe the distribution of modes (mode filling) in multimode fibers is the **effective mode volume (EMV)**:

$$EMV = (D_{eff}\ NA_{eff})^2$$

D_{eff} -   FWHM →near field diameter (spot size)
NA_{eff} -   sine of the half width at half-maximum →far field angle.
          Don't confuse NA_{eff} with →NA, which is taken from the 5%- angle.

The →equilibrium mode distribution (EMD) in a 50 μm graded-index fiber can be described by a spot size of 26 μm and an effective numerical aperture $NA_{eff} = 0.11$ (the correspondent NA is 0.2), yielding an effective mode volume of EMV = 8.18 μm^2.

Mode Scrambler

See →mode filter.

Modes (Fiber-)

Modeling the light propagation in a fiber is usually based on wave optics and "modes". A mode is a 3-dimensional electric field configuration, characterized by a single propagation constant (velocity). A mode represents **one** of the possible solutions of Maxwell's equations for the specific geometry and refractive index profile of the fiber. Only a limited number (N) of modes exist in a fiber. This can be explained with the help of the "wavefront condition": all electric field components in a wavefront of a specific mode must have the same phase. This condition can only be met for modes (rays) which form certain angles with the optical axis.

The simple model of light rays being totally reflected at the boundary between core and cladding cannot explain the limited number of modes and the existence of a →speckle pattern at the end of a graded-index fiber. However, rays and their direction of propagation can help in understanding modes.

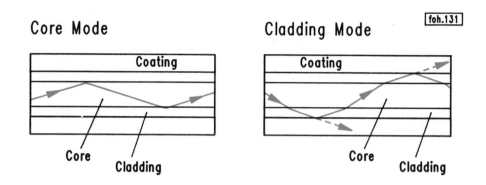

MODES IN A STEP-INDEX FIBER

Fiber modes can be subdivided into guided core modes and radiating cladding modes. Leaky modes have characteristics of both of them.

Core modes: A common mathematical characterization of a fiber is the V-number, also called **normalized frequency**. V combines all essential fiber data **and** the wavelength in a single number.

$$V = \frac{2\pi a}{\lambda} \cdot \sqrt{n_1^2 - n_2^2}$$

a - core radius
λ - wavelength in vacuum
n_1 - refractive index of the core (on the optical axis)
n_2 - refractive index of the cladding

V can be used to calculate the number N of possible modes in the fiber; N includes both possible polarizations of one mode:

$N = V^2/2$ for step-index fibers

$N = V^2/4$ for graded-index fibers with parabolic profile

To find the exact solutions for electric and magnetic fields, Maxwell's equations have to be solved, which leads to complex HE* and EH* modes. A practical approximation has been made by combining HE and EH modes with identical propagation constants to the so-called LP modes; LP stands for **linear polarized**. These modes are **transverse** electromagnetic waves, in which both the electric and the magnetic fields are perpendicular to the direction of propagation and in which the electric fields are oriented in one azimuthal direction only.
* An HE mode is a mode which is nearly transverse magnetic, and an EH mode is a mode which is nearly transverse electric.

The figure shows the electric fields of the fundamental mode and the next-order mode. In the case of the fundamental mode, a small deviation from linear polarization is indicated (exaggerated). There are 2 possible configurations of the next-order (LP_{11}) mode, both of which have the same propagation constant. In both cases, the electric field on the fiber axis is zero : this characteristic makes it easy to detect the LP_{11} mode with the help of a →near-field measurement.

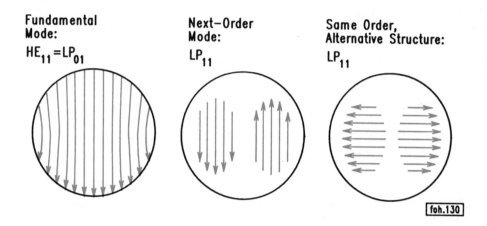

FUNDAMENTAL MODE AND NEXT-ORDER MODE IN A SINGLE-MODE FIBER
(electric fields)

LP modes exist in fibers with low →**refractive index contrast** $\Delta \ll 1$:

$$\Delta = (n_1^2 - n_2^2)/2n_1^2 \simeq (n_1 - n_2)/n_1$$

Such fibers are called **weakly guiding**. All practical fibers fulfil the above condition, which is important to reach high →bandwidth. This can be explained with the help of the →numerical aperture: a low index difference results in a small numerical aperture; therefore the rays only form small angles with the fiber axis. Accordingly, the difference of flight times of different modes is small. The result is low →multimode dispersion and high bandwidth.

Another consequence from the low index difference is that some guided core modes carry fractions of their optical power in the cladding, as a consequence of the electromagnetic boundary conditions. Therefore the cladding must be of good optical quality, too. The power density shows an exponential decay in the cladding. In single mode fibers, the fractional power in the cladding is particularly strong.

The fundamental mode LP_{01} (also called HE_{11} or TEM_{00}) exists at any wavelength. All higher-order modes, starting with the LP_{11} mode, can only propagate at wavelengths shorter than the **cut-off wavelength**. The higher the modal order (i.e. the more complex its electromagnetic field), the shorter its cut-off wavelength. In the case of a step-index fiber, the cutoff-wavelength of the LP_{11} mode is characterized by $V = 2.405$. From this condition, the cut-off wavelength can be calculated with the help of the first equation in this paragraph:

$$\lambda_{cutoff} = 3.7 \, a \, n_1 \, \sqrt{\Delta}$$

The cutoff-wavelength also explains the concept of the single mode fiber: the fundamental mode can always be guided. In contrast, guiding of the next order mode is prevented by making $\lambda > \lambda_{cutoff}$, respectively $V < 2.405$. From the previous equations we find that with $\lambda = 850$ nm, $n_1 = 1.46$, $\Delta = 2 \times 10^{-3}$ the core diameter of a single-mode fiber must be $2a \le 7$ μm. At 1.3 μm the same numbers require $2a \le 10.7$ μm. These small dimensions make it difficult to couple single-mode fibers to light sources and to make single-mode fiber joints; →see coupling.

Each of the modes has different propagation constants. The terms **differential mode attenuation** and **differential mode delay** were created to describe this phenomenon. Differential mode delay is the reason for pulse broadening; see →multimode dispersion. It is not practical to measure the propagation characteristics of the individual modes. Instead, the fiber under test should be driven with an →equilibrium mode distribution, in order to simulate a steady-state modal distribution.

Cladding modes: Optical power which is coupled into the core outside of the numerical aperture cone is not captured by the core. Instead it travels into the cladding and is then partially reflected at the boundary between cladding and coating. These modes can never be recaptured by the core and are therefore called cladding modes. Of course, cladding modes can also be generated by coupling optical power directly into the cladding.

In modern fibers, the coating has a higher refractive index than the cladding. Therefore, most of the optical power travels into the coating and is absorbed there. This type of fiber can be used as →cladding mode stripper, because the attenuation of cladding modes is so high that they are undetectable after a length of only 2 meters.

Cladding modes leave the fiber at angles larger than the angle of the →numerical aperture. Therefore, they can be detected in the fiber's →far field.

Leaky modes: Light energy can be transported by leaky modes over some distance. These modes hold a position in between core modes and cladding modes. For a superficial explanation, let us use rays instead of modes: leaky rays are **skew** rays, i.e. they travel on helical tracks and never touch the optic axis. They can excited close to but outside of the numerical aperture cone. Some fraction of the total power is transported in the core, some in the cladding (similar to cladding modes). Leaky rays exit the end of the fiber at angles equal to or larger than the numerical aperture angle.

In the →far field of the end of a fiber, leaky modes cause a non-abrupt transition of the power density to zero. They also cause a problem in the measurement of the refractive index when using the transmitted →near field method.

Modes (Laser-)

See →spectrum (laser diode-).

Mode Stripper

For some of the fiber measurements, it is important to remove optical power from the fiber cladding (see →modes in a fiber), in order to obtain core modes only.

A 100 m-piece of fiber will perform this task, since the attenuation of the cladding modes is much higher than the attenuation of the core modes. In some instances, it is desirable to remove the cladding modes on a short piece of fiber. To do so, all insulation, buffering and coating must be removed, and the remaining core and cladding must be immersed in a liquid with higher refractive index than the cladding index, i.e. immersion oil, glycerin, and some epoxy materials. A length of a few centimeters is sufficient.

Some fiber coatings have a larger-than-glass refractive index. In this case the coating itself acts like a cladding-mode stripper.

Modulation Index

In the conventional intensity-modulation scheme, the information is digitally coded whith high and low levels of optical power. The best noise performance of such systems coincides with the highest ratio of these 2 levels; this ratio is usually termed →extinction ratio. Another possible description is the more classical **modulation index** m:

$$m = \frac{\text{high level - low level}}{\text{high level + low level}}$$

In connection with frequency-shift keying (FSK) in coherent communication →systems, the term "modulation index" is used to define the relative frequency deviation between marks (ones) and spaces (zeros):

$$m = \frac{f_{mark} - f_{space}}{\text{bitrate}}$$

Modulator (Amplitude-)

Direct light modulation of the laser's drive current causes dynamic effects on the emitted spectrum, such as changes in peak wavelength, spectral bandwidth and the amplitude of the individual cavity modes. The smaller the number of emitted modes (lines), the larger these effects. Other light sources, e.g. gas lasers, may not be capable of being modulated at all. This makes external modulators attractive.

Optical modulators are often based an either the electro-optic effect (induced →birefringence) or on the magneto-optic effect, e.g. the Faraday effect (rotation of the plane of polarization). →Acousto-optical modulators are also quite popular.

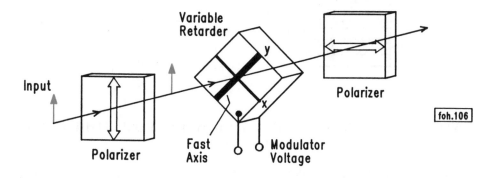

LONGITUDINAL POCKELS CELL MODULATOR

The Pockels cell is the most common optical modulator. It is based on electrically induced →birefringence in certain crystals. Pockels cells are made in either a longitudinal or transverse fashion, meaning that the electric field is applied either parallel or perpendicular to the direction of propagation. In the longitudinal case, transparent or ring-type electrodes are necessary.

A popular material for the longitudinal modulator is KDP (chemical formula KH_2PO_4). In this material, the strength of the **longitudinal** electric field determines the difference of refractive indices in the x- and y-directions. Altogether, the crystal acts as a variable →retardation plate. With no voltage applied, no retardation occurs and the beam is blocked by the second polarizer.

Increasing the voltage consecutively converts the linear input state into the following states: elliptical, circular, elliptical rotated by 90° and linear rotated by 90°. The highest useful voltage creates a **half-wave retarder**, which rotates the input polarization by 90°. In this case, the second polarizer is fully transparent for the output beam. This way, the applied voltage defines the total output power.

Pockels cells have been made with bandwidths from DC to beyond 1 GHz in a travelling wave fashion. Extinction ratios of 100:1 up to more than 1000:1 have been achieved. The disadvantage of usual Pockels cells is the high drive voltage required, typically 2000 Volts or more. A more thorough description of (bulk-type) optical modulators is given in [0.12] and [6.1].

The efforts have concentrated on reducing the drive voltage. One way is using single-mode optical waveguides implanted into an electro-optic material such as lithium-niobate ($LiNbO_3$). This material also exhibits electrically induced birefringence; see →modulator (phase-).

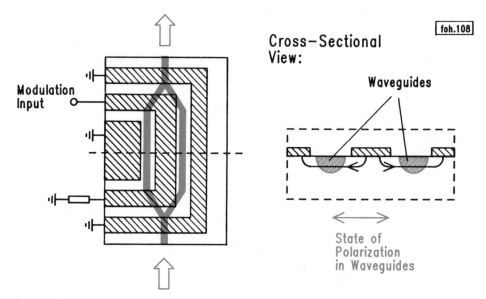

INTEGRATED MACH-ZEHNDER MODULATOR MADE FROM LITHIUM-NIOBATE
(x-cut version)

Most often, integrated amplitude-modulators are based on the structure of a →Mach-Zehnder interferometer. Let us discuss an x-cut Lithium-Niobate device (see the next chapter on the explanation of x-cut). A diffused single-mode optical waveguide is divided into two branches. An electrode configuration is placed on top of the waveguides such that the applied electric field **increases** the velocity in the first arm and **decreases** it in the second arm. After recombining the two branches, total transmission occurs for equal velocity (zero volts drive), and extinction occurs for 180° optical phase difference.

If the interaction length is 1 cm, then around 8 volts must be applied to this modulator in order to achieve extinction (180° phase difference). This number is set by the electrooptic coefficient of Lithium-Niobate and by the specific electrode configuration. Doubling the length cuts the necessary voltage in half. The dependence of the output power is obtained from a geometric addition of the 2 participating electric fields. For a lossless device, we have:

$$P_{out} = P_{in} \cos^2 (V / V_\pi)$$

V - drive voltage
V_π - drive voltage for full extinction (approximately 8 V for 1 cm)

Accordingly, **linear** modulation can only be obtained in the linear region of the $\cos^2$ - function. Sometimes one of the 2 optical waveguides is made 1/4 wavelength longer, in order to create half-on state for 0 volts. In our 1 cm device, this results in: fully on at +4 V, half on at 0 volts, fully off at -4 V.

The **travelling-wave** configuration has 3 advantages: first, the coplanar transmission line can be impedance-matched such that it represents an ohmic resistance at the input. This simplifies the delivery of the drive voltage at high frequencies. Second, the interaction length can be made long without affecting the electrical impedance. This reduces the necessary drive voltage. Third, the modulation bandwidth is increased, because both the electrical and the optical wave travel into the same direction. Ideally, the velocities of both waves should be the same. In this case, the length of the device could be made infinitely long and the drive voltage could be reduced to zero.

Modulation bandwidth: In order to analyze the frequency response, let us apply an electrical impulse (zero-width pulse) to the stripline. The stripline shall have infinite bandwidth. The optical input power shall be constant. The modulator shall be such that zero volts results in zero optical output. Then the **impulse response** will be an optical pulse of finite width; the pulse width $\Delta\tau$ will be equal to the difference in arrival times between the **fast** optical wave and the **slow** electrical wave.

$$\Delta\tau = \frac{L}{v_{el}} - \frac{L}{v_{opt}} = \frac{n_{el} - n_{opt}}{c} L$$

$$\frac{\Delta\tau}{L} \simeq 65 \frac{ps}{cm} \qquad \text{for a lithium-niobate modulator}$$

n_{el} - refractive index for the electrical wave; $n_{el} \simeq 4.1$ in $LiNbO_3$
n_{opt} - refractive index for the optical wave; $n_{opt} \simeq 2.2$ in $LiNbO_3$
L - length of the coupling section
c - speed of light = 3×10^{10} cm/s

With the help of a table of Fourier-transformations, the impulse response can be converted to frequency-domain, which then represents the frequency-dependent conversion gain:

Time Domain		Frequency Domain
Rectangular Pulse: Pulse Width T, Amplitude 1	=>	$\dfrac{T \sin (\pi T f)}{\pi T f}$

This relation is illustrated in the diagram for a modulator of 2 cm length. As expected, the frequency response follows a sin x/x - function. The first zero is at 7.7 GHz. In a practical device, the zeros would be less distinct, due to losses in the stripline. Note that, because of the increased length, this modulator only requires a drive voltage of 4 volts peak-to-peak (as compared to 8 volts above).

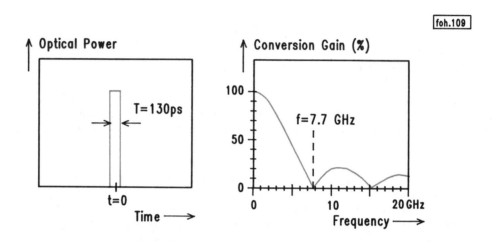

foh.109

IDEALIZED RESPONSES OF A LITHIUM-NIOBATE MODULATOR
(Length = 2 cm)

Mode field: As a first-order approximation, the optical wave both inside and outside the optical waveguide can be described by the mode field of a →Gaussian beam. In order to achieve a good coupling efficiency, the mode-field diameters of the source and the waveguide have to be matched; see coupling (source to fiber-). Practical realizations are attaching fibers to the coupler (pigtailing) or using a lens in order to image the fiber output to the waveguide. This way, typical insertion losses of 3 to 4 dB can be accomplished, including both coupling and attenuation losses. More on waveguide modulators in [6.6].

Modulator (Phase-)

Phase Modulators are important for →coherent communications, in particular for the phase-shift keying techniques (PSK and DPSK). Only integrated versions capable of interfacing with single mode fiber are important in this field. The applied electric field changes the refractive index in the direction of the field. This is then used to create a variable delay of the optical wave.

Because of its strong electrooptic effect, Lithium-Niobate is the most popular material. A single-mode waveguide is created by diffusion or ion-implantation of titanium. There are 2 possible versions, depending on which way the crystal is cut:

Generally, the crystal is cut such that an applied electric field produces the largest possible electrooptic effect. In a z-cut device, mainly the **vertical** component of the electric field is utilized, and the electric field of the optical wave must be oriented vertically. This type of wave is often termed a **TM-wave**. An isolation layer must be inserted between the electrodes and the optical waveguide, because directly adjacent metal would create strong optical losses in the waveguide. In an x-cut device, the **horizontal** component of the electric field is used, and the optical wave must be oriented horizontally. In the same classification scheme, this wave is called a **TE-wave**. x-cut modulators do not require an isolation layer; therefore the necessary drive voltage is reduced. More on this subject in [6.5].

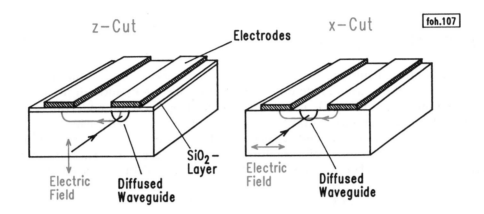

INTEGRATED PHASE MODULATORS IN LITHIUM-NIOBATE

Monochromator

The most common instrument for optical spectrum analysis is the monochromator. A monochromator is a wavelength-tunable narrowband optical filter, based on a →diffraction grating. The grating separates different wavelength spatially. An aperture selects which wavelengths are passed through to the detector. Tuning is accomplished by rotating the grating. The big advantage of a monochromator is its wide tuning range of typically 800 nm.

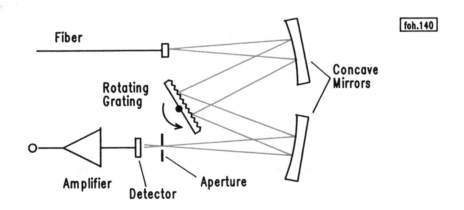

CLASSIC MONOCHROMATOR

The spectral resolution is defined by the aperture size. The finest resolution is on the order of 0.05 nm, which is sufficient to resolve the individual longitudinal modes of a multimode laser diode. The resolution is **not** sufficient for the measurement of the spectral linewidth. A variety of other methods have been invented to measure linewidth, see the paragraph on →spectrum analysis.

Monomode

This term refers to either a single-mode fiber or a laser diode generating a single wavelength (frequency).

Multimode Dispersion

Fiber bandwidth is determined by both →chromatic dispersion and multimode dispersion, see →bandwidth of fibers. Multimode dispersion is also called **intermode** dispersion or, more accurately, multimode distortion. It means pulse broadening on multimode fibers due to the fact that the different fiber modes travel at different effective speeds, which is illustrated in the diagram. To understand multimode dispersion, let us assume that an optical impulse (zero-width pulse) is applied to the input of a multimode fiber of length L. The observed output pulse width shall be Δt_{mod}. Then the multimode dispersion D_{mod} of that fiber is defined by:

$$D_{mod} = \Delta t_{mod} / L \qquad [\,ps/km\,]$$

In case that the frequency response behaves like a Gaussian low pass filter, the 3 dB_{opt} multimode bandwidth is:

$$B_{mod} = \frac{0.44}{L\,D_{mod}} \qquad [\,MHz\,]$$

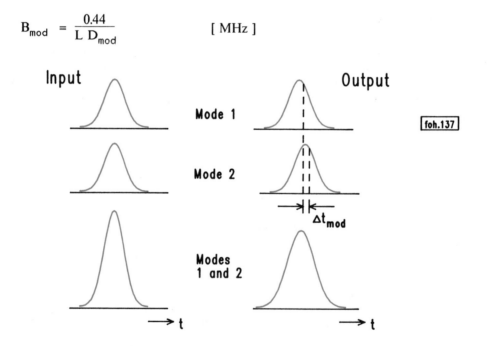

foh.137

ILLUSTRATION OF MULTIMODE DISPERSION

In step-index fibers, a typical number for multimode dispersion at a wavelength of 850 nm is 20 ns/km, corresponding to a 3 $dB_{optical}$ bandwidth of 20 MHz x km. This can be attributed to the difference in path lengths between the fundamental zero-angle mode and the highest order modes.

$$t_{min} \simeq \frac{n_1 L}{c} \quad \text{and} \quad t_{max} \simeq \frac{n_1 L}{c \cos \beta_{max}}$$

with: $n_1 \; \sin \beta_{max} \; = \; NA$ from →fiber (multimode-)

n_1 - refractive index of the core (more accurate is the →group refractive index)
c - speed of light = 3×10^5 km/s
β_{max} - largest guided-mode angle (against the fiber axis)
NA - numerical aperture of the fiber

The output pulse width Δt_{mod} of a **step-index** fiber can now be calculated from the difference between t_{max} and t_{min}, with the assumption that β_{max} is not too large. Note that the following result is based on a full excitation of all guided modes:

$$\Delta t_{mod} \; \simeq \; \frac{NA^2}{2n_1 c} \; L \qquad\qquad [\,s\,]$$

In **graded-index** fibers, the refractive index profile should be optimized in such a way that all the waveguide modes travel at the same effective speed. Accordingly, the multimode dispersion of graded-index fibers can be as low as 50 ps/km, corresponding to a 3 dB (optical) bandwidth of 9 GHz. Practical fibers don't reach this bandwidth due to the problem in exactly controlling the index profile. Also, the optimum profile is wavelength dependent, **double-window fibers** represent a profile compromise for good performance at both 850 nm and 1300 nm.
Note: The term "double-window fiber" is also used for fibers optimized for low **chromatic** dispersion at both 1300 and 1550 nm, see →dispersion shifted-fibers.

In ideal single mode fibers, the multimode dispersion is zero. Finite multimode dispersion arises from different travel speeds of the two possible polarizations of the same mode (polarization dispersion). This problem can be solved by either polarization-preserving fiber or by an optimized production process ("spun fiber"), in order to eliminate differences in propagation constants. 200 GHz x km bandwidth have been achieved this way.

Measurement: Multimode dispersion can be measured by launching a narrow pulse into the fiber, and measuring the pulse width at the end of the fiber. The shortest pulses can be generated by →mode locking. FOTP 30 [1.3] recommends testing in the frequency domain and measuring the 3 dB_{opt}-bandwidth at the end of the fiber. The spectral width must be so small, that →chromatic dispersion does not influence the measurement. Generally, multimode →lasers suffice for step-index fiber measurements. Single mode lasers must be used for high-performance graded-index fibers. The launching conditions influence the measurement, too. FOTP 30 [1.2] suggests overfilling both the core diameter and the numerical aperture. In contrast, the CCITT [1.4] proposes to apply an →equilibrium mode distribution.

Mode mixing means transfer of optical power from one waveguide mode into another, to be observed at connectors, splices and in the fiber itself. One practical consequence is the problem in predicting the pulse broadening of a long fiber. For short lengths, the pulse width rises linear with length. Beyond the so-called coupling length L_c, mode mixing causes the pulse width to rise with the square root of the length (Ref [2.8], k is a constant):

$$\Delta t \; = \; k \, L \qquad\qquad\qquad \text{for } L < L_c,$$

$$\Delta t \; = \; k \, (\, L_c + \sqrt{L\text{-}L_c} \,) \qquad \text{for } L > L_c.$$

Step-index fibers show strong mode-mixing, so the square-root can be applied after only a short length. Modern graded-index fibers have very weak mode coupling, so the square-law is only observed after several km, even up to 20 km. Another popular approximation to length dependence of the pulse width is :

$$\Delta t = k' L^m$$

with a typical m = 0.8, varying between 0.7 and 0.9 (k' is a constant). Also a consequence from mode mixing is the difficulty of predicting the pulse broadening of a concatenated link made of spliced fibers. Ideal mode mixing at each splice would result in a square law dependence, just like cascading a series of decoupled low pass filters. Practical concatenated links show the pulse broadening to be somewhere in between linear with length and linear with the square root of length, in which case the above approximation can be used again. This way, mode mixing at splices leads to the astounding higher bandwidth of a spliced fiber as compared to a one-piece fiber.

NA

See →numerical aperture.

Near Field

This term describes the irradiance (power density) on the surface of a radiating source such as an LED, laser or the end of a fiber. With near field measurements, the refractive index profile of multimode fibers can be measured. Another application is the determination of the fiber's mode filling (see →effective mode volume). In the following chapter, we want to show in which way the power density at the output of a multimode fiber depends on the refractive index profile.

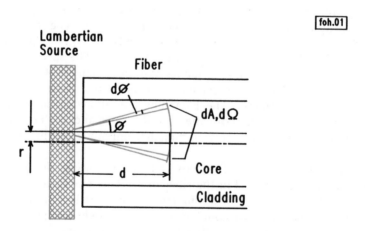

MODEL FOR THE COMPUTATION OF THE NEAR FIELD
(Note that the angle ϕ is the one **before** the fiber)

A →Lambertian source is placed in front of the fiber with the intention of fully exiting all possible modes in the fiber. In order to calculate the power density M(r) at the **input** of the fiber, the following model is established: each fractional solid angle $d\Omega$ contains a fractional power density $dM(\phi)$. Summing (integrating) all fractions $dM(\phi)$ will finally yield the total power density M(r). Following the →radiometric units chapter at the end of this book, we have:

$$dM(\phi) = L_0 \cos \phi \; d\Omega \qquad [\; W/m^2 \;]$$
$$d\Omega = 2\pi \sin \phi \; d\phi$$

L_0 - maximum radiance of the →Lambertian source (perpendicular to the surface), assumed to be constant over the fiber input

$d\Omega$ - solid angle as defined by a ring of the area dA at the distance d

Only those fractions $dM(\phi)$ will be guided which fall into the fiber's maximum angle of acceptance $\phi_{max}(r)$:

$$\sin \phi_{max}(r) = \sqrt{n(r)^2 - n_2^2} = NA_{local}$$

$n(r)$ - refractive index of the fiber core as a function of the radius

n_2 - refractive index of the fiber cladding

Optical power outside of ϕ_{max} will be cut off, i.e. absorbed in the cladding. A →cladding mode stripper is recommended. The cut-off process can be expressed in the following integral which leads to the "guided" power density M(r):

$$M(r) = \int_{\phi=0}^{\phi_{max}(r)} 2\pi \; L_0 \cos \phi \sin \phi \; d\phi$$

$$M(r) = \pi \; L_0 \sin^2 \phi_{max}(r) = \pi \; L_0 \; [\; n(r)^2 - n_2^2 \;] = \pi \; L_0 \; NA_{local}^2$$

$$M(r) \simeq 2\pi \; L_0 \; n_2 \; [\; n(r) - n_2 \;]$$

The same power density will also be observed at the **end** of the fiber. This is based on 2 assumptions. First, an infinite number of modes should exist; this will be provided by the large spectral width of an LED. Second, the modal distribution should remain constant; this assumption is valid on a short piece of fiber (typically less than 1 m). Therefore, the near field at the output of a fully excited short piece of multimode fiber represents the refractive index profile.

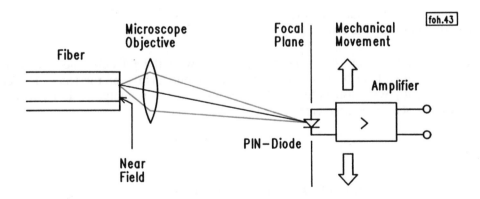

TRANSMITTED NEAR-FIELD MEASUREMENT

Because of the typically very small emitting areas, the near field cannot be measured directly, instead imaging techniques must be applied. A microscope objective with a magnification of 40 to 100 is used to generate a much larger image via projection, in this case of a fiber core. The 50 μm core of a graded-index fiber can thus be converted to a 5 mm diameter image, still being quite small but large enough to be inspected or digitized.

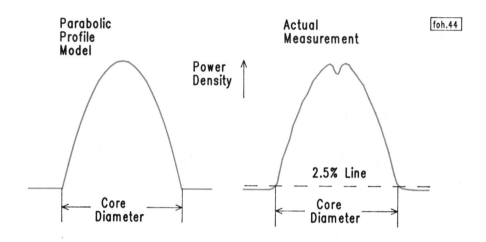

NEAR-FIELDS AND CORE DIAMETER OF A GRADED-INDEX FIBER

The parabolic model is based on a graded-index fiber with parabolic index profile, see →fiber (multimode). The actual measurement reveals a small index dip at the fiber center which is typical for graded-index fibers. It is caused by the specifics of the manufacturing process. Under the influence of non-avoidable leaky →modes, the measured intensity profile slightly differs from the actual refractive index profile. In order to determine the core diameter, the EIA's FOTP 58 [0.3] therefore suggests to intersect the measurement curve with a line defined by n_3:

$$n_3 = n_2 + k \, (n_1 - n_2) \, , \text{ with } k = 0.025.$$

n_1 - maximum refractive index of the core
n_2 - refractive index of the cladding

A more accurate index measurement can be made with the refracted near-field method, in which case a focused laser beam is used to scan the input surface of the fiber. Different from before, the output power distribution of non-captured modes is analyzed. For further information on core diameter measurements, refer to [2.5].

NEP

For noise equivalent power (NEP), see →noise (photodiode-).

Network (Local Area)

The family of computer networks, industrial control networks, airplane and ship buses, and other short distance - multiuser links is called local area networks. Today, most of these are still electrical networks. Examples are the IEEE 802 "Ethernet" bus type network and the MIL 1553B twisted pair bus. However, a large percentage of the newly installed LANs are based on optical fibers, or on a mixture of electrical and optical transmission. The reason for the strong interest in optical networks can be found in the advantages of fibers in comparison to electrical cables: noise immunity, eliminated ground loops, high bandwidth and low weight.

The classical network topologies like bus, loop, star and hybrids are also possible with fibers, but their implementation is different from electrical networks. This is a consequence from the lack of direct fiber access. Instead, directional →couplers must be used for tapping. Couplers can only receive from or transmit into **one** direction of the bus. Here we present 3 popular fiber-network topologies: bus, ring and star. All of these networks are capable of exchanging information between each of the participating terminals.

Bus - type networks are used in networks with a fixed number of terminals which are separated by relatively short distances. Examples are airplanes and ships. Our example is based on passive couplers, and the structure is such that each terminal can directly communicate with each other terminal. The reason for the limited number of users is the subsequent losses of optical power in the couplers, when the signal travels along the bus. Each of the receivers is driven with a different power level, which causes another complication.

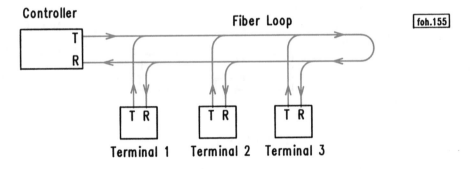

BUS-TYPE NETWORK WITH PASSIVE DISTRIBUTION

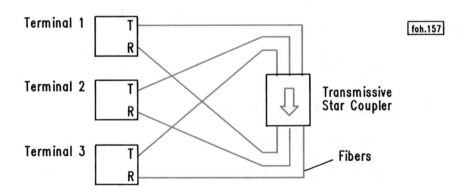

STAR-TYPE NETWORK WITH PASSIVE DISTRIBUTION

Star - type networks are a different solution for the same problem. The star requires a higher amount of wiring, but offers a number of advantages. The signal levels at all receivers are identical if the fibers have the same length. Most important, the star can accomodate more terminals because of its lower losses. In a star network the power (in units of dB_{opt}) only decays with the logarithm of the number of terminals, whereas there is a linear decay in bus networks.

The above networks are generally made with large core, large numerical aperture step-index fibers and LEDs for simplicity reasons. The lower bandwidth of these fibers is well suited to the required data rates, which usually is a few megahertz maximum.

More challenging are long-range, high-capacity computer networks. One example is the "Fiber Distributed Data Interface", **FDDI**, which is proposed as a standard for computer networking. It is based on 1300 nm LEDs and graded-index fiber with either 62.5/125 μm or 85/125 μm core/cladding diameters. Each terminal receives optical information from the preceding terminal, converts it to an electrical signal, processes it or reconverts it to an optical signal for the next terminal. Our example contains 2 fiber rings, one of which is used as backup, should the first ring fail. Maximum data rate is 100 Mbit/s, and maximum distance between two neighboring terminals is 2 km.

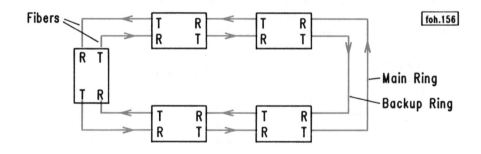

FDDI-RING NETWORK

The FDDI protocol is based on **token passing**, which means that the authorization of transmitting data is passed around the ring from terminal to terminal. If a terminal is ready to transmit, then it holds the token and sends the data.

Noise (Birefringence-)

Birefringence noise is only observed in single mode fibers. See →modal noise.

Noise Equivalent Bandwidth

The noise equivalent bandwidth B_n is different from the signal bandwidth B_s (which is usually the $3dB_{el}$-frequency). Instead, B_n is determined this way: the square of the (electrical) transfer function is approximated by a rectangle of equal area, with the height of the rectangle being the maximimum of the transfer curve and the width being the noise equivalent bandwidth. A practical result for systems with 1 pole is:

$$B_n = \pi \, B_s \, / \, 2$$

This formula can also be used for Gaussian low pass filters and first order resonant filters. If one assumes a constant (electrical) power density, p_n, the the total noise power is $p_n \times B_n$.

Noise Equivalent Power (NEP)

The noise of optical receivers, or of entire transmission systems, is often expressed in terms of noise equivalent optical power (NEP). The NEP is a measure for the smallest detectable optical power at a given bandwidth.

Imagine an optical receiver: even with no optical input, an output noise voltage is observed. This voltage can be thought of as being generated by a noiseless receiver, the optical input of which driven by a fictitous optical power, the NEP. The NEP should be expressed in units of RMS optical **amplitude** [watt]; there is no continuous optical power involved. A spectrum analyzer is frequently used to measure the NEP. Therefore the NEP is sometimes given in units of watt/$\sqrt{Hz}$, not in watt. The NEP and the output noise voltage of any optical receiver are related by:

$$v_{output}{}^2 (RMS) \;=\; NEP^2 r^2 R_t{}^2 B_n \qquad [\, V^2 \,]$$

NEP - noise equivalent power; watt (RMS),
    the peak-to-peak amplitude of the NEP is 6 to 10 times as large
r   - responsivity of the photodetector
R_t - transimpedance resistor of the amplifier
B_n → noise equivalent bandwidth of the meter (e.g. the spectrum analyzer)

Here is benefit from using the NEP-model: with the help of the average input power to the receiver, P_{opt}, the signal-to-noise ratio can be calculated:

$$SNR \;=\; 10 \log (P_{opt} / NEP) \qquad [\, dB_{opt} \,]$$

Also see: →noise of photodiodes and →bit errror rate.

Noise (Fiber Output-)

A substantial amount of noise is frequently observed at the end of optical fibers, so that the signal/noise ratio is rarely better than 15 dB_{opt}. This is the reason why optical fibers are mostly used for transmission of **digital** signals. What are the noise sources ?

1. **Mode competition noise**: the driving laser diode may generate noise, because the optical power is statistically exchanged between the modes. This effect increases with the length of the fiber, because the laser modes (colours) split in time due to →chromatic dispersion. See →noise (laser diode). LEDs don't generate mode competition noise.

2. **Optical feedback noise**: the driving laser diode is sensitive to changes of the reflected optical power, e.g. from an optical connector. These changes are usually caused by vibrations of the fiber. The strongest effect is observed when a laser drives a multimode fiber: in this

case, a →speckle pattern is reflected to the laser, with the speckles moving across the emitting surface of the laser diode. The change in power level may be several dB. The combination of laser and single mode fiber exhibits smaller noise levels. In this case, there is no speckle pattern; most likely, the noise is caused because the fiber acts as a resonator and vibration changes the length of the resonator.

3. **Modal noise** always occurs when more than one fiber mode travel through a mode selective device, such as a sharp bent in the fiber or a connector with lateral offset. The necessary mode changes are again caused by vibrations of the fiber. This effect is obvious in multimode fibers; it also exists in single mode fibers because of the propagation of higher order modes near the source, see →cutoff wavelength.

4. **Polarization noise**: in a single mode fiber, the state of polarization changes when the fiber is bent or vibrated. If polarization-selective devices (e.g. beam splitters, diffraction gratings) are part of the fiber path, then polarization noise is observed.

Noise (Laser Diode-)

Two types of noise may be generated by a laser diode. Phase noise (see →coherence) is most disturbing in coherent transmission systems. This paragraph is about **amplitude noise**, which may have several causes. Whenever light is converted to an electrical signal, **shot noise** is generated; see →noise (photodiode-). In lasers, additional noise is caused by the laser emission process. Typically, the noise power increases with rising optical power, reaches a maximum at the threshold level, and decays at higher power levels. An **example** of laser intensity noise is presented in the chapter →optical signal analyzer. Also see the chapter →relative intensity noise.

A third noise generating effect is **mode competition noise**, also called **mode partition noise** when observed at the end of a fiber. In a multimode laser, all of the longitudinal modes are in competition, causing the spectral distribution to be time-dependent. The normal spectral distribution (→spectrum of the laser diode) is only a time-average. Looking at one single mode only, its signal-to-noise ratio SNR can be 15-20 dB_{opt} worse than the SNR associated with all the modes. In single mode lasers, this effect does not exist. As each of the modes corresponds to a different colour, →chromatic dispersion of the fiber separates these modes. This not only lowers the system bandwidth, but also increases the noise level, 10 dB_{el} higher noise level is a typical number for a multimode laser and a graded-index fiber of 1 km length.

A fourth effect is **optical feedback noise**. Light reflected back into the laser (from the fiber input, fiber output or connectors) causes the laser oscillation to be disturbed. Generally, fiber bending increases the noise. The strongest effect is obtained from the combination of a laser diode with a graded-index fiber. The reason is the →speckle pattern, which can be expected at both ends of the fiber (transmitted and reflected). The combination of laser diode and single-mode fiber is more stable, because bending will only change the **phase** of the reflected signal. Note that even the backscatter signal may change the characteristics of the laser.

Not only the amplitude may change, but also the modal distribution and the spectral bandwidth. This effect is particularly troublesome in coherent transmission →systems. Single-mode lasers (e.g. DFB lasers) are disturbed by only 10^{-6} of the generated power, multimode (gain-guided) lasers are sensitive to a fraction of 10^{-3} to 10^{-4}.

One way to avoid reflections is to use optical isolators. A tapered fiber (see →coupling) is a less effective solution. Also see →modal noise.

Noise (Modal-)

See →modal noise.

Noise (Mode Competition-)

For mode competition noise, see →noise (laser diode-).

Noise (Mode Partitioning-)

For mode partitioning noise, see →noise (laser diode-).

Noise (Optical Feedback-)

For optical feedback noise, see →noise (laser diode-).

Noise (Photodiode-)

In this chapter, the noise-generating mechanisms of PIN-diodes and of avalanche photodiodes (APDs) shall be presented.

foh.17

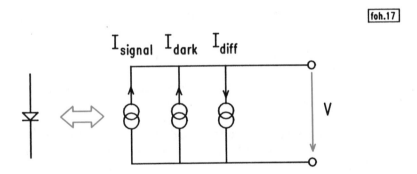

NOISE-GENERATING CURRENT SOURCES IN A PIN-DIODE

The dominant noise source in PIN-diodes is **shot noise**, which is generated by the statistical process of single electrons passing the pn-junction. Shot noise is closely related to the statistical arrival of photons at the detector. Limited by the bandwidth of the diode only, shot noise is "white", which means that the (electrical) noise power is proportional to the bandwidth. There are several current flow (I) mechanisms in a photodiode, each of which creates a mean square noise current; time average is indicated by brackets < > :

$$< i_n^2 > \; = \; 2e \, I \, B_n \qquad\qquad [A^2]$$

e - electron charge, 1.6×10^{-19} As
B_n - see →noise equivalent bandwidth

With the model established in the →pin-diode chapter, the above equation should read as follows. The "|" indicates that all currents shall be **added**, independent of their direction):

$$< i_n^2 > \;=\; 2e\,B_n\,(\,|\,I_{signal}\,| + |\,I_{dark}\,| + |\,I_{diff}\,|\,),\quad \text{with}$$

I_{signal} - current caused by optical power: $I_{signal} = r\,P$,
I_{dark} - dark current (at negative bias)
I_{diff} - diffusion current caused by applied voltage: $I_{diff} = I_{dark}\,\exp(-V/V_t)$

r   → responsivity, in units of [A/W]
P   - incident optical power
V   - applied voltage
V_t - temperature-dependent voltage, $V_t = kT/e = 26$ mV at 300 K (25° C);
      see →constants at the end of the book

Two cases shall be distinguished:

A) The **zero-bias** mode is mostly used in optical power meters, where bandwidth is of no concern. Here it is important to generate the lowest possible current with no light on the photodiode. In this mode, the total DC current is zero, because I_{dark} and I_{diff} cancel each other. However, they do not cancel each other in terms of noise generation:

$$< i_n^2 > \;=\; 2e\,B_n\,(\,|I_{dark}| + |I_{diffusion}|\,)\qquad [A^2]$$
$$\phantom{< i_n^2 >} \;=\; 4e\,B_n\,I_{dark}$$
$$\phantom{< i_n^2 >} \;=\; 4kT\,B_n\,/\,R_d,\qquad \text{with } R_d = kT\,/\,(e\,I_{dark}) = V_t\,/\,I_{dark}$$

R_d - the photodiode's differential resistance at zero bias.

Note that, according to the last equation, the generated noise current is exactly the one expected from a pure ohmic resistor R_d.

B) The **photoconductive (backbiased) mode** is used in most optical receivers, where bandwidth is important and bias currents are not. In this mode, and under the assumption of no light, $I_{diff} = 0$. The RMS noise current is:

$$< i_n^2 > \;=\; 2e\,B_n\,I_{dark}\qquad [A^2]$$

In this case, the square of the noise current is only one half of the one in the zero-bias mode. However, this only applies if the "backbiased" dark current is the same that defines the R_d at zero volts, which may not always be true. Note that the noise due to **signal** current can be substantial, with the consequence that the signal-to-noise ratio is degraded.

The noise of PIN-diodes is often expressed in terms of **noise equivalent optical power** (NEP), which is a measure for the smallest detectable optical power for the given bandwidth. The NEP is defined as a fictitious noise power at the input of the photodiode; it is usually given in units of RMS optical **amplitude**:

$$NEP = \frac{1}{r}\,< i_n^2 >^{1/2}\qquad [W]$$

A) $\quad$ NEP $= \dfrac{1}{r} \left(4e\, B_n\, I_{dark} \right)^{1/2} \qquad = \dfrac{1}{r} \left(4kT\, B_n\, /\, R_d \right)^{1/2} \qquad$ zero-biased

B) $\quad$ NEP $= \dfrac{1}{r} \left(2e\, B_n\, I_{dark} \right)^{1/2} \qquad\qquad\qquad\qquad$ backbiased

Some typical device characteristics at a temperature of 25° C are given in the table. Note that, in contrast to the above definition, the NEP is given in units of $W/\sqrt{Hz}$. For a fair comparison, the dark current should be scaled by the active area, whereas the NEP should be scaled by the **diameter** of the active area.

Technology	Diameter of active area	Dark current	NEP $[\,W\,/\,\sqrt{Hz}\,]$
Silicon	1 mm	5 nA	8×10^{-14} (800 nm)
Germanium	0.2 mm	500 nA	1×10^{-12} (1300 nm)
InGaAs	0.1 mm	60 nA	3×10^{-13} (1300 nm)

NOISE CHARACTERISTICS OF PIN-DIODES

In the receiver, additional noise sources like resistors and transistors increase the NEP (see →receiver).

Shot noise also exists in **avalanche photodiodes** (APDs). Again, any current flow mechanism in the diode adds to the total noise. Different from the PIN-diode model, I_{diff} can be neglected, because APDs are always operated a high enough bias voltage. Instead, there may be a leakage current I_{leak} caused by the usual high voltage applied.

In an APD, the avalanche process causes a multiplication of the photocurrent. As the multiplication is another statistical process, the square of the noise current (i.e. the electric noise power) is not only multiplied by M^2; instead it is multiplied by $M^2 \times F(M)$. F(M) is called **excess noise factor**. Note that only multiplied currents create excess noise (i.e. not I_{leak}):

$$\langle i_n^2 \rangle \quad = 2e\, B_n\, I_o\, M^2\, F(M) + 2e\, B_n\, I_{leak}$$
$$= 2e\, B_n\, [\, (I_{signal} + I_{dark})\, M\, F(M) + I_{leak}\,]$$

e $\qquad$ - electron charge, $e = 1.6 \times 10^{-19}$ As
I_o $\qquad$ - original current (before multiplication)
B_n $\qquad$ - see →noise equivalent bandwidth
I_{signal} $\quad$ - actual current due to signal (after multiplication)
I_{dark} $\qquad$ - actual dark current (after multiplication)
I_{leak} $\qquad$ - leakage current (does not undergo multiplication)

F(M) is usually measured by illuminating the detector such that the generated photocurrent is much larger than both the dark current and the leakage current. As a result of the noise current, a noise voltage at a load resistor can be measured with either a true-RMS voltmeter or with an (electrical) spectrum analyzer. Finally, F(M) can be extracted from the above equation, using the known bandwidth of the measurement system, B_n.

Near breakdown, F(M) can be approximated by:

$$F(M) = M^{\alpha}$$

α = 0.2 - 0.5   for silicon diodes
α = 0.9 - 1   for germanium diodes
α = 0.7 - 0.8   for germanium diodes

Like in the case of a PIN-diode, the noise of an APD can be expressed in terms of noise equivalent optical power (NEP). To do this, we set $I_{signal} = 0$:

$$NEP = \frac{1}{rM} < i_n^2 >^{1/2}$$

$$NEP = \frac{1}{r} \left[(2e\, B_n) (I_{dark}\, F(M)/M + I_{leak}/M^2) \right]^{1/2}$$

r - non-multiplied $\rightarrow$responsivity, in units of [A/W]

I_{dark}/M is identical to the original PIN-diode's dark current (before multiplication). Now, compare the NEP of an APD with the NEP of a PIN-diode: if the contribution of I_{leak} can be neglected, then the NEP of an APD is higher than the NEP of a PIN-diode by the square root of F(M).

If this is true, what is the advantage of using an APD ? Answer: the photodetector always drives an ohmic resistor. In the APD case, the noise contribution of this resistor is scaled down by M. If well designed, this results in lower NEP of the entire $\rightarrow$receiver, as compared to a PIN-diode receiver.

Typical data of commercial APDs, at the manufacturer-recommended bias point (around 0.9 x V_{br}), are given in the table below. Note that, for a fair comparison, the dark current should be scaled by the active area, whereas the NEP should be scaled by the diameter.

Technology	Diameter of active area	M	I_{dark} (total)	Exponent α	Calculated NEP [W/$\sqrt{Hz}$]
Silicon	0.8 mm	100	150 nA	0.30	81×10^{-15} (850 nm)
Germanium	0.1 mm	18	500 nA	0.95	480×10^{-15} (1300 nm)
InGaAs	0.05 mm	13	23 nA	0.75	76×10^{-15} (1300 nm)

TYPICAL NOISE PERFORMANCE OF APDs
(at 0.95 x breakdown voltage and 25°C ambient temperature)

Noise (Polarization-)

Polarization noise is only observed in single mode fibers. See $\rightarrow$modal noise, $\rightarrow$multimode dispersion.

Noise (Quantum-)

See $\rightarrow$quantum noise.

Noise (Receiver-)

See →receiver.

Noise (Shot-)

For a discussion of shot noise, see →noise (photodiode-).

Normalized Frequency

The normalized frequency (abbreviation V, dimensionless) allows to describe the characteristics of a single-mode fiber as a function of a single variable (an operating point). The number of →modes, the →spot size, the →cutoff wavelength, the propagation constant and the →chromatic dispersion can be calculated with the help of V. For the basic step-index profile, V is given by:

$$V = \frac{2\pi a}{\lambda} \sqrt{n_1^2 - n_2^2} = \frac{2\pi a}{\lambda} NA = \frac{2\pi a}{\lambda} n_1 \sqrt{2\Delta}$$

a - radius of the fiber core
λ - wavelength in vacuum
n_1 - refractive index of the fiber core
n_2 - refractive index of the fiber cladding
NA - numerical aperture
Δ → refractive index contrast; $\Delta = (n_1^2 - n_2^2) / 2n_1^2 \simeq (n_1 - n_2) / n_1$

For example, a (step-index) single-mode fiber supports one mode only, if $V \leqslant 2.405$. The analysis of V suggests that a 10% reduction of V can be accomplished with either a 10 % reduction of the core diameter **or** with a 10 % reduction of the refractive index contrast.

Numerical Aperture (NA)

For a lens or a fiber, the NA historically is defined as the sine of half the maximum angle of acceptance, α:

$$NA = \sin \alpha, \quad \text{with} \quad 2\alpha = \text{full acceptance angle.}$$

For a multimode fiber, only →meridional rays leading to guided core modes are considered.

$$NA = \sin \alpha = \sqrt{n_1^2 - n_2^2}$$

n_1 - core refractive index
n_2 - cladding refractive index

In the case of **step-index fibers**, this equation is rather simple. In the case of **graded index fibers**, n_1 depends on the core profile: the largest acceptance angle is measured at the core center. Accordingly, the core center's index must be used to calculate the NA. Typical NA numbers are 0.3 - 0.4 for step-index fibers, 0.2 - 0.3 for graded-index fibers.

As the direction of the light rays is reversible, the NA is usually determined by the maximum far-field angle of the fiber output. Slightly different from the figure, the power density (irradiance) is **not** measured on a plane, but on a sphere. See the paragraph on →far field.

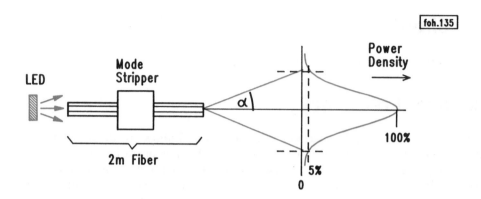

NUMERICAL APERTURE MEASUREMENT

Since these measurements do not show a clear cut-off angle, one proposed standard for measuring the NA of graded-index fibers suggests the evaluation of the →far field of a 2 m piece of fiber. The sine of the 5% optical power angle, corresponding to -13 dB_{opt}, has been found to be in best agreement with the NA. At the input, the fiber must be overfilled with a large spot size, and a →mode stripper must be used to remove the cladding modes. This results in →skew rays being excited, too, but **graded-index** fibers show smaller than maximum acceptance angles for skew rays. Therefore, skew rays do not affect the NA-measurement of graded-index fibers.

Step-index fibers have larger acceptance for skew rays than for meridional rays, so the above measurement method is questionable in this case. In order to only launch meridional rays, a small spot excitation at the center of the fiber has been proposed.

Defining the NA by the refractive indices of core and cladding can also be applied to **single mode** fibers. This leads to the typical NA = 0.1 of single-mode fibers. In contrast to the above, the NA does not describe the fiber's far field, because the ray-model cannot be applied to single-mode fibers. An accurate, but expensive method is the measurement of the refractive index profile. However, the disagreement between the NA and the sine of the 5 % - far field angle is usually small; see the example in the chapter →far field.

Optical Density

The optical density D characterizes the power budget or power density budget of light when transmitted through a layer of material at normal incidence.

$$D = \log P_0/P_1$$

P_0 is the input power, P_1 the output power. The associated loss may be caused by reflection and absorption. The optical density should be multiplied by -10 to calculate the loss in dB_{opt}.

Optical Feedback Noise

See →noise (laser diode-).

Optical Signal Analysis

An optical signal analyzer measures the **modulation** of an optical carrier, either in the time-domain or in the frequency-domain.

An example is a conventional (electrical) spectrum analyzer with a PIN-diode front end. See the product section of this book for an example in which this concept has been optimized in terms of bandwidth and sensitivity: the HP 71400A Lightwave Signal Analyzer. Although it measures only intensity modulation, it can also be used for the measurement of the linewidth (i.e. the frequency modulation) of laser diodes. See the chapters on →Mach-Zehnder interferometer and →self-hetero/homodyning to understand how frequency modulation can be converted to intensity modulation.

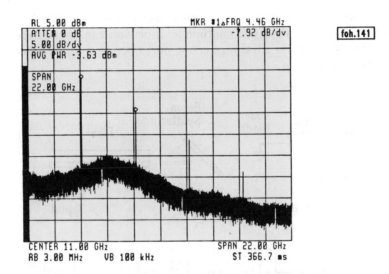

MODULATED LASER SIGNAL IN THE FREQUENCY-DOMAIN
(Display of the HP 71400A Lightwave Signal Analyzer)

On the left side of the screen, you see a "Power Bar" which is an analog display of the average optical power being measured (-3.63 dBm). The signal being measured is generated by a sine-wave modulated laser diode. The laser's transfer function is nonlinear. The result is harmonic distortion, which is -7.92 dB_{opt} (corresponding to -15.84 dB_{el}) in this case. Also shown is the laser's **intensity noise**, which peaks up at about 6.6 GHz. This noise peak is a function of bias, modulation level and modulation frequency, and, along with the intensity noise at all in-band frequencies, is of great interest to many system designers.

Optical Spectrum Analysis

Optical Spectrum Analysis (OSA) is necessary for the measurement of the spectrum of LEDs and laser diodes. Another important application is the measurement of optical filters, such as those used for →wavelength-division multiplexing. 2 categories of OSA can be distinguished by their spectral resolution:

a) **Wideband** analysis is capable of measuring the coarse spectrum of laser diodes and LEDs. These measurements are typically made with a →monochromator, which is based on a →diffraction grating. Typical monochromator characteristics: resolution is 0.05 nm, tuning range 800 nm.

b) **Narrowband** analysis is necessary for the measurement of the linewidth of laser diodes. A large variety of measurement principles has been developed, all of which are based on optical interference: see the chapters on →self-heterodyning/homodyning, →Michelson interferometer, →Mach-Zehnder interferometer, →Fabry-Perot interferometer. The characteristics of these instruments can vary widely. Typical tuning ranges are less than 0.1 nm (18 GHz), with resolutions from MHz to kHz.

Optical Time Domain Reflectometer (OTDR)

An OTDR is an important tool for the characterization of a fiber's attenuation, uniformity, splice loss, breaks and length. Even multimode dispersion can be measured with a suitable, short pulse width OTDR. Its main advantage is one-port operation at the fiber input with no need to access the fiber output.

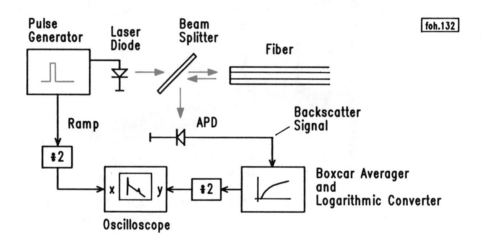

OTDR INSTRUMENT PRINCIPLE

A typical OTDR arrangement is shown in the figure. A pulse generator drives a laser **diode** which then launches optical pulses (10 mW or more) into the fiber. The pulse widths range from nanoseconds to microseconds at repetition rates of 1 kHz (for long fiber lengths) up to 20 kHz (for short fiber lengths). The repetition rate must be chosen such that the signals returning from the fiber do not overlap. The returning signal is separated from the launched signal by a directional coupler, such as a twisted-pair →coupler or a polarizing →beam splitter.

An →avalanche photodiode is often used as a detector. Its signal is fed to an amplifier and a digitizer. A →boxcar averager usually improves the signal-to-noise ratio. The signal is then displayed in logarithmic form. A division by 2 is performed because the vertical scale should be in **one-way** fiber attenuation; see below. Horizontal scaling is also in **one-way** fiber length.

Let us now calculate the signal arriving at the photodiode. The Fresnel →reflection from the fiber input is usually the largest signal; its magnitude may be up to 4 % or -14 dB of the launched optical power. If the laser emits polarized light, then the front reflex can be suppressed by using a polarizing →beam splitter. The splitter separates the polarized front reflex and the unpolarized backscattered light.

According to the →backscattering theory, the backscattered signal P_{bs} begins with a level that can be calculated by setting the length parameter z = 0:

$$P_1 = P_{bs}(0) = S \, \alpha_s \, \Delta z \, P_0 \, T_s$$

with: $\Delta z = w \, c / n_{gr}$

α_s - scattering coefficient, [1/km]. Use α_s [1/km] = 0.23 α_s [dB/km].
See →backscattering theory.
S - backscattering factor (dimensionless), see →backscattering theory
P_0 - launched power in the fiber, [watt]
Δz - pulse length on the fiber, [m]
T_s - round-trip transmission of the beam splitter, dimensionless.
w - pulse width, [s]
c - speed of light = 3×10^5 km/s
n_{gr} - group refractive index, see →group velocity

The backscattering amplitude P_2 from the end of the fiber is obtained with the help of the round-trip attenuation $2\alpha L$:

$$P_2 = P_{bs}(L) = S \, \alpha_s \, \Delta z \, P_0 \, T_s \, 10^{-2\alpha L/10 \, dB}$$

The signal P_3 due to the reflection from the end of the fiber does not depend on the backscattering factor S. P_3 can be calculated from the input power P_0, the round-trip loss $2\alpha L$ and the →reflection coefficient r at the end of the fiber, which is 4% (-14 dB) if the end is polished. Also, we assume no amplitude reduction due to fiber dispersion:

$$P_3 = r \, P_0 \, T_s \, 10^{-2\alpha L/10 \, dB}$$

From these formulas, the table below was calculated.

Fibers:	Graded-Index λ = 850 nm	Graded-Index λ = 1300 nm	Single Mode λ = 1300 nm	Single Mode λ = 1550 nm
α	3.5 dB/km = 0.81/km	0.5 dB/km = 0.115/km	0.4 dB/km = 0.092/km	0.2 dB/km = 0.046/km
α_s	0.65/km	0.09/km	0.074/km	0.036/km
NA	0.2	0.2	0.1	0.1
n	1.5	1.5	1.5	1.5
S	4.44×10^{-3}	4.44×10^{-3}	9.8×10^{-6}	9.8×10^{-6}
P_1/P_0	-32.4 dB	-41.0 dB	-48.4 dB	-51.5 dB

TYPICAL NUMBERS DETERMINING THE BACKSCATTER SIGNAL
(Calculated with: pulse width w = 1 μs, beam splitter transmission T_s = 100 %)

When comparing the attenuation α with the scattering coefficient α_s, it is evident that scattering is by far the strongest attenuation mechanism (80 to 90%).

The diagram below shows calculated OTDR signal levels for a single-mode fiber of 20 km length. Of course, the diagram may be used for other lengths by extrapolation. In order to calculate power levels (P) in units of dBm_{opt}, use the following relation:

$$P_{dBm} = 10 \log (P / 1 \, mW) \qquad [\, dBm \,]$$

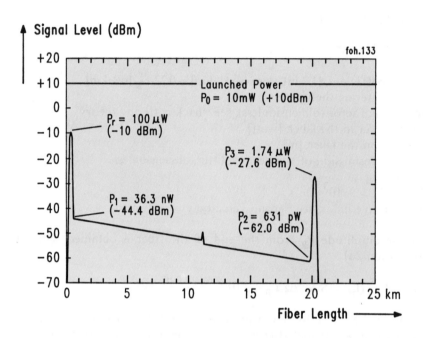

OTDR SIGNAL LEVELS FOR 20 km SINGLE-MODE FIBER AT 1300 nm
Pulse amplitude: 10 mW, pulse width: 1 μs, round-trip coupler loss: 6 dB.
Both fiber ends polished with 4 % reflection.
Splice with 0.8 dB loss at 11 km (resulting in 1.6 dB loss of signal).
Note that, for an OTDR display, the signal must be compressed by the factor 2 !

The diagram shows the backscattered signal rapidly falling below the sensitivity of usual receivers. Often, the P_1 level is already near the noise-equivalent power (NEP) of the receiver. The typical method for enhancing the signal-to-noise ratio is **averaging**. This method effectively leads to a reduction of the NEP, see →boxcar averaging.

The logarithm of the received signal decays with 2 x α. Therefore, the signal trace in the above diagram must be vertically compressed by a factor of 2, in order to construct the desired OTDR display. The result is that the display directly allows to extract the attenuation of the fiber in units of dB, or dB/km. The maximum measurable length of fiber is usually expressed in terms of the dynamic range. The most important definition is:

Dynamic range for a signal-to-noise ratio of 1:
Half the dB-difference between the maximum backscatter signal (P_1) and the NEP of the receiver. The division by 2 is due to the fact that the logarithm of the backscatter signal decays with 2xα.

Note that the peak noise amplitudes are a factor of 3 (approximately) larger than the RMS-based NEP of the receiver. Compression by 2 leads to peak noise amplitudes of **2.3 dB** above the NEP level on the OTDR display.

An important capability of an OTDR is **splice loss** analysis: it can be shown that, in order to measure a splice loss of 0.1 dB with an accuracy of ± 0.05 dB, the (one-way) OTDR trace must be **8.2 dB** above the NEP level. This number sets the dynamic range for splice loss measurements.

Another characteristic of an OTDR is the capability of detecting the end of a fiber. Two cases shall be distinguished: if the fiber end is nonreflecting, we obtain:
Detectable Length = (Dynamic range - 2.3 dB) / Attenuation.
If the fiber end is polished, then the displayed reflection is 17 dB* above the backscatter signal. In this case, the result is:
Detectable Length = (Dynamic Range + 17 dB* - 2.3 dB) / Attenuation
The latter defines the maximum useful fiber length (L_{max}) of the OTDR. Note that the backscatter signal from L_{max} will be hidden in the noise. Both ranges are set by the condition that the signal from the fiber end must be larger than the peak noise level; therefore, consider them as approximate only !
* 17 dB for a single-mode fiber at 1300 nm, with a pulse width of 1 µs.

For the largest possible backscatter signal, one would be tempted to use a long pulse width, because the backscatter signal is proportional to the pulse width. On the other hand, this would reduce the length resolution:

The 2-point **length resolution** is a measure of the closest spacing between 2 fiber discontinuities which the OTDR can separate. Let us construct an example: the launched pulse width shall be 1 µs, which corresponds to a geometrical pulse length on the fiber of 200 m. 2 fiber discontinuities shall be 101 meters apart. After reflection from the discontinuities, there will be 2 pulses running back, each 200 m long. Their positive slopes will be separated by 202 m. Assuming that the sampling rate is sufficiently high, this leads to the following result : the 2-point resolution equals the displayed pulse length, or half the physical pulse length (in meters).

OTDR-performances: Most of today's OTDRs exhibit a dynamic range of around 22 dB after 15 minutes of averaging. This means that a fiber attenuation of 22 dB will cause the signal to drop down to the receiver's NEP level (after improvement by averaging). As stated above, the dynamic range for splice loss measurements is reduced by approximately 8 dB. The resulting 14 dB means a maximum length for splice measurements of 35 km (at 1300 nm, with 0.4 dB/km).

Hewlett-Packard's HP 8145A OTDR offers a dynamic range of 28 dB during the same time. This means 20 dB for splice loss measurements, or 50 km (again, at 1300 nm). These numbers refer to a pulse width of 4 µs, corresponding to a 2-point resolution of 400 m. In the comparison of dynamic ranges and averaging times, the following rule can be applied: an improvement of 3 dB in dynamic range costs a factor of 16 in time.

HP's improved performance in terms of dynamic range was accomplished by sending a coded pulse stream into the fiber, this way increasing the total pulse energy. No penalty in terms of 2-point resolution must be taken into account, because the complex backscatter signal is converted to a single-pulse backscatter signal with the help of correlation techniques. For a detailed description of this technique, see [7.3].

As an example, a single-mode fiber of 50 km length was tested with the HP 8145A OTDR, using a wavelength of 1300 nm. The diagram was generated during approximately 15 minutes averaging time. Note that the end of the useful backscatter signal was visible after only 6 seconds; the rest of the time was spent for averaging down to the noise level. As usual, the OTDR signal diagram is scaled in units of one-way attenuation.

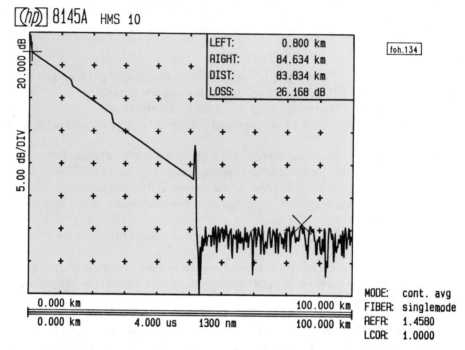

50 km SINGLE-MODE FIBER, DISPLAYED ON THE HP 8145A OTDR SIGNAL
(wavelength 1300 nm)

Results from **attenuation** measurement by time-domain reflectometry are not identical with those obtained by classical two-port measurements. For example: the OTDR signal may exhibit a step into the positive direction at a location where the fiber's numerical aperture changes. This certainly does not mean a gain in the fiber. To explain this behaviour, let us analyze the situation at a splice between a fiber A and a fiber B. The displayed power levels shall be P_A and P_B. When assuming equal power transmission into either direction one obtains a splice loss of [7.2]:

$$A_{splice} = 5 \log \frac{P_A}{P_B} - 5 \log \frac{S_A \alpha_{sA}}{S_B \alpha_{sB}}$$

Different scattering properties (expressed by $S \times \alpha_s$) thus result in an uncertainty of splice loss and connector loss, even a "gain" is possible. This problem can only be solved with a measurement from both ends of the fiber: the average of the 2 losses is the "exact" number.

The big advantage of the backscattering method is the "inside view" of the fiber. Thus many fiber manufacturers measure fiber attenuation by backscattering **and** by two-port measurement. Optical time domain reflectometry is also suitable for multimode **bandwidth/dispersion** measurements. To do so, a narrow subnanosecond pulse is launched and the pulse width of the end reflection is measured.

Paraxial Ray

This term is used for both lenses and fibers. A light ray intersecting and forming a small angle with the optic axis is called paraxial. In this case, the sine of the angle can be replaced by its argument. Paraxial rays are a special class of →meridional rays.

PCS Fiber

Abbreviation for →plastic clad silica fiber, a fiber with a silica core and a plastic cladding. This construction improves the fiber's flexibility, but increases its attenuation.

Phase Velocity

The speed of light in a medium is called phase velocity v_{ph}, which for a uniform medium is:

$$v_{ph} = c/n = \omega/\beta$$

c - speed of light in vacuum; 2.998×10^8 m/s
n - refractive index
ω - 2π x optical frequency
β - propagation constant

For glass with n = 1.5, the phase velocity is around 20 cm/ns. While the phase velocity in a material is usually lower than the speed of light in vacuum, it can also be higher: some metals have a refractive index of less than 1. However, the →group velocity, which is the transportation speed of **energy**, can never be higher than the speed of light in vacuum.

Photocurrent

The current caused by conversion of photons into electrons in a →pin-diode or in an →avalanche photodiode (APD) is termed "photocurrent". Additional current due to multiplication in an APD is not part of the photocurrent, neither is dark current.

Photodiode

See →pin-diode, →avalanche photodiode and →noise (photodiode-).

Photometric Units

These units use the human eye as wavelength-dependent measurement standard. To convert them to absolute units see →units at the end of this book.

Photon

A quantum of light is called photon. Its energy E_{ph} depends on the wavelength:

$$E_{ph} = h\,f = h\,c/\lambda$$

h - Planck's constant, h = 6.62×10^{-34} Ws^2
f - optical frequency
c - speed of light, c = 2.998×10^8 m/s
λ - optical wavelength

At a wavelength of 850 nm, the energy of a photon is 23.4×10^{-20} Ws. At 1300 nm, the energy is 15.2×10^{-20} Ws.

Photovoltaic Effect

The photovoltaic effect causes a non-terminated PIN-diode to generate a voltage equal to the logarithm of the optical power. See →PIN-diode.

Pigtail

For the ease of connection to a fiber, some manufacturers supply sources and photodiodes with a short length of fiber, called pigtail.

PIN-Diode

The PIN-diode is the most important detector type due to its simplicity, stability and bandwidth. This is its principle of operation: whenever the energy of an entering photon is larger than the bandgap energy of the material, the photon energy is **absorbed** and an electron-hole pair are generated in the i-zone (intrinsic zone, a zone of low conductivity) of the diode. An ideal photodiode with negligible recombination would generate one electron-hole pair per photon. This mechanism creates a responsivity which is proportional to the wavelength; see the chapter →responsivity.

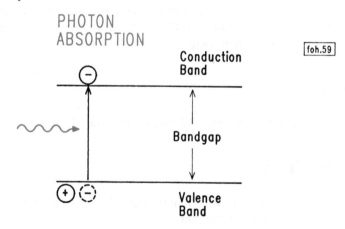

PHOTON ABSORPTION

The photon's energy is inversely proportional to the wavelength. At the **cutoff wavelength**, the photon's energy falls below the bandgap energy. This leads to a more or less abrupt drop of the responsivity; the material appears to be transparent to those wavelengths.

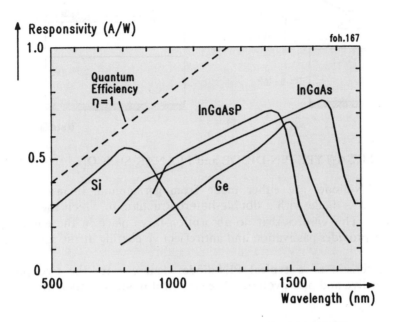

RESPONSIVITY OF TYPICAL PHOTODIODES

Because of the respective bandgap energies, silicon is the common material for the near-infrared (850 nm) - region, whereas germanium, InGaAs or InGaAsP are used for wavelenghts above 1 µm. The cutoff wavelength of the InGaAsP - system can be selected by "tuning" the alloy. The broader wavelength range of InGaAs detectors (in comparison to InGaAsP detectors) are accompanied by higher dark currents.

Note that the observed cutoff-wavelengths of **germanium** are on the order of 1.4 µm. In contrast, the theoretical cutoff-wavelength is 1.85 µm, as dictated by the formula given in the chapter →responsivity. The discrepancy is due to the more complex structure of the energy bands in germanium (indirect bandgap); a certain fraction of the photon energy is absorbed in creating lattice vibrations.

Material	Bandgap	Cutoff-Wavelength	
Si	1.11 eV	1.12 µm	Silicon
InGaAsP	0.89 eV	1.4 µm	Indium-Gallium-Arsenide-Phosphide
InGaAs	0.77 eV	1.6 µm	Indium-Gallium-Arsenide
Ge	0.67 eV	1.4 µm	Germanium

TYPICAL PHOTODIODE MATERIALS

The usual construction consists of highly conductive p- and n-zones enclosing the i-zone. An electric field is established in the i-zone, which pulls the generated carriers to the contacts. The input p-zone should be very shallow in order to prevent absorption there.

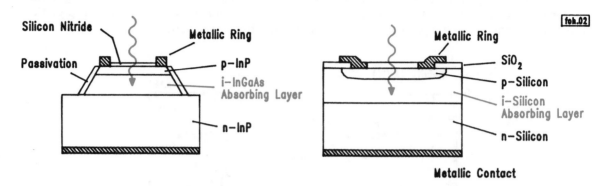

InGaAs MESA-TYPE PIN-DIODE and PLANAR SILICON PIN-DIODE

Long-wavelength PIN-diodes are either made from germanium, InGaAs or InGaAsP. The figure shows an InGaAs-diode with a **double-heterostructure**, in which the absorbing layer has the lowest bandgap. This ensures that no absorption takes place in the enclosing layers. The silicon nitride layer provides passivation and antireflective coating at the same time.

The output characteristic of a typical PIN-diodes demonstrates the two possible operating modes: photoconductive and photovoltaic. The electrical model covers both modes.

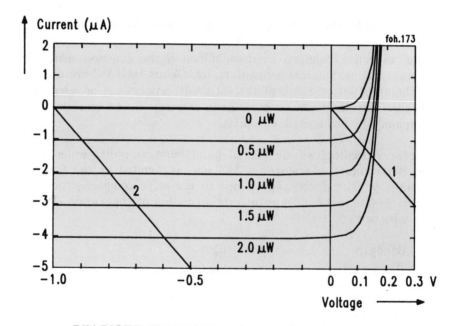

PIN-DIODE ELECTRICAL CHARACTERISTIC

Referring to the model the following equations can be established:

$$I_{ph} = r\, P_{opt}$$
$$I_{diff} = I_{dark}\, \exp(V_i/V_t)$$

r   → responsivity
P_{opt} - incident optical power
I_{diff} - diffusion current of the diode
I_{dark} - dark current, measured at reverse bias
V_t - temperature voltage, $V_t = kT/e = 26$ mV at 300 K

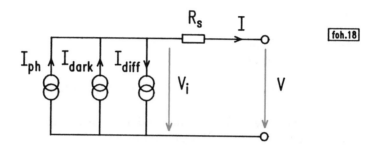

foh.18

PIN-DIODE MODEL

The **photovoltaic** mode refers to operation in the right quadrant with no voltage source required. Line 1 in the diagram represents a 100 kΩ load resistor. There is no current in the "dark" condition, which makes this mode attractive for detection of low light levels.

The model shows the photocurrent I_{ph} being shunted by an ordinary pn-diode, and an intrinsic series resistor R_s limiting the maximum current from the diode. Typical series resistance is 50 Ω for a silicon photodiode of 1 mm diameter. In agreement with this model, the PIN-diode generates a voltage which is the logarithm of the incident optical power, if no load resistor is connected:

$$V = V_t \ln (1 + r P_{opt} / I_{dark})$$

In a typical power meter, the diode drives the virtual ground of an operational amplifier, which represents a short circuit. The diode then equals a differential resistor R_d:

$$R_d = V_t / I_{dark}$$

This resistor, in conjunction with the offset voltage of the amplifier, is capable of generating an output voltage even in the "dark" condition. Even worse, R_d is strongly temperature-dependent (because of the temperature dependence of I_{dark}, see below), which makes a compensation of the offset difficult.

PIN-diodes exhibit excellent linearity over more than 6 decades of optical power in the (photovoltaic) short-circuit mode. At the high-power end, the increasing voltage drop across the series resistor R_s starts limiting the photocurrent. Nonlinearity typically starts at a power level of 1 mW, depending on the type of diode and on its active area. The real drawback of the photovoltaic mode is its lower bandwidth due to much larger capacitance.

In the **photoconductive** (backbiased) mode a voltage source is applied, which dramatically decreases the junction capacitance and increases the bandwidth. Unfortunately, a temperature-dependent dark current is also generated, resulting in problems with measuring low light levels.

Therefore, this mode is less sensitive than the photovoltaic mode. However, it offers good linearity up to high power levels, because the voltage drop across R_s has no effect. Line 2 in the diagram represents a bias of 1 V with a series resistor of 100 kΩ.

Technology	Dark Current at 25 °C	Dark Durrent doubles every:
Silicon	5 nA	7 °C
Germanium	12 μA	8 °C
InGaAs	12 μA	10 °C
InGaAsP	6 μA	10 °C

DARK CURRENTS OF 1 mm - DIAMETER PIN-DIODES

Dark current is the reason why germanium and InGaAs-diodes have very small active areas, typically diameters are 0.1 - 0.2 mm. Dark currents depend exponentially on temperature.

Evaluation of the bandwidth of PIN diodes usually represents the biggest measurement problem, particularly because these diodes are used for data rates of more than 5 Gbit/s and because laser diodes with high bandwidth are difficult to obtain. Three methods are available:
1. Testing in the time domain requires picosecond pulse widths. One way is applying a short pulse to a laser diode and utilizing the laser's first relaxation oscillation. Another way is →mode locking.
2. Testing in the frequency domain requires a network analyzer and a high-bandwidth laser diode.
3. A sine-wave electrical current up to many gigahertz can be generated in the PIN diode by adding the outputs of 2 external cavity lasers on the surface of the diode, just like in →coherent detection. Of course, the laser must exhibit extremely high frequency stability and narrow spectral bandwidth. This method is sometimes termed **two-tone method**.

Planck's Constant

$h = 6.62 \times 10^{-34}$ Ws^2. See →constants at the end of this book.

Plastic Clad Silica (PCS) Fiber

A step-index (multimode) fiber made from a silica core and a plastic cladding, such as silicone. The idea of such a fiber is a large core while maintaining a good flexibility. The result is good coupling efficiency and large →numerical aperture, but higher loss. Such a fiber may have advantages up to a link length of a few hundred meters.

Plastic Fiber

Plastic fibers are entirely made from plastic. Their advantage is low price and easy of use, due to large core diameters. Because of their much higher attenuation in comparison with glass fibers, they can typically span distances of 50 m. For a review of some characteristic properties of plastic fiber, let us use Hewlett-Packard's HFBR-351X series plastic fiber (typical numbers):

Attenuation	0.31 dB/m at 665 nm (visible !)
Numerical Aperture	0.5
Core Diameter	1.0 mm
Jacket Diameter	2.2 mm
Refractive Index (Core)	1.5 (velocity 0.2 m/ns)

A simple step-index profile defines core and cladding. Using the formula in →multimode dispersion, the bandwidth due to the different mode velocities can be calculated from:

$$B_{mod} = \frac{0.44}{L\,D_{mod}} \quad \text{with} \quad D_{mod} = \frac{NA^2}{2n_1 c}$$

B_{mod} - multimode bandwidth   [MHz]
L - length of the fiber
D_{mod} - multimode dispersion [ns / km]
n_1 - refractive index of the core
c - speed of light = 3×10^8 m/s

With a numerical aperture of 0.5, the multimode bandwidth of this fiber is estimated to be:

$$B_{opt}\,L = 1.57 \ \text{MHz} \times \text{km}$$

For a fiber length of 50 m, the multimode bandwidth is therefore much higher than typically required. Therefore, systems with plastic fiber fall under the category "attenuation-limited".

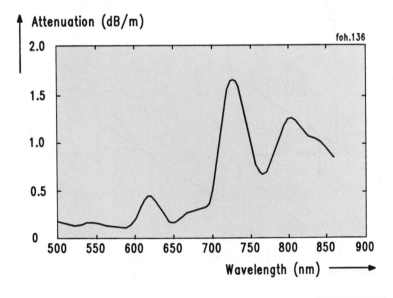

SPECTRAL ATTENUATION CURVE OF A PLASTIC FIBER

Pockels Cell

A crystal exhibiting voltage-dependent optical birefringence, mostly used as an optical modulator. See →modulator.

Polarization

Electromagnetic theory requires the electric and magnetic field vectors of an unbound wave to be in a plane perpendicular (transverse) to the direction of propagation. This can be applied to both free-space radiation far from the source and to the output of single-mode fibers. Transverse electromagnetic (TEM) waves can be subdivided into unpolarized and polarized. In an **unpolarized** TEM wave, the electric fields are evenly distributed in all directions of the transverse (azimuthal) plane, and the phase relation between them changes statistically. In a **polarized** TEM wave, all field components in the transverse plane are related by a fixed phase difference.

An emission with a spectral width of zero **must** be polarized, because all field vectors can be added to a resulting vector in this case. An example is the emission from a narrow-linewidth laser diode. A source with a wide spectral width, such as an LED, is usually unpolarized. It can be made polarized by passing its output through a polarizer.

The term **linear polarization** is used when the electric field is oriented in only one direction of the transverse plane. The projection of the field vectors to the plane is a simple line. Modern laser diodes generate nearly 100 % linear-polarized radiation. The term **circular polarization** is applied to a wave in which the electric field vector rotates by 360° within one wavelength. In this case, the projected field vectors form a circle. The figure shows the field vectors of both types at a fixed time. In free space, both of the packages of vectors travel at the speed of light, c.

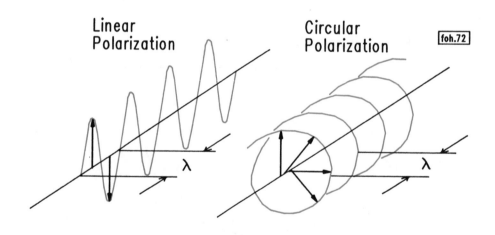

TYPES OF POLARIZATION
(linear polarization and clockwise rotating circular polarization)

At the output of ordinary single-mode fibers, **elliptical polarization** is usually observed, meaning that the projected field vectors form an ellipse. Elliptical **and** circular polarization can always be constructed from 2 linear-polarized waves which are oriented in the x- and y- directions of the coordinate system.

Let us mathematically split an elliptical state of polarization into 2 partial waves, E_x and E_y, which are 90° out of phase. A →**quarter-wave retarder** shall be oriented such that E_y travels faster than E_x. Then the 2 partial waves are **in phase** at the output of the retarder. This way, linear polarization can be reconstructed, as illustrated in the figure. In order to prevent a possible confusion, note that a quarter-wave retarder is usually much thicker than a quarter of the wavelength.

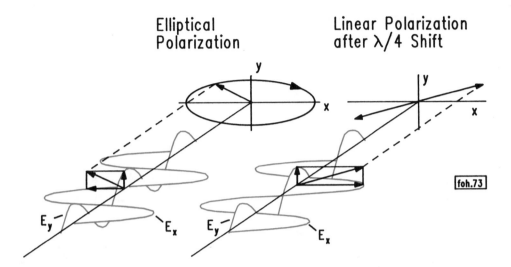

Elliptical Polarization

Linear Polarization after λ/4 Shift

foh.73

ELLIPTICAL POLARIZATION AND ITS CONVERSION TO LINEAR POLARIZATION

If the main axes of the ellipse coincide with the axes of the system (as shown in the figure), then there is a 90° phase difference between the 2 waves. Generally, the main axis of the ellipse forms an angle Θ_a with the x-axis. Again, linear polarization can be reconstructed with a quarter-wave retarder: this time, one of the axes of the retarder must be oriented at the angle Θ_a.

In the general case of Θ_a being unequal 0, the phase difference ϕ between E_x and E_y is different from 90°. The correct value of ϕ can be extracted graphically from the drawing of the ellipse, as illustrated.

Ratio of Axes, b/a	Direction of Main Axis	Phase Delay ϕ	State of Polarization
0	any direction	not applicable	linear
1	not applicable	90°	circular
< 1	horizontal or vertical	90°	elliptical
< 1	**not** horizontal or vertical	> or < 90°	elliptical

RELATIONS BETWEEN PHASE DELAY AND ELLIPSE

The diagram was produced with the assumption that the electric fields are pure sine waves. Eliminating the time-dependence yields an analytical form of the ellipse. Unfortunately, the ellipse equation does not readily supply the graphic information a, b, Θ_a.

Field vectors:

$$E_x(t) = A \cos \omega t$$
$$E_y(t) = B \cos (\omega t - \phi)$$

Ellipse:

$$\frac{E_x^2}{A^2} + \frac{E_y^2}{B^2} - \frac{2 E_x E_y \cos \phi}{A B} = \sin^2 \phi$$

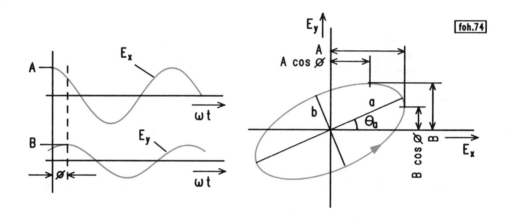

RELATION BETWEEN ELECTRIC FIELDS AND POLARIZATION ELLIPSE
(field vector rotates counter-clockwise in this case)

All of the above can only be applied to **polarized** waves. The question on whether the radiation is polarized can be answered with the help of a quarter-wave retarder and a →polarizer: with the appropriate orientation of the retarder, linear polarization remains unchanged and circular polarization will be converted to linear polarization. The polarizer (analyzer) will then detect the linear state, by passing the electric field in one plane and suppressing the field in the perpendicular plane. Ideally, the output is zero when the axis of the analyzer and the electric field are perpendicular. A **partially polarized** wave yields a minimum position. An **unpolarized** wave results in a constant output at any azimuthal position of both the quarter-wave plate and the analyzer.

Once the polarized state is verified, a simple analyzer is sufficient to measure the polarization ellipse. Note that the output of the analyzer does not directly produce the desired ellipse. Let us use the illustrated example:

Orientation of input wave:	linear in x-direction.
Electric field amplitude:	A.
Orientation of analyzer:	Θ.
Electric field after analyzer:	$A \cos \Theta$.
Output of power meter:	$k A^2 \cos^2 \Theta$ (k is a constant).

In this case, the ellipse is a simple line in x-direction. In contrast, the analyzer produces an output which is proportional to $\cos^2 \Theta$. Therefore, the ellipse should be constructed from the angle Θ_a (the analyzer orientation at maximum output) and the square roots of the analyzer outputs at Θ_a and $\Theta_a + 90°$. Taking the square root is necessary because the ellipse represents electric fields, not optical power. The detection of the sense of rotation would require an additional quarter-wave retarder.

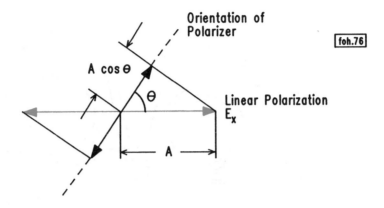

LINEAR-POLARIZED INPUT TO A POLARIZER

Here are some alternatives for a complete description of the state of polarization:

1. Field vectors with parameters A, B, ϕ
2. Polarization ellipse in analytical form, using the parameters A, B, ϕ and the sense of rotation (CW or CCW)
3. Polarization ellipse in graphical form, using the parameters a, b, Θ_a and the sense of rotation
4. Jones vector (see the chapter on →Jones calculus)
5. The Poincaré sphere (not explained here, see [0.6])

A large number of passive optical components are based on polarized waves, e.g. →polarizers, →polarization controllers, →retardation plates, →isolators, →modulators, →beam splitters and →polarization-maintaining fibers. See the appropriate chapters.

Polarization Control

Controlling the state of →polarization is important because many modern fiber optic components require a well defined state of polarization. In coherent communications, a polarization controller is one of the key components. Therefore, the most important methods of polarization control shall be explained. Of course, retardation plates can be used for polarization control, see the chapters on →polarization and →retardation plate. More elegant, however, is polarization control which does not require an interruption of the fiber.

The first **fiber-based polarization controller** (PC), consisting of 3 single-mode fiber coils, was published by H.C. Lefevre [6.3]. The basic idea is that a loop of single-mode fiber can replace a →retardation plate. This can be explained with the "water hose effect": bending a water hose changes its cross section to an ellipse. In the fiber, bending causes an increase in the material's density in the plane which is perpendicular to the plane of the coil. This increases the refractive index in that plane; the change in the plane of the coil is much smaller, because pressure and tension tend to cancel each other. Lefevre calculated an index difference of:

$$\Delta n = a \ (\ r/R \ )^2 , \quad \text{with } a = 0.133 \ \text{(constant)}$$

r - radius of the fiber, typical number: 2r = 125 μm
R - radius of the curvature

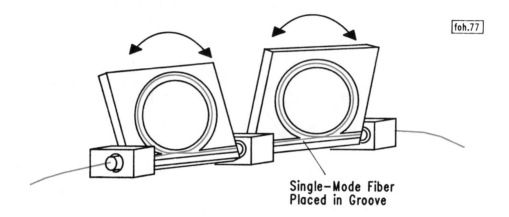

Single—Mode Fiber
Placed in Groove

foh.77

FIBER-BASED POLARIZATION CONTROL

Let us now calculate the radius R of a **single fiber loop** which leads to a phase difference of 90°; this is the requirement for a quarter-wave →retarder. The phase condition for this case is:

$$\Delta \beta \ 2 \pi R = \pi / 2 , \quad \text{with}$$

$$\Delta \beta = 2 \pi \ \Delta n / \lambda$$

Δβ - difference of propagation constants for the 2 possible linear polarizations
λ   - wavelength in air

Combining all 3 equations leads to the necessary loop radius R:

$$R = 8 \pi \ a \ r^2 / \lambda = 10.04 \ \text{mm (at 1300 nm)}$$

Experiments with a standard single-mode fiber at a wavelength of 1300 nm resulted in a radius of approximately 8 mm, which is in good agreement with the above number. The 8 mm - number was obtained from experiments with a half-wave retarder, which consists of 2 loops of the same radius. A half-wave →retardation plate simply rotates the polarization ellipse without changing the ratio of the axes, if the radius is correct. Due to this characteristic, the proper radius can be found without knowing the input state of polarization.

See the chapters on →polarization and →retardation plate for an explanation of the function of retarders. The practical use of the fiber-based PC is very similar: rotation of the coil means rotation of the fast and slow axes of the coil with respect to the incoming electric field, even though the field is in the same fiber. If a conversion of an arbitrary input field to an arbitrary output field is desired, then a combination of 3 coils is recommended: quarter-wave, half-wave and quarter-wave. The first coil will convert any input state to linear polarization, the second coil will rotate it, and the third coil will convert it to the desired state. It can be shown that two quarter-wave coils perform the same task; however, their function is not so obvious.

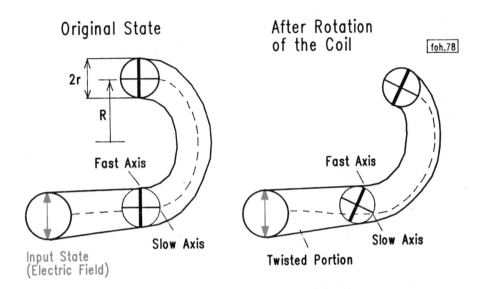

Original State

After Rotation
of the Coil

foh.78

2r

R

Fast Axis

Slow Axis

Input State
(Electric Field)

Fast Axis

Slow Axis

Twisted Portion

CROSS-SECTIONAL VIEW OF THE FIBER COIL

A parasitic twist of the fiber is caused by rotating the coils. This twist causes circular
→birefringence in the fiber, which tends to reduce the **effective** rotation of the coil. Using a
half-wave retarder, Lefevre measured a necessary coil rotation of 48.6°, instead of the ideal 45°,
in order to produce a 90° rotation of the incoming field. Experiments at Hewlett-Packard
showed a much smaller deviation from the ideal behaviour, indicating that the used fiber was
less sensitive to twist.

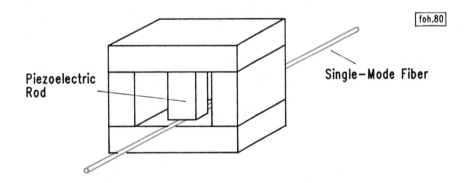

foh.80

Piezoelectric
Rod

Single–Mode Fiber

POLARIZATION CONTROL WITH FIBER SQUEEZER

Electronic control of the state of polarization is possible with **fiber squeezers**. With the help of
a piezoelectric crystal, lateral pressure is applied to the fiber. This way, a variable retardation in
one fiber axis is generated. In reference [6.4], four squeezers were arranged in the following
azimuthal orientations: 0°, 45°, 0°, 45°. This way, a fixed linear output state could be generated
from any arbitrary input state. The optimum state of polarization was detected by coherent
detection (see →coherent communications). Two remarkable features were accomplished: First,
the system can accomodate an arbitrary number of 360° rotations of the input state (endless
polarization control). Second, the control voltages for the squeezers were derived from the
output of the coherent receiver only.

Twisting a polarization-maintaining fiber (PMF) is another method of polarization control. A PMF is capable of maintaining a linear state of polarization, if linear polarization is coupled into one of the main axes of the PMF. Measurements at Hewlett-Packard with a bow-tie PMF (see →polarization-maintaining fiber) showed that a twist of 17 x 360° of a 55 cm long fiber rotated the linear state 17 times, without conversion of the linear state to an elliptical state. This demonstrates the excellent polarization-holding capability of this type of fiber. However, a simple rotation of a linear state of polarization may not be sufficient. More desirable is the conversion from any state to any other state.

Polarization Dispersion

In single mode fibers, the group velocity depends on the input state of polarization. Called polarization dispersion, this is a special form of →multimode dispersion. See the chapter on →birefringence (in fibers).

Polarization Noise

This effect is only observed in single-mode fibers, see →modal noise.

Polarization-Maintaining Fiber (PMF)

A well defined state of polarization at the end of the fiber is important for the proper function of many fiber optic components, and it forms the basis of →coherent communications. Several measurement techniques, like the spectral bandwidth measurement of laser diodes via →self-heterodyning, also rely on a fixed state of polarization. Regular single-mode fiber is not capable of maintaining a fixed state of polarization. Therefore, the polarization-maintaining fiber (PMF) was invented.

Even in a regular single-mode fiber 2 field orientations can be found which lead to a maximum difference in propagation velocity. This effect is caused by rotational unsymmetries in the fiber. It may be characterized as relative difference in (effective) refractive indices, Δn, of the "fast" and "slow" axes. In regular single-mode fibers, Δn is very small, on the order of 10^{-6}. See the chapter on →birefringence (in fibers).

Let us call the waves travelling along the preferred axes "fast" and "slow" waveguide modes. These modes are normally very similar; the fiber optic literature uses the term **degenerated**. In this case, optical power can easily be exchanged between the 2 modes. **Twist** is one of the possible causes for the exchange of power. In fact, the "rotating-coil" →polarization controller utilizes this possibility.

PMFs are based on the concept of a **large** difference in velocity, i.e. large →birefringence. Under those circumstances, the exchange of optical power between the 2 modes is minimized because of their different propagation characteristics. Compare this with 2 coupled resonators: the more different the 2 resonant frequencies, the smaller the exchange of energy between the resonators. The desired index difference can be introduced by lateral pressure on the fiber. Several types of fiber have been invented to produce this type of stress, the most popular types being the **Bow-Tie** fiber and the **PANDA** fiber. So far less successful are fibers utilizing geometric deformation, an example of which is the **elliptical-core** fiber.

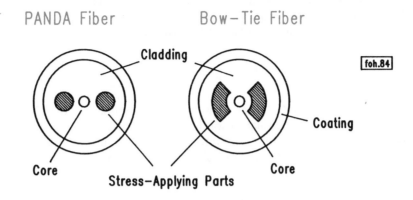

TYPES OF POLARIZATION-MAINTAINING FIBERS

The performance of PMFs is basically set by 3 figures: birefringence B, mode-coupling parameter h and attenuation. The birefringence is simply the difference of refractive indices, Δn, between the 2 preferred axes. It is directly related to the difference of velocities between the fast and slow modes, because the phase velocity is the speed of light divided by the refractive index.

Birefringence: $B = \Delta n$

Typical numbers are $B = 3$ to 5×10^{-4}, whereas the birefringence in standard single-mode fibers is typically 10^{-5} to 10^{-6}. The **measurement** of birefringence can be based on analyzing the polarization ellipse; see the chapter on →birefringence (in fibers).

Another possibility is the measurement of the beat length Λ, which is the length of fiber after which the 2 preferred waves are out of phase by 2π. In the measurement, a linear-polarized wave is coupled at 45° against the main axes. A strong electromagnet is then moved along the fiber and the state of polarization (SOP) at the fiber output is observed. Due to the →Faraday effect in quartz, the polarized wave in the fiber is modulated depending on the actual SOP. This way, the SOP at the **end** of the fiber is periodic with a movement of the magnet of one beat length [3.8]. Actual beat lengths of PMFs are on the order of 1 to 3 mm.

Beat length: $\Lambda = \lambda / B$

The mode-coupling parameter, h, allows a quantization of the amount of power coupled into the unwanted mode. Note that in the normal use of the PMF, there is no difference between coupling into the fast or slow axis. With increased length of the fiber, z, the unwanted coupling is increased. This mechanism can be described by the extinction ratio, ER, which is the ratio of power in the wrong orientation to the one in the original orientation:

Extinction ratio: $ER = \tanh(hz) = \dfrac{\exp(hz) - \exp(-hz)}{\exp(hz) + \exp(-hz)}$

Crosstalk: $CT = -10 \log ER$ $[\, dB_{opt} \,]$

Reference [3.9] lists a PANDA with a mode-coupling parameter of $h = 0.5 \times 10^{-6}$ per meter. This corresponds to a **crosstalk** of -26 dB_{opt} after 5 km, or -23 dB_{opt} after 10 km. It should be mentioned that birefringence B and mode-coupling parameter h are **not directly** related.

An **unintentional rotation** ϕ of a linear-polarized input against one of the main axes of the PMF will also degrade the extinction ratio. In this case, the electric field component in the wrong direction is proportional to the sine of the electric field, and the extinction ratio (i.e. the power ratio) is :

$$ER = \sin^2 \phi$$

Today's standard single-mode fibers show a typical attenuation of 0.2 dB/km at a wavelength of 1550 nm. In PMFs, good polarization-holding performance is usually accompanied by high attenuation. PMFs have been steadily improved through design optimization, so that the fiber with $h = 0.5 \times 10^{-6}$ / m (as above) exhibits an attenuation of 0.25 dB/km. Even 0.22 dB/km have been reported.

Despite of these advances, many fiber-optic system designers believe that coherent communications will utilize standard single-mode fiber, together with some sort of →polarization control at the end of the fiber. In contrast, polarization-holding fibers are well accepted in the field of fiber-optic sensors.

Polarizer

A polarizer creates linear polarization by transmitting one plane of vibration, whereas the perpendicular plane is absorbed, reflected or refracted at a different angle. Polarized light can be easily produced by using the reflection from a glass plate oriented at **Brewster's angle** (see →reflection and refraction). A more effective polarizer is a pile of glass plates oriented at Brewster's angle, reference [1.2]. Here, the amount of polarized light is increased by adding the reflections from each surface. A practical realization is a multilayer dielectric film cemented into glass prisms. This way, high reflection of one plane of polarization is achieved, whereas the other plane of polarization is almost completely transmitted. A variable attenuator can be realized using two polarizers and rotating one polarizer with respect to the other.

A second polarizer type is the **calcite** (calcium-carbonate) →beamsplitter cube, which is based on the calcite's birefringence effect: the crystal exhibits different refractive indices for different polarizations of light. This effect is used to construct total reflection for one polarization and total transmission for the other.

A third type of polarizer is realized with plastic **dichroic film**, by stretching the film into one direction. Thus the molecules are oriented in a special way, which allows only one polarization to pass.

The main quality criterium for polarizers is the **extinction ratio**. In order to measure it, two polarizers are arranged in series and exposed to light. First the polarizers are oriented perpendicularly, then identically. The ratio of the two transmitted powers is called extinction ratio e. Typical values are $e = 10^{-2}$ for multilayer dielectric films, 10^{-4} for dichroic films and 10^{-5} for calcite cubes.

Power Measurement

Let us assume an optical beam with a uniform power density H which fills an area A. If the spectrum is monochromatic, then the power contained in the beam can be calculated from the (uniform and transversal) electric field E, see the paragraph on →electric field. The result is:

$$H = E^2 / 2Z_0 \qquad [\,W/m^2\,]$$

and $\qquad P = H\,A \qquad\qquad [\,W\,]$

H - time-average power density (irradiance)
E - amplitude of the electric field
Z_0 - characteristic impedance of air : 377 Ω
P - time-average optical power
A - area of the beam

In a situation where the power density is non-uniform, the power is defined by the integral over the area A.

In the measurement of optical power, the strongest concern is accuracy. At Hewlett Packard, accuracy is subdivided into 2 categories: **calibration accuracy** means the accuracy obtained at the condition where the calibration was made, namely the power level, the wavelength and the temperature. The **absolute accuracy** is the one obtained when leaving these condition, i.e. changing the power level, the wavelength and the ambient temperature. These are the most popular methods for the measurement of the fiber-optical power:

1. **Parallel beam to a large-area PIN - diode:**
   In this context, large area means a diameter of approximately 5 mm. This method offers good absolute accuracy (typically better than 5 %) at reasonable cost. Here are the reasons: the optical-to-electrical conversion accuracy can be easily verified, because all national standard laboraties use parallel beams. With affordable effort, the large area can be analyzed for uniformity. In the practical application, the large area is well capable of capturing even cladding modes from the output of a fiber. The parallel beam can be obtained from a conventional light source with the help of lenses and apertures; in the case of a divergent beam from the end of a fiber, a lens can be used to generate a collimated (parallel) beam. In any case, the wavelength should be known, because all PIN - diodes exhibit a wavelength-dependent conversion factor (→responsivity).

   A larger dark current (and the associated drift) and an increased noise-equivalent power (due to the diode's low differential resistance) are disadvantages of the large area. In the HP 8152A / 81521B Optical Power Meter, this problem is solved by cooling and temperature-stabilizing the germanium detector at -10° C.

2. **Focused beam to a small-area PIN - diode:**
   Small area means diameters of less than 1 mm. Due to the small area, the main advantages of this method are better sensitivity (less noise) and lower cost. However, it is difficult to verify the calibration accuracy; therefore, the accuracy is reduced, typically to worse than 5 %. The verification of the uniformity is also non-trivial.

3. **Parallel beam and wavelength-independent detectors:**
   Because this "classic" method is based on the measurement of the **temperature**, the exact wavelength need not be known. However, the sensitivity is far inferior to the photon detection in PIN-diodes : 1 µW against 1 pW (typical numbers). 2 different detector types are commonly used: the first is the pyroelectric radiometer, which is basically a temperature-dependent dipole/capacitor. The second is the thermopile, which is a series connection of thermoelements. In both cases, **electrical-substitution radiometry** (ESR) is applied, which means that the measurement is based on achieving an equilibrium between optically-generated and electrically-generated temperature. Chopping switches between the two

types of excitations. Both types of excitations are applied with the help of chopping. All national laboratories are based on ESR. International comparisons between such detectors demonstrated accuracies of better than 0.5 %.

Large inaccuracies can be caused by ghost images on the detector: If the reflection from the diode hits another reflecting surface, then the reflection from that surface can add to the total incident power. In the HP 81521B Optical Head, this problem was solved with the help of an aperture, antireflective coating and tilting the detector.

Another problem is the reduced accuracy in the measurement of LEDs, because of their wide spectral width. This is explained in the paragraph →LED.

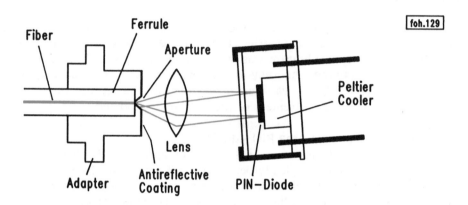

STRUCTURE OF THE HP 81521B OPTICAL HEAD

In the power-measurement of laser-based systems, it is recommended to avoid reflections from the surface of the photodiode back to the laser, because of the laser's backreflection-sensitivity. Of course, diodes with antireflection coatings can be recommended. In the parallel-beam case, tilting is another contribution. In the case of a focused beam, tilting does not help: the photodiode will always reflect back to the source; this is a consequence of basic lens optics. For further information on the accuracy of optical power measurements, see [5.4].

Going back to PIN-diodes, it should be mentioned that very high accuracy can be obtained by **self-calibrating** PIN-diodes. These diodes come close to ideal photodetectors, because their quantum efficiency (the number of generated electrons per photon) is very near to 1. A typical number is 0.999. For a better understanding of this concept, let us recall the →responsivity of a PIN-diode:

$$ r(\lambda) \quad = \frac{I}{P} = \eta \; \lambda \; \frac{e}{h\,c} \qquad\qquad [\,A/W\,] $$

I - photocurrent
P - incident optical power
η - quantum efficiency
e - electron charge ; $e = 1.6 \times 10^{-19}$ As
h - Planck's constant ; $h = 6.62 \times 10^{-34}$ Ws^2
c - speed of light; $c = 2.998 \times 10^{8}$ m/s

With a quantum efficiency of 1, the responsivity turns out to be dependent on natural constants only. Therefore, this method seems attractive if such diodes can be made. Claimed accuracies are on the order of 0.1 %. For further information on self-calibrating PIN-diodes, see [5.3] .

Preform

A glass rod from which the final fiber is drawn. The necessary differences in refractive index are accomplished by various techniques, e.g. chemical vapor deposition (CVD).

Profile

For a fiber's refractive index profile, see →fiber.

Profile Dispersion

Profile dispersion is part of the →chromatic dispersion, thus contributing to the pulse broadening on a fiber. The refractive indices of **both** core and cladding (usually expressed in terms of the →refractive index **contrast** or **-profile**), affect the group velocity in a fiber. Accordingly, the cause for profile dispersion is the different wavelength-dependences of the refractive indices of core and cladding; this is due to different materials involved. Profile dispersion is defined as the change of group travel time per km of fiber per change of wavelength [ps/km nm].

In graded-index (multimode) fibers, profile dispersion is an important design parameter, because the profile can only be optimized for **one** wavelength (e.g. 850 nm or 1300 nm). A change of the profile with wavelength causes profile dispersion. In single mode fibers, profile dispersion is often treated as being part of the →waveguide dispersion.

Quantum Efficiency

The quantum effiency η of a photodetector is the ratio of the number of generated electron-hole pairs to the number of incident photons. As the generation process is of statistical nature, η only describes a time-average. η depends on wavelength, detector material and angle of incidence. It is always <1. Typical numbers range from 50 to 90 %. Nearly 100 % have been obtained in self-calibrating PIN-diodes; see the chapter →power measurement.

A certain fraction of the incident optical power is reflected from the surface of the detector. Therefore, a reduced number of photons actually arrives in the junction. Nevertheless, quantum efficiency is usually based on the incident optical power; it is then termed **external** quantum efficiency. Otherwise the term **internal** quantum efficiency is used.

Quantum Noise

Quantum noise arises from the particle nature of light: single photons are generated in a light source at random times. One of the results from the photon statistics is the number of necessary photons in order to detect a single bit in an ideal direct-detection* →receiver: 21 photons are necessary to achieve a →bit error rate of 10^{-9}, assuming a →quantum efficiency $\eta = 1$. This

is called **quantum limit** and establishes the ultimate sensitivity of receiver utilizing direct detection. Practical systems always operate well above the quantum limit, e.g. at 400 photons per bit. Note that receivers bases on →coherent detection may require less than 21 photons per bit.
*   Direct detection means conversion of the incident flow of photons to an analog current, with the help the →responsivity of the detector, in contrast to →coherent detection.

Q-Switching

Besides →mode locking, Q-switching is an attractive form of optical pulse generation. Again, a laser with an external cavity (e.g. a gas laser) is required. An element, which is capable of switching between a low-attenuation state and a high-attenuation state, is inserted into the cavity. In the high-attenuation state, the laser cavity is open, so that no lasing oscillation can be generated. During this time, the energy of the pumping source is stored by excited atom states.

When the switch is set to the low-attenuation state, the cavity gain (Q) is raised to a value which allows lasing. The stored energy will suddenly be released in a giant pulse burst which lasts for around 20 ns. It is important to remember that, in contrast to mode locking, Q-switching requires no synchronism with the round-trip frequency in the cavity.

Q-switching is important for many applications where short optical pulses of high energy are required. One fiber-optic example is the →Raman dispersion measurement. For further information on this subject see [0.13].

Radiance

Radiance is one of the →radiometric terms, see the end of the book. In the visible wavelength range, radiance corresponds with the observed brightness of a source. The term is best explained with the measurement setup below. A lens is used to image the source area or a part of it to the detector. The light cone should overfill the aperture.

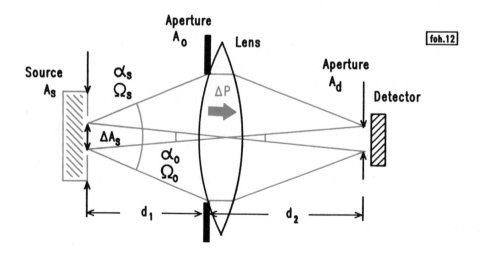

RADIANCE MEASUREMENT OF AN OPTICAL SOURCE

The radiance L is defined as the power per solid angle per area of the source:

$$L = \frac{\Delta P}{\Delta A_s \, \Omega_s} \qquad [\frac{W}{m^2 \, sr}]$$

ΔP - fractional power on the detector
ΔA_s - fractional source area
Ω_s - solid angle, as defined by the aperture area A_0 and the distance d_1

The following relation is utilized in the actual measurement:

$$\Delta A_s \, \Omega_s = \Delta A_s \, A_0 / d_1^2 = A_0 \, \Omega_0 \simeq A_0 \, \pi \alpha_0^2 / 4$$

α_0 - full linear angle, as defined by A_d and d_2

Law of Brightness (Invariance of radiance): According to the principles of optics, no lens system is capable of increasing the radiance of a source. A reduced source image is always connected with a larger solid angle. If the source can be described by a numerical aperture NA and a total emitting area A_s, then the law of brightness can be expressed by:

$$A_s \, \Omega_s \simeq A_s \, \pi \, NA^2 = constant$$

with: $\qquad NA = \sin(\alpha_s / 2)$

This equation explains, why it is impossible to achieve a good source-to-fiber coupling efficiency with a large, divergent source such as an LED: no lens system can convert an LED to a smaller source with smaller beam divergence.

Radiometric Units

The fiber optics community uses radiometric units, in contrast to photometric units. See →units at the end of the book.

Raman Dispersion Measurement

The Raman scattering mechanism is now commonly used for the measurement of the →chromatic dispersion of single mode fibers [3.3]. The measurement was first mentioned in 1977, reference [2.4].

An Neodym-YAG laser is →mode locked at 100 MHz and →Q-switched at 1 kHz. The same 1 kHz frequency also drives the modulator, which then extracts a single pulse from the comb of pulses. The single pulse is still repeated at a 1 kHz rate; it has the following characteristics: wavelength 1060 nm, pulse power 1 kW, pulse duration 200 ps. It is launched into a single mode fiber of 100 m length which acts as nonlinear medium, so that the 1.06 µm line is converted to a non-uniform spectrum with so-called Stokes lines (longer wavelength lines); altogether, there are about 6 broad lines ranging from 1120 to 1510 nm. The Raman effect is caused by molecular vibration which is generated by the interaction between the electric field of the optical wave and the quartz molecules. The generated spectrum is filtered with a monochromator and then launched into the long test fiber. Analysis of the pulse delay in comparison to the reference pulse is utilized to determine the chromatic dispersion, which is the combined effect of waveguide and material dispersion.

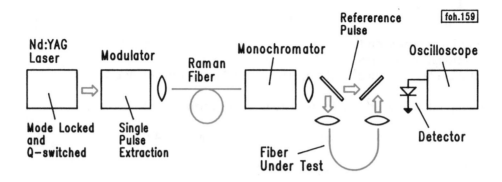

foh.159

DISPERSION MEASUREMENT USING THE RAMAN EFFECT

Receiver

This paragraph describes the realization of practical receivers with special attention to their noise performance.

The photodiode, the conversion resistor and the amplifier contribute to the total noise in an optical receiver. Additionally, the received optical power may also carry amplitude noise, such as laser noise, →mode partitioning noise or →modal noise. The noise of the detector is dominated by **shot noise**, see the paragraph →noise (photodiode-). In this paragraph, a common **detector model** was established for PIN and APD detectors.

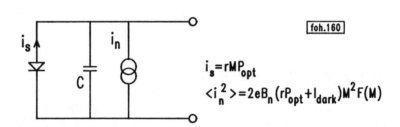

foh.160

$$i_s = rMP_{opt}$$

$$\langle i_n^2 \rangle = 2eB_n(rP_{opt} + I_{dark})M^2F(M)$$

ELECTRICAL MODEL FOR PIN AND APD DIODES

r — non-multiplied responsivity of the photodetector [A/W]
M — multiplication factor, M = 1 for PIN-diodes
P_{opt} — optical power
e — electron charge, 1.602×10^{-19} As
B_n — →noise equivalent bandwidth
I_{dark} — primary dark current (before multiplication)
F(M) — excess noise factor in APDs, F(M) = 1 for PIN-diodes.

The mean square noise term in the figure indicates the statistical nature of the noise currents. As the noise term is proportional to the →noise equivalent bandwidth B_n, it is called "white" noise. The amplitude statistics can be assumed to be Gaussian, with the standard deviation σ being the square root of the noise term. Accordingly, the peak-to-peak amplitude is around 6 times σ.

One consequence from the noise term is its dependence on the absolute optical power. This explains why a "one" in a binary sequence always appears to be more noisy than a "zero". It further explains the system designer's desire for a high →extinction ratio, and why the discriminator level in a system receiver is often set to a more negative level than the →mesial power level.

The **resistor model** also shows a white noise behaviour. The terms in the figure are:

k   - Boltzmann's constant, see →constants at the end of this book
T   - absolute temperature in Kelvin
B_n - see →noise equivalent bandwidth.

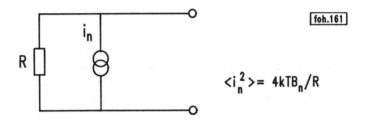

$$\langle i_n^2 \rangle = 4kTB_n/R$$

foh.161

NOISE MODEL OF A RESISTOR

The noise sources of practical **amplifiers** can be almost completely attributed to the input stage. These noise sources generally are not white, because all transistors exhibit higher noise intensity at low frequencies, which is called 1/f noise. In the following example, the amplifier noise is omitted for simplicity.

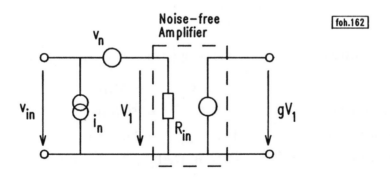

NOISE MODEL OF AN AMPLIFIER

As an example we will compare the noise performance of two practical receivers: the **low-impedance** type, the bandwidth of which is determined by the RC-time constant of the input, and the **transimpedance** type. The bandwidth of both receivers shall be 100 MHz, suitable for a bit rate of 100 Mbit/s with a non-return-to-zero (NRZ) format.

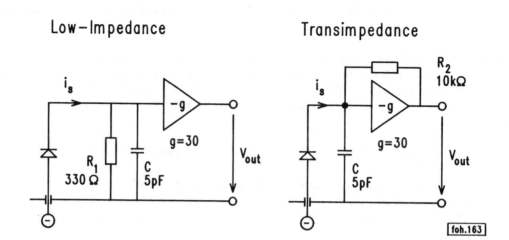

Low-Impedance

Transimpedance

foh.163

PRACTICAL EXAMPLES OF CLASSICAL OPTICAL RECEIVERS

The voltage gain of the common amplifier cell is assumed to be $g = 30$, with an infinite input resistance. For equal bandwidth, the conversion resistor of the transimpedance amplifier can be made larger (10 kΩ) than the resistor in the low-impedance amplifier (300 Ω). This advantage of the transimpedance amplifier is the result of its bandwidth **not** being determined by $1/2\pi R_2 C$, but by a larger $g/2\pi R_2 C$.

Both amplifiers are assumed to be noiseless. PIN-diodes shall be used as photodetectors. We assume the following data: $r = 0.4$ A/W, $M = 1$, $F(M) = 1$. We also assume an even distribution of "ones" and "zeros". For the analysis we further set:

$$
\begin{aligned}
P_1 \text{ ("1"-level)} &= 1\ \mu W &&= -30\ \text{dBm} \\
P_0 \text{ ("0"-level)} &= 0 \\
P_{avg} &\simeq 0.5\ \mu W &&= -33\ \text{dBm} \\
I_{dark} &= 5\ \text{nA} \\
T &= 300\ \text{K}
\end{aligned}
$$

Here are the approximate results for the **low-impedance** receiver:

Signal Bandwidth	B_s	$= 1/2\pi R_1 C$	$= 96$ MHz
Noise Equ. Bandwidth	B_n	$= 1/4 R_1 C$	$= 150$ MHz
Average Output Level	v_{avg}	$= -R_1 g\, r P_{avg}$	$= -2$ mV
Average Output Noise	$\langle v_n^2 \rangle$	$= g^2 R_1^2 B_n [2er P_{avg} + 2e I_{dark} + 4kT/R_1]$	
		$= 1.5 \times 10^{16} [6.4 \times 10^{-26} + 1.6 \times 10^{-27} + 5 \times 10^{-23}]$	
		$= 7.4 \times 10^{-7}\ V^2$	
Input-Related Noise	NEP	$= v_n(\text{RMS}) / (gr R_1)$	
		$= 217\ nW_{avg} = -37.7$ dBm	
Signal/Noise Ratio	SNR	$= 10\ \log(P_{avg} / \text{NEP})$	
		$= 6.65\ \text{dB}_{opt}$	

In this case, the resistor noise dominates the other terms. Instead of 0.5 μW, an average power of 1.3 μW (-28.8 dBm) would be needed to achieve an SNR of 10.8 dB_{opt}, which is required in a digital binary transmission for a bit error rate of 10^{-9} (see →bit error rate). In other words: the sensitivity of the low-impedance receiver is -28.8 dBm at a bit error rate of 10^{-9}

The analysis of the **transimpedance** amplifier yields the following approximate results:

Signal Bandwidth	B_s	$= g/2\pi R_2 C$	$= 96$ MHz
Noise Equ. Bandwidth	B_n	$= g/4RC$	$= 150$ MHz
Average Output Level	v_{avg}	$= -R_2\, r\, P_{avg}$	$= -2$ mV
Average Output Noise	$<v_n^2>$	$= R_2^2 B_n\, [2erP_{avg}+2eI_{dark}+4kT/R_2]$	
		$= 1.5\text{x}10^{16}[6.4\text{x}10^{-26}+2\text{x}10^{-27}+1.7\text{x}10^{-24}]$	
		$= 2.78 \times 10^{-8}$ V^2	
Input Related Noise	NEP	$= v_n(RMS)/(rR^2)$	
		$= 41.7$ $nW_{avg} = -43.8$ dBm	
Signal/Noise Ratio	SNR	$= 10\ \log(\,P_{avg}\,/\,NEP\,)$	
		$= 13.8$ dB_{opt}	

Having an SNR which is 7.15 dB_{opt} better than before, the sensitivity of the transimpedance amplifier is -36 dBm (0.25 μW_{avg}) for a bit error rate of 10^{-9}. This is due to the lower noise generated by the larger resistor in the transimpedance scheme. In addition to the lower noise, the transimpedance receiver is also more stable and linear, because its parameters do not directly depend on the gain of the active components.

A modification of the low-impedance receiver is the **high-impedance** receiver: in this case, the detector drives a much higher impedance. Accordingly, the bandwidth of the input stage is much lower than required by the system's bitrate. Therefore, equalization networks must be inserted after the amplifier in order to emphasize the high-frequency components of the signal. The integrating behaviour of the input stage also necessitates a larger dynamic range. The advantage is an improved sensitivity of typically -40 dBm at a bit error rate of 10^{-9} and 100 Mbit/s, even when taking the amplifier noise into account.

Amplifiers with junction FETs or bipolar transistors in conjunction with PIN-detectors perform equally well at 100 Mbit/s: as stated before, the sensitivity is around -40 dBm. Beyond 100 Mbit/s amplifiers with bipolar transistors or GaAs-FETs offer better sensitivity. Below 100 Mbit/s FET amplifiers are preferred: at 10 Mbit/s the FET amplifier's sensitivity can be improved to -55 dBm.

Highest performance systems use APDs instead of PIN-diodes. The sensitivity can be improved by another 6 to 8 dB_{opt} this way. A much more thorough article about the design of optical receivers can be found in [5.1].

Reflectance

The ratio of reflected power to incident power. See →reflection and refraction.

Reflection and Refraction

At the boundary of two dielectric media, or of air and a dielectric medium, reflection occurs upon the transition of light. This effect plays a key role in fiber optics. To name a few examples:

Optical guiding in a →fiber is only possible by total internal reflection at the core-cladding boundary. It thus defines the →numerical aperture of a fiber, too. Reflection also causes loss of optical power in various combinations of fibers, and it causes additional →noise when transmitted back to a laser. Dielectric reflection can be utilized to construct partially transparent mirrors for power splitting and monitoring purposes. Polarizing →beam splitters are also based on reflection. Finally, →Fabry-Perot resonators (including laser diodes) utilize the mechanisms of reflection.

Reflection is mostly treated using **Fresnel's laws**, see below. Here we present a different approach. The concept of →characteristic impedance, well-known by electronic engineers, can be applied to understand reflection. The characteristic impedance Z_n of an isotropic dielectric medium is:

$$Z_n = Z_0/n, \quad \text{with:} \quad Z_0 = 377 \, \Omega$$

Z_0 - characteristic impedance of vacuum
n - refractive index of the dielectric material, n = 1 for air, n ≃ 1.5 for glass

For normal incidence (beam vertical to the boundary) the classical transmission line theory then provides the field-reflection factor r, which is the ratio of the reflected electric field amplitude R to the incident amplitude E.

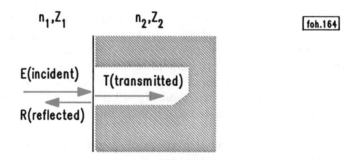

A LIGHT RAY PROPAGATING FROM RARE TO DENSE

$$r = \frac{Z_2 - Z_1}{Z_2 + Z_1} \quad \text{with} \quad Z_1 = \frac{Z_0}{n_1}, \quad Z_2 = \frac{Z_0}{n_2}$$

$$r = \frac{n_1 - n_2}{n_1 + n_2}$$

For an air-to-glass transition the amplitude reflection factor is r = -0.2, indicating a change of phase. For a glass-to-air transition, we find r = 0.2 with no phase change. As the reflected power density is proportional to the square of the reflected amplitude, the resulting power-reflection factor r^2 (normally called "reflection factor" only) is:

$$r^2 = \left(\frac{n_1 - n_2}{n_1 + n_2} \right)^2 \qquad \textbf{Fresnel Reflection}$$

This equation gives the same result for a rare-to-dense or vice-versa transition: for a glass-to-air-transition the reflection factor is $0.2^2 \approx 4\%$, be it external or internal reflection. At normal incidence, the power densities on either side must be equal:

$$n_2 T^2 = n_1 (E^2 - R^2)$$

Notice that the terms on either side contain their refractive indices. This stems from power density H being defined by:

$$H = \frac{1}{2} \frac{E^2}{Z_n} = \frac{n}{2} \frac{E^2}{Z_0}$$

E   - electric field amplitude
Z_n - characteristic impedance of a dielectric with index n
Z_0 - characteristic impedance of vacuum

Summarizing the electric field amplitudes, with $|\ |$ indicating the absolute value:

$$R = \left| \frac{n_1 - n_2}{n_1 + n_2} \right| E$$

$$T = \frac{2n_1}{n_1 + n_2} E$$

So far, only normal incidence has been considered. For **oblique incidence**, the transmitted ray path is bent according to **Snell's law**:

$$n_1 \sin \phi_1 = n_2 \sin \phi_2$$

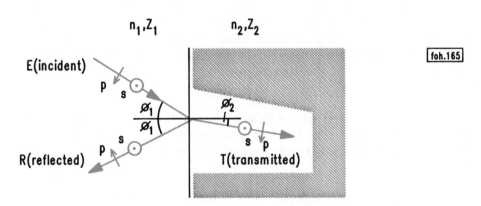

REFLECTION AND REFRACTION AT OBLIQUE INCIDENCE
(Rare to dense transition)

Total reflection only occurs at parallel incidence ($\phi_1 = 90°$) for a rare-to-dense transition. For a dense-to-rare transition ($n_1 > n_2$) total reflection occurs when the refracted ray reaches $\phi_2 = 90°$. For this case the **critical angle** of total reflection ϕ_c in the dense material can be calculated using Snell's law:

$$\sin \phi_c = n_2/n_1 \qquad \textbf{Angle of total reflection}$$

Using $n_1 = 1.5$ for glass and $n_2 = 1$ for air, the critical angle is $\phi_1 = \phi_c = 41.8°$.

Fresnel's laws of reflection allow to calculate the reflected and transmitted **amplitudes** in the case of **oblique** incidence. Normal incidence is a special case of Fresnel's laws. The incident wave must first be split up into its two planes of polarization: p for parallel to the plane of the paper, s for perpendicular (German: senkrecht). Each of these polarizations reacts differently upon the transition. Here are Fresnel's laws:

$$\frac{R_s}{E_s} = r_s = - \frac{\sin (\phi_1 - \phi_2)}{\sin (\phi_1 + \phi_2)}$$

$$\frac{R_p}{E_p} = r_p = \frac{\tan (\phi_1 - \phi_2)}{\tan (\phi_1 + \phi_2)}$$

$$\frac{T_s}{E_s} = t_s = \frac{2 \sin \phi_2 \cos \phi_1}{\sin (\phi_1 + \phi_2)}$$

$$\frac{T_p}{E_p} = t_p = \frac{2 \sin \phi_2 \cos \phi_2}{\sin (\phi_1 + \phi_2) \cos (\phi_1 - \phi_2)}$$

E   - incident electric fields
T   - transmitted electric fields
R   - reflected electric fields
p, s - orientations parallel, perpendicular to the plane of the paper

Note that E, R and T are electric **field** amplitudes, not power densities. The evaluation of these formulas shows that the phase of the s-polarized part of the reflection is always changed by 180°. The p-polarized part is not phase-changed for small angles of incidence, according to the usual convention of positive field directions shown in the figure. As before, the actual power densities are proportional to the squares of the amplitudes. The diagram displays power densities. It should be noted that the transmission-line theory can also be applied to oblique incidence.

Analyzing the above graphs we find the reflected power being 4% for both internal and external reflection at normal incidence. The two polarizations separate with growing angle, until at **Brewster's angle** ϕ_B, there is total transmission of the p-polarization and the reflection is totally s-polarized:

$$\phi_1 = \phi_B = \arctan (n_2/n_1) \qquad \textbf{Brewster's Angle}$$

This was calculated from the condition $r_p = 0$ which yields: $\phi_1 + \phi_2 = 90°$. A ray of light entering a glass plate at the external Brewster's angle intersects the second surface at the corresponding internal Brewster's angle. Thus a glass plate oriented at Brewster's angle supplies total transmission of one polarization (assuming no absorption). Making the angle even larger increases the reflection, until total reflection is reached. Also see →antireflection coating, →interference.

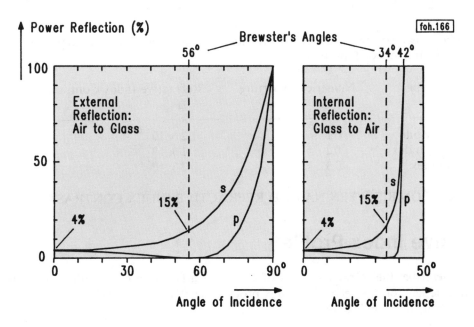

REFLECTION FROM GLASS/AIR INTERFACES
(arrows indicate positive field directions)

Refracted Near-Field Method

A special method for the determination of the refractive index profile and the core diameter of a fiber. In contrast to the more common analysis of the transmitted →near field at the end of a fiber, the refracted near-field method analyses radiation which is not captured by the fiber input; the fiber input is excited with a focused beam, the aperture of which is larger than the acceptance of the fiber. This method has been described by various authors: see, for example, [0.14].

Refractive Index (n)

A material's refractive index n is the ratio of the speed of light c in vacuum to the speed of light v in the material. More accurately, "speed of light" should read "→phase velocity". n is identical to the square root of the relative dielectric constant ϵ_r, except that ϵ_r is mostly measured at much lower (electrical) frequencies.

See →fiber and →near field for the refractive index profile of a fiber.

Refractive Index Contrast

In conjunction with fibers, the refractive index contrast Δ expresses the differences in refractive indices between n_1 of the core center and n_2 of the cladding. It can also be expressed in terms of the →numerical aperture NA:

$$\Delta = (n_1^2 - n_2^2) / 2n_1^2 \simeq (n_1 - n_2) / n_1$$
$$\Delta = NA^2 / 2n_1^2$$

This number has a strong influence on the fiber →modes, and thus also influences →multimode dispersion. Examples for typical fibers:

Fiber Type	Numerical Aperture NA	Refractive Index Contrast Δ
Single-Mode	0.1	2×10^{-3}
Graded-Index	0.2	1×10^{-2}
Step-Index	0.3	2×10^{-2}

RELATION BETWEEN NA AND REFRACTIVE INDEX CONTRAST

Refractive Index Profile

This term describes the refractive index of a fiber as a function of its radius. All relevant fiber parameters depend on the refractive index profile; see →fiber, →numerical aperture, →multimode dispersion, →refractive index contrast.

The most popular profiles are the step-index and the graded-index profile, see →fiber. More complex profiles are used in the →dispersion-shifted fibers, in order to reduce the →chromatic dispersion. There are 2 methods of measurement of the refractive index profile:

A) Transmitted →near-field method: if the fiber input is overfilled, e.g. with an LED, then the power density at the output is proportional to the refractive index profile. For details, see →near-field.

B) Refracted near-field method: different from before, the rays which are **not** captured by the fiber are used for the determination of the profile. This method has been described by various authors: see, for example, [0.14].

Refraction

See the paragraph: →reflection and refraction.

Relative Intensity Noise (RIN)

This term describes the fluctuations of a laser diode's optical power. The measurement system consists of the device under test (laser), a pin-diode, a load resistor and a spectrum analyzer (or selective voltmeter) for the noise measurement. In the first step, the PIN-diode is excited with a "white" light source, which is usually a tungsten lamp. Let use the term P_{shot} for the detector's total noise power, which is only shot noise in this case; see the chapter noise (photodiode-).

$$P_{shot} = 2eB_n rP_{opt}R_l \qquad [W]$$

P_{shot} - the detector's noise power at R_l from a white light source
e - electron charge; 1.6×10^{-19} As
B_n - noise equivalent bandwidth; [Hz]
r - responsivity of the pin-diode; [A/W]
R_l - load resistor

In the second step, the PIN-diode is excited with a laser at the same power level as before. Now: RIN is defined as the change of electrical noise power divided by the total electrical power (the useful signal) and the bandwidth:

$$RIN = \frac{P_{laser} - P_{shot}}{P_{total}\ B_n} \qquad [\ \% / Hz\ ]$$

$$P_{total} = r^2 P_{opt}^2 R_l$$

P_{laser} - combined noise power of the laser and the detector at R_l
P_{total} - total electrical power at R_l

The noise power of the system's remaining noise sources, i.e. the resistor and the analyzer, should be subtracted from the measurements, in order to measure only the noise contributions from the PIN-diode and the laser.

It should be mentioned that the concept of →noise equivalent power (NEP) is another powerful method for quantifying the noise contribution of lasers. Very simply, the NEP of a laser just adds to the total NEP of the system.

Reliability

The reliability of semiconductors (e.g. integrated circuits, lasers or LEDs) is typically given in the form of either failure rate λ or mean time between failures (MTBF):

$$\lambda = MTBF^{-1} \qquad [\ h^{-1}\ ]$$

λ - failure rate = average number of failures of a device per unit of time
MTBF- mean time between failures of a device,
in the case of (non-repairable) semiconductors: mean time to failure of the device

Of course, the measurement of either number should always include a large number of devices in order to improve the statistical basis **and** in order to reduce the measurement time. A frequent question is the dependence of the MTBF on the operating temperature of the device. Following the model of Arrhenius, one obtains:

$$MTBF = c \exp\left(\frac{E_a}{kT}\right) \qquad [\ h\ ]$$

c - device-typical constant
E_a - activation energy, mostly given in units of eV
e - electron charge; 1.6×10^{-19} As
k - Boltzmann's constant; 1.38×10^{-23} Ws
T - absolute temperature in units of K; $273.2 + °C$

Arrhenius' model suggests an exponential decrease of the MTBF with rising temperature. As an example, let us imagine an LED with these data at a given operating point: MTBF (25 °C) = 10^6 h, activation energy E_a = 0.9 eV. Question: what is the MTBF at 35 °C ? The result of using the above equation is:

$$MTBF\ (35\ °C)\ /\ MTBF\ (25\ °C)\ =\ 0.32$$

The elevated temperature reduces the MTBF to 32 % of the original 10^6 hours.

Repeater Spacing

A long repeater spacing is the prime motivation for the installation of fiber optic communication systems. We will use an example to show the calculation of repeater spacing in an "attenuation-limited" digital →system. In such a system the receiver performance is not influenced by the dispersion of the fiber. This situation is typical for many of today's commercial fiber systems. Our system utilizes a laser diode source, a graded-index fiber and a receiver with an avalanche photodiode (APD).

Power into the fiber (2mW)	+ 3 dBm
Attenuation of 2 connectors	4 dB
System margin	5 dB
Receiver sensitivity (100 Mbit/s)	- 50 dBm
Attenuation between repeaters	44 dB
Fiber attenuation (850 nm)	3 dB/km
Splice attenuation (1 splice / km)	0.3 dB/km
Reserve for repair splices	0.3 dB/km
Cable attenuation	3.6 dB/km
Repeater spacing (44 / 3.6)	12.2 km

This is a typical repeater spacing for systems using the 850 nm wavelength. Direct-detection systems using a wavelength of 1300 nm span 50 km or more. The 1550 nm wavelength allows up to 100 km, based on a narrow-linewidth laser. →Coherent detection at 1550 nm allows a repeater spacing of up to 200 km.

Resonator

Narrow-band optical filtering is possible with optical resonators. The most popular resonators are →Fabry-Perot resonator and the fiber-based →ring resonator. See the appropriate chapters.

Responsivity

The responsivity of a detector is the ratio of its output current to the incident optical power. The term "sensitivity" is a formerly-used obsolete term for responsivity.

Ideal photodiodes generate one electron-hole pair per incident photon. An important condition, however, is that the energy of the photon is larger than the bandgap of the absorbing layer. The energy of a single →photon is inversely proportional to the wavelength:

$$E_{ph} = h\,f = h\,c\,/\,\lambda$$

h - Planck's constant, 6.62×10^{-34} Ws^2
f - optical frequency, $f = c/\lambda$
c - speed of light, 3×10^8 m/s
λ - wavelength in air

Therefore, a longest wavelength exists beyond which the photon energy falls below the bandgap energy: the **cutoff wavelength**. At longer wavelengths, the responsivity drops rapidly to zero; see the responsivity curves in the chapter →PIN-diode. Setting the bandgap energy E_g equal to the photon energy E_{ph} yields the cutoff wavelength λ_c. Note that the center wavelength of LEDs and laser diodes is defined by exactly the same equation.

$$\lambda_c = 1.24\ \mu m\,/\,E_g$$

E_g - bandgap energy in units of [eV]

In the following, the responsivity shall be calculated for wavelengths which are shorter than the cutoff wavelength. The number n_{ph} of photons contained in a time slot Δt with the optical power P_{opt} can be calculated from the energy contained in each photon:

$$\Delta t\,P_{opt} = n_{ph}\,E_{ph} = n_{ph}\,h\,c\,/\,\lambda$$

Each photon statistically generates η electron-hole-pairs. Then the photocurrent is defined by:

$$\Delta t\,I\,/\,e = \eta\,n_{ph}$$

e - electron charge, 1.6×10^{-19} As

Now the photodetector's **responsivity r** (the ratio of generated current to absorbed optical power) can be calculated using the above equations:

$$r = I/P_{opt}$$
$$= \frac{\eta\,e}{h\,f} = \frac{\eta\,e\,\lambda}{h\,c}$$
$$= 0.8\ \eta\ \lambda/\mu m \qquad [A/W]$$

At wavelengths which are shorter than the cutoff wavelength, the responsivity turns out to be a function of the quantum efficiency and the wavelength only.

Retardation Plate

Retardation plates are made from birefringent materials, such as calcite. The effect of →birefringence causes different orientations of polarization to travel at different speeds inside the crystal, whenever the direction of propagation is perpendicular to the optic axis of the crystal.

A quarter-wave retarder converts linear →polarization to circular polarization (or vice-versa). To do so, the input beam's electric field must be oriented at 45° against the fast (or slow) axis of the crystal. This way, it can be mathematically split into two electric fields of equal amplitude but orthogonal polarizations, one being in the slow direction (ordinary ray in calcite), one being in the fast direction (extraordinary ray in calcite).

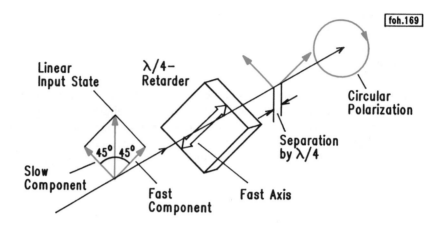

FUNCTION OF A QUARTER-WAVE RETARDER

The figure shows how the two input fields are separated in time, until at the end of the plate they have a quarter wave difference. This is the characteristic of circular →polarization. The quarter-wave retarder can be used to build a simple type of →isolator.

A half-wave retarder rotates the plane of polarization by 2α, if α is the angle between the plane of a linear polarized input and the "fast" axis of the crystal.

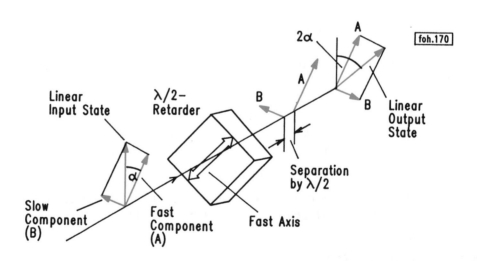

FUNCTION OF A HALF-WAVE RETARDER

Looking at a fixed point on the beam, we notice that the B-field is rotated by 180°, whereas the A-field has kept its orientation. This corresponds to the mentioned 2α-rotation of polarization.

Rotating the crystal results in a twice as large rotation of the polarization. It should be mentioned that the rotation is not restricted to linear input states: elliptical states will experience the same rotation.

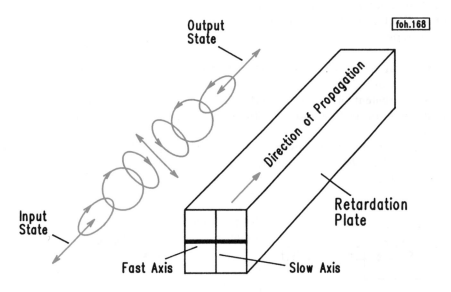

STATE OF POLARIZATION IN A FULL-WAVE RETARDER
(linear input state coupled at 45°)

Finally we want to discuss the effect of a retardation plate of arbitrary length. The figure shows linear polarization coupled at an azimuthal angle of 45° into a birefringent crystal. In our terminology, the crystal is a full-wave retarder. During its pass through the crystal, the polarization goes consecutively through the following states: linear, elliptical, circular, elliptical rotated by 90°, linear rotated by 90° and so on. After a full-wave retardation, the original state reappears. Note that elliptical polarization can also be generated by coupling at other-than-45° angles into a quarter-wave retarder.

Return Loss

The return loss of an optical component is the ratio of the incident optical power P_{in} to the reflected optical power P_{back}, in units of dB_{opt}. Therefore, return loss is usually a **positive** number.

$$\text{Return Loss} = 10 \log (P_{in} / P_{back}) \quad [dB_{opt}]$$

Because of the laser's sensitivity to back-reflection, the return loss of optical components (such as connectors) is gaining attention. Today's best connectors, which are based on physical contact, exhibit a return loss of 40 dB_{opt}.

An →optical time-domain reflectometer (OTDR) can be used for the **measurement** of the return loss measurements. Such an instrument may be calibrated with the help of a known device, e.g. the well-cleaved end of a fiber which provides 14.5 dB return loss; this is based on a fiber refractive index of 1.46. Often, the OTDR does not offer the necessary length resolution, because of the short lengths of fibers involved.

A second method is based on a fused fiber coupler, together with a continuous laser source and an optical power meter. The laser source is recommended because of the dynamic range of the measurement. Let us discuss the return loss measurement of a single-mode connector pair (DUT). In this setup, the DUT is connected to the coupler with a first jumper cable, because connector 4 (the termination of the coupler) should not be part of the DUT. The procedure consists of 3 steps:

Step A: Calibration of setup for -14.5 dB return loss with connector 6 open. The power meter now reads: P_1.

Step B: Measurement of the unwanted reflections from pair 4/5 with connector 6 immersed in oil, in order to avoid reflections from the end of the fiber. The power meter now reads: P_2.

Step C: Measurement of the device under test (DUT: pair 6/7) plus the unwanted reflections. The end of the second jumper cable is now immersed in oil. The power meter now reads: P_3.

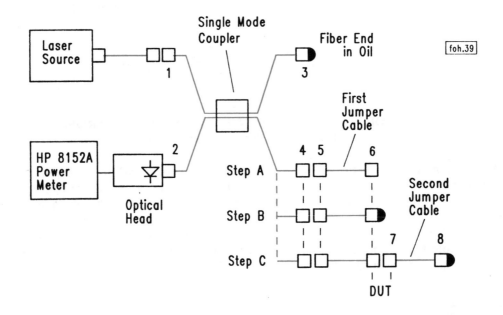

SETUP FOR MEASUREMENT OF CONNECTOR RETURN LOSS

The reflection from the DUT shall be calculated by subtracting P_2 from P_3. Our experiments show that this method is capable of measuring return losses of 40 dB and more. These are the critical points of the measurement:

1. The length of the first jumper cable should be longer than the coherence length of the source, because the measurement is based on the addition of the reflected **powers** (not electric fields) from pairs 4/5 and 6/7.

2. In terms of return loss, pair 4/5 should at least be as good as the DUT. Otherwise, the dynamic range of the measurement will suffer.

3. The impedance matching in steps B and C should produce a reflection well below the reflection from the DUT. Note that the quality of impedance matching with oil depends on how well the fiber end is polished. Introducing one or two additional knots in the fiber before the oil termination will help. This is based on experiments with a single-mode fiber

in which a knot diameter of 10 mm introduces a one-way loss of 20 dB. Strong dependence on the type of fiber was found in that experiment.

The return loss of multimode connectors can be measured the same way; this time, a multimode coupler must be used.

Ring Resonator

A ring resonator based on single-mode fiber is capable of narrow-bandwidth optical filtering. Similar to the →Fabry-Perot resonator, the ring resonator exhibits a comb-like filter characteristic. Its advantage is that the length of the ring can be made very long; therefore the resonances can be spaced very densely on the frequency scale. Another advantage is that the ring resonator is non-reflecting; therefore the driving source is not disturbed.

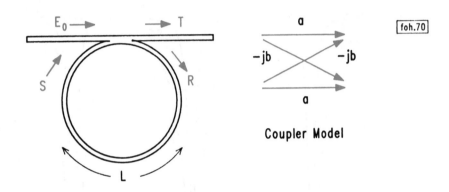

FIBER RING RESONATOR AND COUPLER MODEL

The analysis of the ring resonator can be based on classical network analysis. The coupler model was borrowed from the chapter on →couplers. The fiber is modeled as a delay line, and its attenuation is described by the parameter c:

$$R = -jb\, E_0 + a\, S$$
$$S = c\, R\, \exp(-j\beta L)\,,\ \text{resulting in:}$$

$$S = -jbc\, E_0\ \frac{\exp(-j\beta L)}{1 - ac\, \exp(-j\beta L)}$$

$$T = a\, E_0 - jb\, S$$

$$T = E_0\ \frac{a - c\, \exp(-j\beta L)}{1 - ac\, \exp(-j\beta L)}$$

E_0 - electric field at the input of the resonator
R - electric field coupled into the ring
S - electric field at the end of the ring
T - electric field at the output of the resonator

a^2 - power coupling coefficient between connected coupler arms
b^2 - power coupling coefficient between coupled arms
c^2 - power at the end of the ring divided by the power at the input of the ring
L - length of the ring
β - propagation constant, $\beta = 2\pi n / \lambda = 2\pi n f / c$
n - effective refractive index for the fundamental fiber mode
λ - wavelength in vacuum
f - optical frequency $= c/\lambda$
c - speed of light, $c = 3 \times 10^8$ m/s

The transmitted field was calculated with the energy-conservation law for the coupler:

$$a^2 + b^2 = 1$$

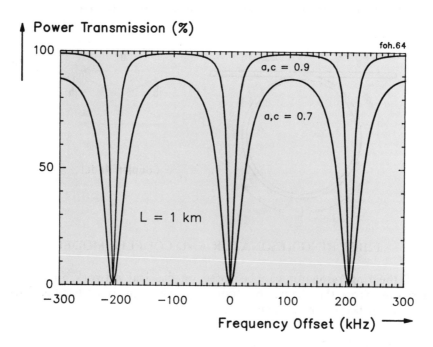

FILTER CHARACTERISTICS OF A 1 km RING RESONATOR

The power-transmission curves in the diagram were obtained by squaring the absolute value of T. The spacing of the resonant frequencies, i.e. the **free spectral range (FSR)**, can be calculated from the resonance condition:

$$\beta L = 2m \pi, \qquad m = \text{positive integer}$$

yields: $\quad FSR = \dfrac{c}{nL} \qquad$ [MHz]

The condition **a = c** is necessary to achieve zero power transmission in resonance. Low bandwidth of the individual filter curves is obtained with a high value of a, i.e. with a low coupling factor b. Setting the power transmission to 50 % allows to calculate the FWHM bandwidth of the individual curves, Δf, and the **Finesse** F:

$$\Delta f \simeq \frac{c}{nL} \frac{2\,b^2}{\pi\,(\,2-b^2\,)} \qquad\qquad [\ \text{MHz}\ ]$$

$$F \simeq \frac{FSR}{\Delta f} = \frac{\pi\,(\,2-b^2\,)}{2\,b^2} = \frac{\pi\,(\,1+a^2\,)}{2\,(\,1-a^2\,)}$$

Using the example a = c = 0.9, one obtains a finesse F = 14.96 ; note that better finesses can easily be realized with reduced coupling into the ring, i.e. higher values of a.

Another condition for the proper function of the resonator is that the orientation of the electric fields at the coupler must be identical, in order to allow optical interference. This can be achieved with the help of either a →polarization controller or a **polarization maintaining fiber**.

At resonance, there is no output power when a = c. This seems to violate the law of energy conservation. However, a more careful analysis reveals that zero output power is based on the cancellation of 2 electric fields. In the ring, there is a much higher optical power than the input power. This is easily obtained by analyzing the expression for S. Let us use the the example a = c = 0.9; then **power magnifiction** M, i.e. the ratio of the power in the ring to the input power, is:

$$M = a^2\,/\,b^2 = 420\ \%$$

Similar to scanning a Fabry-Perot resonator, a **scanning ring resonator** is based on shifting the comb a maximum of 1 free spectral range. The necessary change in length, which is λ/n, can be obtained by winding the fiber on a piezoelectric ring.

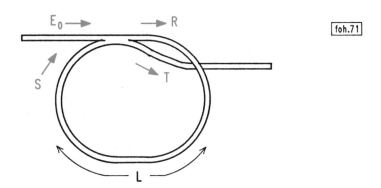

ALTERNATIVE FIBER RING RESONATOR

Another possibility for a ring resonator is reversing the output arms of the coupler [6.2]. In contrast to the first resonator, the coupling factor b^2 should be made as large as possible in this case. Similar filter characteristics are obtained. An advantage of this configuration is that the entire resonator can be made from one fiber, i.e. without cutting the fiber.

Fiber rings with long fibers are very sensitive to air turbulence and vibration, because this often produces a scanning of many free spectral ranges (due to length variation of the fiber). This limits the useful fiber length.

RIN

Abbreviation for →relative intensity noise, which is a measure for the additional noise generated by a laser diode.

RMS Pulse Duration

Abbreviation for "root-mean-square pulse duration". This term describes the $1/e$ - pulse duration of a Gaussian pulse, which is the full width at half maximum (FWHM) multiplied by 0.43. See →Gaussian pulse.

Safety (Laser Products)

Lasers may cause eye damage by absorption of light energy on the human retina. Most of the standardization in this field was initiated by the American National Standards Institute (ANSI) and was later adopted by the International Electrotechnical Commission (IEC). The IEC provides worldwide guidelines, although national standards may differ. In 1984, the IEC Committee 76 (laser equipment) published the IEC 825 Standard "Radiation Safety of Laser Products, Equipment Classification, Requirements, and User's Guide" [0.1]. In the USA, laser safety is regulated by the Food and Drug Administration (FDA); their rules [0.2] differ from the IEC 825 rules.

Depending on the potential danger, the IEC 825 demands all laser equipment to be classified to one of these classes: 1, 2, 3A, 3B or 4. The basis of the classification is set by the **Maximum Permissible Exposure (MPE)**. The MPE establishes the maximum safe radiation levels at the human eye's entrance surface, the cornea. Please refer to the IEC 825 for numbers.

The IEC 825 distinguishes between point sources and extended sources; the analogous viewing conditions are termed "intrabeam viewing" and "extended source viewing". The criterion is the angle α, at which the source appears to the observer. For the special case of continuous operation (CW) we extract the following full angles:

$$\alpha \leqslant 24 \times 10^{-3} \text{ rad } (1.38°): \qquad \text{this is intrabeam viewing}$$
$$\alpha > 24 \times 10^{-3} \text{ rad } (1.38°): \qquad \text{this is extended source viewing}$$

According to a new IEC TC 76 draft, the angle α shall be measured at a 100 mm distance from the apparent source. Based on this, most of the fiber optic sources can be considered point sources. With this precondition, the IEC 825 - classification procedure can be greatly simplified.

Classification should be made according to the **Accessible Emission Limits (AEL)**, which are different for each class. The AEL values are given in the IEC 825 as a function of emission duration and wavelength. Here, we only extract classification limits for CW lasers. The exposure time used for the classification of CW laser instruments is 1000 seconds, if the instrument is not designed for intentional viewing of the beam. For the special case of Class 3A, a time base of 100 s is proposed in the new IEC draft. Depending on the class, these are the necessary classification measurements:

1. Measurement of the power (Watt) or energy (Watt sec) within an aperture of 80 mm diameter. For point-type sources, this means the measurement of the total power output.

2. Measurement of the irradiance (power density: W/m^2) or radiant exposure (Ws/m^2) averaged over a 7 mm diameter aperture stop. This measurement must be taken at the point of highest irradiance (generally directly at the output); however, the new IEC draft relaxes the distance to 100 mm for all wavelength from 400 to 1400 nm. The 100 mm are considered to be the minimum focal distance of the eye; therefore observation of a laser source at a distance of 100 mm is considered most dangerous.

Note that in the case of any **single** component failure, the emission must remain within the limits of the class assigned.

Class 1 laser products are considered to be inherently safe. The table lists AEL values for the typical fiber optical wavelengths and CW operation. Only the power criterion must be met.

AEL (Class 1)	λ = 850 nm	λ = 1050 to 1400 nm	λ > 1400 nm
Power	0.24 mW	0.6 mW	0.8 mW

AELs FOR CLASS 1 LASER PRODUCTS (CW OPERATION)

Class 2 is used for visible laser products emitting wavelengths from 400 to 700 nm. Within this range, the human eye protects itself via the blink reflex, which is assumed to respond within 0.25 seconds. Thus the CW power from such sources may be 1 mW maximum.

AEL (Class 2)	λ = 400 - 700 nm
Power	1 mW

AELs FOR CLASS 2 LASER PRODUCTS (CW OPERATION)

Class 3A products are safe except if viewed with optical instruments. The table lists the AELs for typical fiber optical wavelengths and CW operation. Note that the most restrictive of the 2 limits must be used for the classification.

AEL (Class 3A)	λ = 850 nm	λ = 1050 to 1400 nm	λ > 1400 nm
Power	1 mW	3 mW	4 mW
Irradiance	6.4 $W\,m^{-2}$	16 $W\,m^{-2}$	1000 W/m^{-2}
.. averaged over:	7 mm	7 mm	1 mm

AELs FOR CLASS 3A LASER PRODUCTS (CW OPERATION)

For the typical point sources used in fiber optics, the irradiance limits are the more stringent. The 1984 document of the IEC allows averaging of the irradiance over 7, 7 or 1 mm apertures. Using a measurement distance of zero, this method yields power levels which are identical to the ones of Class 1. Therefore, in the case of point sources, complying with the limits of Class 3A automatically means compliance with the limits of Class 1.

For point sources, the 100 mm distance and the 100 s time base mean higher power levels in Class 3A. The maximum power levels P can be estimated with the allowed irradiance H_{max}:

$$H_{max} = \frac{P}{\pi\,NA^2\,L^2} \qquad \text{for step index fibers,}$$

$$H_{max} = \frac{2P}{\pi\,NA^2\,L^2} \qquad \text{for graded index fibers,}$$

$$H_{max} = \frac{0.95\,P}{NA^2\,L^2} \qquad \text{for single mode fibers,}$$

$$H_{max} = \frac{P}{\pi\,L^2\,\sin\alpha\,\sin\beta} \qquad \text{for lasers and LEDs}$$

P   - total optical power output (W)
NA - the sine of the 5 % power density angle in the far field
α,β - angles of the 5 % power density in the far field
L   - measurement distance from the (point) source; now 0 mm, will be changed to 100 mm

Class 3B products may emit dangerous radiation. The limitation in CW operated Class 3B products is 0.5 Watt maximum power in the wavelength range from 315 nm up to 1 mm.

AEL (Class 3B)	$\lambda = 315 - 10^6$ nm
Power	0.5 W

AELs FOR CLASS 3B LASER PRODUCTS (CW OPERATION)

Class 4 is assigned to products exceeding the limits of Class 3B. These products are dangerous. Care must be taken to avoid even exposure to diffuse reflections.

SAFETY REQUIREMENTS: For **all** laser products the following requirements have been established by the IEC. Safety information is normally required in local language.

* Protective housing to prevent higher than classified emission.
* Safety interlock in the housing to prevent access to non-classified emission levels.
* Classification labels on the product and in the promotional literature.
* Caution labels on service panels, interlocked or not
* User safety information in operator and service manuals

Class 2 additional requirements:

* Laser warning label.

Class 3A additional requirements to all of the above:

* Key control
* Beam stop to automatically disable the laser if no access is required
* Audible or visible "laser on" warning

Users should remove the key when the instrument is not in use. Also they should wear protective glasses if other protection methods fail. User training is recommended. According to the new IEC draft, key control and beam stop are likely to be removed from the Class 3A list.

Class 3B requirements to all of the above are:

* Remote control switch to allow disabling the laser by a door circuit
* Aperture label to indicate the location of the radiation output.

Class 4 reqirements are identical to those of class 3B. Avoid reflections!

Self-Calibrating PIN-Diode

This diode is a special type of a PIN-diode, in which the quantum efficiency (the number of generated electrons per incident photon) is very near 1. See the chapter on →power measurement.

Self-Heterodyning/Homodyning

Measurement of the linewidth of laser diodes is important for →coherent communications. One of the most efficient ways of linewidth measurement is self-heterodyning. The idea of this measurement is mixing the spectrum with itself, in order to produce a spectral image at low frequencies. Mixing is obtained from a simple photodiode, with the help of its quadratic field-to-current conversion. The low frequency spectrum can then be observed with a conventional (electrical) spectrum analyzer.

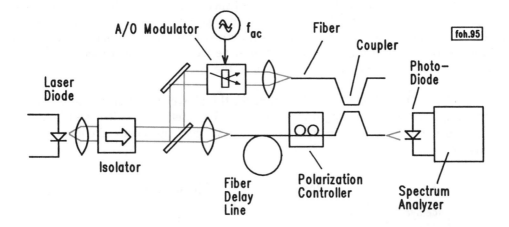

LINEWIDTH MEASUREMENT BY SELF-HETERODYNING

The measurement setup is basically a →Mach-Zehnder interferometer. Before the mixing, the signal under test is split by a semitransparent mirror. Then one channel is frequency-shifted with an acousto-optic modulator, in order to produce a difference frequency which is larger than zero. The other channel is delayed by a fiber, the length of which is much larger than the coherence length of the laser radiation. This way, the 2 electric fields add with a random phase difference.

If one assumes a Lorentz-type spectrum (see →spectrum of laser diodes), then the low-frequency spectrum has **twice** the width of each of the high-frequency spectra. A simple explanation is:

1. Difference frequency between points 1 and 4: $f_{ac} + \Delta f$,
2. Difference frequency between points 2 and 3: $f_{ac} - \Delta f$,
3. Low-frequency spectral width (line 1 - line 2): $2 \Delta f$.

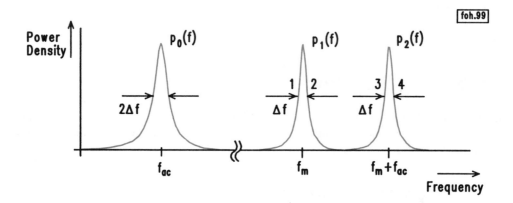

foh.99

LOW-FREQUENCY SPECTRUM OBTAINED BY SELF-HETERODYNING

As a practical example, let us assume a spectral linewidth (at the optical frequency) $\Delta f = 30$ MHz. This is typical For →DFB lasers. The correspondent coherence length in the fiber is $l_c = c/(n \, \Delta f) = 7$ meters. For the non-correlated addition of the 2 electric fields, the length of fiber should be much larger than l_c. In practical experiments, a fiber length of 5 times the coherence length was found to be sufficient, i.e. the obtained spectrum did not change when longer fibers were inserted. Therefore, a fiber length of 35 meters would be sufficent in this case. An additional component in the measurement setup is the →polarization controller, because the orientation of the electric fields at the coupler input must be identical. Also advisable is an isolator, in order to prevent any disturbing reflections back to the laser.

Omission of the A/O modulator greatly simplifies the above measurement setup. In this case, the center frequency of the mixing product is zero. The method is called **self-homodyning**; it can be applied if the expected spectral width is larger than the lowest frequency of the spectrum analyzer.

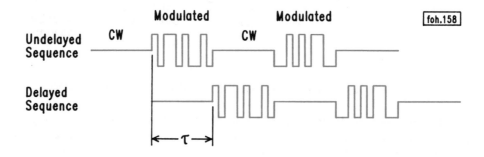

foh.158

OPTICAL SIGNALS IN THE 2 ARMS OF A MACH-ZEHNDER INTERFEROMETER
FOR THE MEASUREMENT OF LASER CHIRP

At Hewlett-Packard, self-homodyning has been successfully applied to the measurement of laser →**chirp**. To do this, the laser diode under test is modulated e.g. with a pseudorandom bit sequence which is gated on and off with a **period** equal to twice the delay difference (τ) between the 2 arms. This way, the modulated signal is always mixed with an unmodulated signal. The result is that the spectrum analyzer will display the time-average of the chirp-induced frequency-offset (chirp).

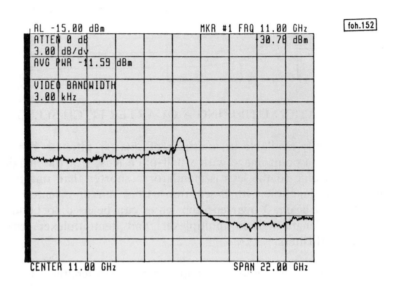

CHIRP MEASUREMENT WITH THE HP 71400A OPTICAL SIGNAL ANALYZER

The reproduction of the display of the optical signal analyzer shows the spectrum of a DFB laser broadened by chirp. In the measurement, the laser was amplitude-modulated with a pseudo-random sequence, the bitrate of which was 50 MHz. The effective linewidth is 12.2 GHz, as compared to 65 MHz when unmodulated.

Selfoc Lens

SELFOC® is a tradename of the Nippon Sheet Glass Co. Their lenses are actually rod lenses with a graded refractive index profile, similar to graded-index fiber but larger in diameter. They are increasingly used instead of conventional lenses for various fiber optic imaging tasks. The reasons for this popularity are small size relative to numerical aperture, flat surfaces and the possibility to permanently attach a fiber to one of the surfaces (due to the focal point being on the surface). It should be noted that the imaging quality of Selfoc lenses is inferior to the one of good spherical lenses, since the index profile cannot be as perfectly controlled as the radius of a spherical lens.

While in a conventional lens the rays are refracted at the lense's surface only, a SELFOC lens is based on **internal** ray bending. This is caused by a refractive index which decreases quadratically with the distance from the lens axis. Accordingly, the lense's numerical aperture also decreases with the distance from the lens axis. Thus the lens resembles a graded-index fiber. A certain wavelength dependence arises from the lense's material dispersion.

The sketched beam collimation is achieved by careful control of the lense's length, which is a quarter of a total ray cycle in this case. When the beam direction is reversed, a collimated beam can be focused onto a fiber or a small-area detector. Two of these lenses may form a pair of connectors, the coupling loss of which is insensitive to radial and axial misalignments.

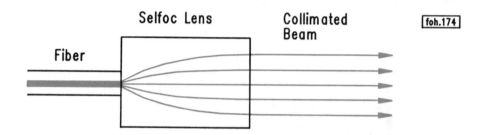

BEAM COLLIMATION UTILIZING A QUARTER-PITCH SELFOC LENS

SELFOC lenses are normally available in multiples of quarter pitches. For example, a point source can be converted to a point image with a half-pitch lens. For the imaging of a semiconductor laser, a certain spacing to the lens is mandatory: shorter than quarter pitch lenses are used for this task. In conjunction with a semitransparent mirror oriented at 45° against the wavefront of a collimated beam, 3 quarter-pitch lenses can be used to build a power splitter with fiber ports. →Wavelength-division multiplexers and demultiplexers can be made with SELFOC lenses and optical filters.

Typical SELFOC lens data are: diameters 1 - 2 mm, quarter pitch lengths 3.3 - 6.5 mm, numerical apertures 0.37 - 0.46. Lens surfaces with antireflection-coating are also available.

Sensitivity

The sensitivity is the minimum optical power amplitude at the input of a →receiver in order to achieve a certain bit error rate (BER). Based on the assumption of a Gaussian distribution of noise amplitudes, a signal-to-noise ratio of around 10 dB_{opt} is required in order to obtain a BER of 10^{-9}. In this context, the **signal** is the difference between high level and low level at the output of the fiber; the **noise** is the noise-equivalent optical power (NEP) contained in the bandwidth of the receiver. Therefore, the sensitivity can only be improved by reducing the NEP, i.e. by selecting the right components for the receiver.

The strongest noise source of the receiver is usually the **shot noise** of the detector; see the chapter →noise (photodiode-). The NEP scales with the active diameter of the detector; therefore the diameter should be chosen as small as possible. For best sensitivity, APDs are preferred before PIN detectors. Other important noise sources are the input resistor and the first transistor in the →receiver. Junction FETs are preferred at lower frequencies. At higher frequencies, bipolar transistors and GaAs-FETs produce lower noise.

An **empirical** formula for the sensitivity attainable with InGaAs-PIN detectors, which is in good agreement with measured results, is given in reference [8.3]:

$$S = -33 + 14 \log B \qquad [dB_{opt}]$$

S - receiver sensitivity in units of dB_{opt}
B - bitrate in Gbit/s

The above formula yields the following sensitivities for **PIN**-type receivers. Note that APDs allow a 5 to 10 dB_{opt} improvement.

S	=	-33 dB_{opt}	at	1	Gbit/s
S	=	-47 dB_{opt}	at	100	Mbit/s
S	=	-61 dB_{opt}	at	10	Mbit/s

Typical Sensitivities

Don't confuse the term "sensitivity" with →responsivity.

Shot Noise

See →noise (photodiode-).

Signal-to-Noise Ratio

See →receiver and →bit error rate.

Single Mode

This term is used to describe both single **waveguide**-mode in conjunction with fibers and single **wavelength** in conjunction with lasers. See →fiber (single mode), or →laser diode and →spectrum (laser diode-).

Skew Ray

In a lens or fiber, skew rays are those rays which are not parallel to the optic axis and do not intersect it. In fibers, reflection at the core-to-cladding boundary causes the skew rays to form a spiral-like trace about the fiber axis. In contrast, →meridional rays intersect the optic axis. Leaky rays (modes) belong to the class of skew rays; see →modes (fiber-).

Snell´s Law

Snell's law quantifies a light ray's angle of refraction upon transition between two different materials. See →reflection and refraction.

Solid Angle

The geometric radiation characteristics of optical components may be expressed in terms of the solid (spherical) angle Ω, in units of steradian. The solid angle of 1 steradian is defined by an area of A of 1 cm^2 on the surface of a sphere with the radius r of 1 cm.

$$\Omega = A/r^2, \qquad \text{unit steradian [sr]}$$

The largest possible angle (4π sr) is defined by a whole sphere. For small angles, the linear **half-angle** ϕ and the solid angle Ω are related by:

$$\Omega = \pi \, \phi^2 \, , \qquad\qquad [\phi \text{ in units of rad}]$$

See →units at the end of the book, and →coupling efficiency.

Speckle Pattern

This term is used for the typical appearence of the →near field or →far field of graded-index fibers: a pattern of randomly distributed light spots. It is caused by optical →interference of different fiber →modes. See the paragraph →modal noise for an illustration of the speckle pattern.

Spectrum (Laser Diode-)

Due to the process of stimulated emission, laser diodes emit basically monochromatic light. The peak wavelength is determined by its material, whereas the fine structure is formed by its resonant cavity. Typical GaAlAs (850 nm) lasers of the double-heterostrucure type with gain guiding (see →laser diode) show 10 - 20 longitudinal modes with a typical overall spectral width between 2 and 5 nm and a mode spacing of about 0.2 nm. InGaAs (1300 nm) lasers of the index-guided type typically exhibit 3 - 5 modes with a mode spacing of 0.8 nm: index-guiding reduces the number of modes. Distributed-feedback lasers (see →DFB laser) exhibit the cleanest spectrum with only 1 line, adjacent modes usually are more than 25 dB$_{opt}$ down.

The resonant cavity of a laser diode is a →Fabry-Perot resonator. The spacing of the longitudinal modes in the cavity is defined the cavity's resonant conditions: the round-trip cavity length 2L must coincide with an integer number m of wave cycles in the cavity:

$$2Ln = m \, \lambda_1 \qquad\qquad \text{Mode no. m}$$

$$2Ln = (m + 1) \, \lambda_2 \qquad \text{Mode no. m + 1}$$

λ - wavelengths in air
n - refractive index inside the cavity

From these equations, the mode spacing $\Delta\lambda$ between two adjacent modes and the corresponding frequency difference are:

$$\Delta\lambda \simeq \lambda^2/(2L\,n) \qquad \text{Mode spacing in units of wavelength (in air)}$$

$$\Delta f = c/(2L\,n) \qquad\qquad \text{Mode spacing in units of frequency}$$

with: $\qquad \Delta f = c\Delta\lambda/\lambda^2 \qquad\qquad$ Relation between Δf and $\Delta\lambda$

It is important to mention that the displayed spectra are time-average spectra. In a time-resolved display, one would see a statistical exchange of power between the different modes.

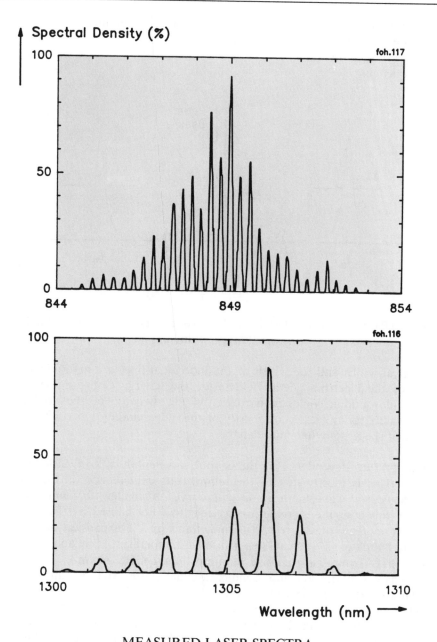

MEASURED LASER SPECTRA
850 nm GaAlAs measured at the end of a graded-index fiber, and
1300 nm InGaAsP laser measured at the end of a single-mode fiber

Stimulated emission would ideally result in individual lines of zero spectral bandwidth. However, a fine analysis shows that the individual lines exhibit a finite spectral width, which is caused by the remaining spontaneous (LED-type) emission. The spectral density is most often assumed to follow a **Lorentz**-type function. In the symmetric Fourier-type notation, the spectral density is:

$$p(f) \quad = \frac{B}{2} \left[\quad \frac{1}{1 + k(f - f_m)^2} \quad + \quad \frac{1}{1 + k(f + f_m)^2} \quad \right] \qquad [W/Hz]$$

B - constant, proportional to the optical power contained in the line
k - factor expressing the bandwidth, $k = 4/\Delta f^2$
Δf - FWHM spectral bandwidth
f_m - center frequency

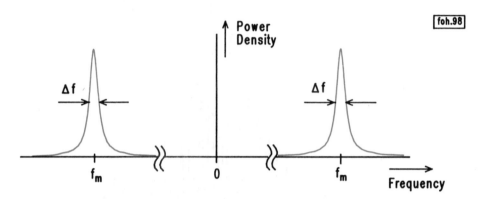

SPECTRUM OF AN INDIVIDUAL LONGITUDINAL LASER MODE
(Lorentz-type spectrum)

The overall spectral width **and** the width of the individual lines are determined by the quality of the guiding of the electromagnetic field inside the cavity. Gain-guiding results in larger width, whereas index-guiding yields in narrower width. Because of the need for lasers with narrow spectral width, today's lasers are mostly of the index-guiding type. Unfortunately, lasers tend to widen their spectrum when modulated.

The typical **temperature** dependence of the central wavelength of conventional laser diodes is +0.3 nm per °C. This is mostly due to the temperature-dependence of the bandgap energy, which defines the central wavelength of the gain curve. A smaller +0.08 nm per °C is observed in DFB lasers. In this case, the increase in wavelength is not caused by the changing bandgap energy, but by the increase of the refractive index and by the expansion of the cavity. A related problem is **chirping**: a current step causes a temperature rise and a decrease of the frequency (red-shift). Typical is a change of more than 1 GHz per mA. Before warming up, carrier-induced changes of the refractive index dominate; 100 MHz per mA are typically observed. This causes a **transient increase** of the frequency after the rising edge of the pulse (blue-shift). The net effect is a broader linewidth, which usually causes stronger chromatic dispersion. Chirp can be measured by demodulation on one of the slopes of a narrowband filter, e.g. a Fabry-Perot filter. Another method is described in →self-heterodyning/homodyning.

The overall spectrum and the line spacing can be analyzed with a good monochromator. Monochromators do not supply the necessary resolution for the measurement of the **width of an individual line**. This task is usually accomplished with one of these 3 methods:
a) Spectrum analysis with tunable optical filters (e.g. →Fabry-Perot-interferometer or →ring resonator),
b) Spectrum analysis with a conventional (electric) spectrum analyser. This method is based on heterodyning the spectrum with a delayed and frequency-shifted version of itself; see →self-heterodyning/homodyning,
c) Measurement of the coherence length; see →coherence and →Michelson interferometer.

Some typical spectral characteristics of laser diodes are listed below.

Laser Type	Center Wavelength	Number of Lines	Line Spacing	Line Bandwidth
GaAlAs (GG)	850 nm (350 THz)	10-20	0.2 nm (80 GHz)	5×10^{-3} nm (1 GHz)
InGaAs (IG)	1300 nm (230 THz)	3-5	0.9 nm (160 GHz)	1×10^{-3} nm (180 MHz)
InGaAs DFB	1300 nm (230 THz)	1	- -	1x10-4 nm (18 MHz)

TYPICAL SPECTRAL CHARACTERISTICS OF LASER DIODES
(GG: gain-guided, IG: index-guided, DFB: distributed feedback)

The spectral characteristics of 1550 nm laser diodes are similar to those of 1300 nm lasers. Because of the fiber's large →chromatic dispersion at 1550 nm, fiber systems utilizing 1550 nm are typically limited by chromatic dispersion. This, in addition to the requirements of coherent →systems, is the reason for the intense research in the field of narrow-linewidth lasers.

Spectrum (LED-)

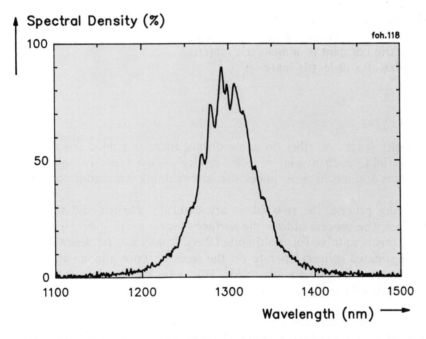

MEASURED SPECTRUM OF AN EDGE-EMITTING InGaAsP LED
(measured at the end of a graded-index fiber)

In contrast to the laser diode, an LED has a continuous spectrum. The spectral distribution is approximately Gaussian. In our measurement example, the additional comb structure indicates partially stimulated emission; this is due to the fact that edge-emitting LEDs are similar to laser diodes. In a surface-emitting LED, the comb would not be observed. Typical full width at half maximum (FWHM) is 30 - 50 nm for 850 nm LEDs, and 50 - 100 nm for 1300 / 1550 nm LEDs.

The large spectral width causes pulse broadening; see →chromatic dispersion. This limits the bandwidth of LED systems, in addition to the LED's **inherent** lower bandwidth. On the other hand, LEDs are not sensitive to backreflection, which make them attractive for power- and attenuation measurements. Also, →modal noise and →mode partitioning noise do not exist in LED-based systems.

Speed of Light

In this book, the term "speed of light" means the →phase velocity of an optical wave. In vacuum, both phase velocity **and** →group velocity are the same.

$$c_0 = \frac{1}{\sqrt{\mu_0 \epsilon_0}} = 2.998 \times 10^8 \text{ m/s.}$$

$$c_m = \frac{1}{\sqrt{\mu_0 \epsilon_0 \epsilon_r}} = \frac{c_0}{\sqrt{\epsilon_r}} = \frac{c_0}{n}$$

c_0 - phase velocity in vacuum, identical to group velocity in vacuum
c_m - phase velocity in a dielectric material
μ_0 - permeability of vacuum; 1.257×10^{-6} $\Omega s/m$
ϵ_0 - dielectric constant of vacuum; 8.85×10^{-12} $s/(\Omega m)$
ϵ_r - relative dielectric constant of a dielectric material
n - refractive index of a dielectric material

Splice

Because of the finite length of fiber on cable drums, there is a need for durable, permanent fiber joints in the field. Such a joint is called "splice". Two types of splices are commonly applied: fusion splices and mechanical splices, the latter gaining more and more attention.

In the fusion-splicing process, the two fibers are carefully aligned and then joined by arc-welding. Very often, the process utilizes the surface-tension of glass for self-alignment of the two fibers. While this is suitable for multimode fibers, it may not be desirable for single mode fibers. More sophisticated splicers operate on the basis of core alignment, joining the fibers whereever the lowest insertion loss is observed. This point can be detected by observation of the optical power radiated from a sharp bend **after** the joint.

Mechanical splices utilize V-grooves and optical cement. One popular version is called "elastomeric" splice. In this case, the V-groove and the opposing lid are made from polyester. They form a triangular cavity, in which the fiber resides with a small lateral pressure for self-alignment. Index-matching fluid reduces return loss and eases the problem of end separation. Strain relief is provided by an outer housing. Compared to fusion splicing, this technique is quite simple. It therefore is becoming very popular.

Typical splice loss is 0.1 - 0.2 dB$_{opt}$ for both graded-index and single-mode fibers. See the paragraph →insertion loss for the measurement of splice-loss.

Spot Size

This term is used to describe the diameter of the fundamental mode in a single mode fiber. The power density in the spot follows a Gaussian shape , see →Gaussian beam. By international convention, e.g. FOTP 165 [1.3], the spot diameter is defined by the point of $1/e^2$ - power density. At wavelengths longer than the →cutoff wavelength, the spot diameter is always larger than the core diameter. It has a strong influence on the fiber's bending sensitivity and on the propagation characteristics, namely the →waveguide dispersion. For an ideal step-index single mode fiber, most of the fiber-optic literature uses the following formula [3.10] for the dependence of the spot size on the →normalized frequency, V:

$$w_0 = a \left(0.65 + 1.619 / V^{3/2} + 2.879 / V^6 \right)$$

w_0 - beam radius at the point of $1/e^2$ - power density
a - core radius of the single mode fiber

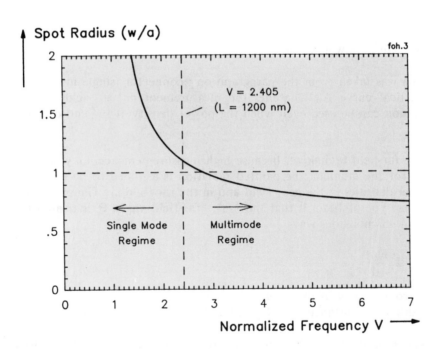

SPOT RADIUS OF A SINGLE-MODE FIBER WITH STEP-PROFILE

The parameter V, the **normalized frequency**, contains the core radius a (not to be confused with spot radius w_0), the refractive index contrast Δ and the wavelength λ. An advantage of using V instead of λ is that V describes both the fiber **and** the wavelength. With the definition of an "equivalent step-index profile", it can even be applied to more exotic profiles.

$$V = \frac{2\pi a}{\lambda} \sqrt{n_1^2 - n_2^2} = \frac{2\pi a}{\lambda} \ NA = \frac{2\pi a}{\lambda} \ n_1 \sqrt{2\Delta}$$

Spot Size

with: $\Delta = (n_1{}^2 - n_2{}^2) / 2n_1{}^2 \simeq (n_1 - n_2) / n_1$

and: $NA = \sqrt{n_1{}^2 - n_2{}^2}$

Δ - refractive index contrast
λ - wavelength in air
n_1 - refractive index of the core
n_2 - refractive index of the cladding
$NA \rightarrow$ numerical aperture

There are several methods for the measurement of the spot size: the most obvious is the determination of the $1/e^2$ - points in the →**near field**. Because of the small dimensions involved, other methods are more practical:

In the **transverse offset** method, the ends of 2 identical fibers are brought in close proximity (e.g. less than 10 µm) and then laterally shifted against each other with the help of a piezoelectric drive. If one assumes →Gaussian beams in both fibers, then the following equation describes the ratio A(r) of the coupled power to the input power :

$$A(r) = \exp(-r^2 / w_0{}^2) \quad \text{[dimensionless]}$$

r - lateral offset
w_0 - spot radius ($1/e^2$ - power radius)

The above formula was taken from the paragraph on →connector (single mode-). Varying w_0, until the mathematical curve A(r) matches the measurement curve, yields the desired spot radius. This definition can be used even when the power density at the end of the fiber is not Gaussian.

Most elegant is the **far-field technique**, because high measurement accuracy is easily obtained; see →far field. If, for the moment, the emitted radiation is assumed to be perfectly Gaussian, then both the power densities in the near field **and** in the far field are Gaussian. A remarkable characteristic of this type of beam is that the $1/e^2$ - far-field angle, Θ, is related to the $1/e^2$ - spot radius w_0 in an unambiguous way:

$$\tan \Theta = \frac{w(d)}{d} = \frac{\lambda}{\pi w_0}$$

d - distance from the end of the fiber
$w(d)$ - beam width at the distance d, as defined by the $1/e^2$ - power density

This equation was adopted from the paragraph on →Gaussian beam. If the wavelength is known, then w_0 can be easily calculated. The method is complicated by the fact that the far field of a single-mode fiber is Gaussian only as a first-order approximation; see →far field. Therefore, mathematical corrections should be made as proposed in [3.11]. Note that a different definition of the spot size is used there !

Finally, the measured far field can be used to **calculate** the near field. This is based on the fact that in a circular-symmetric situation, the far field is the **Hankel transform** of the near field. The method is also described in [3.11].

Standards

These are the most active groups in measurement standardization in the world of fiber optics:

1. EIA (Electronics Industries Association), which sets standards for the US industry
2. CCITT (International Telegraph and Telephone Consultive Committee), which sets worldwide postal standards
3. IEC (International Electrotechnical Commission), which sets worldwide standards for the electronics industry.

Find a list of their most important publications in section [1] of the literature index.

Star Coupler

Star couplers are used for the distribution of optical signals to a group of terminals. See →coupler.

Steady-State Distribution

See →Equilibrium Mode Distribution.

Step-Index Fiber

Fibers with a refractive-index profile forming a rectangle are called "step-index". See →fiber (multimode-).

Steradian

The geometric radiation characteristics of optical components may be expressed in terms of the solid (spherical) angle Ω, expressed in units of steradian. See the chapter →solid angle and the chapter →units at the end of the book.

Sterance

See →units at the end of this book.

Subscriber Network

A typical subscriber network is cable television. In this case, the subscriber expects random access to a multiple of channels. There are several choices for a subscriber network in fiber optics form: the most straightforward, but most expensive form would be parallel fibers to each of the subscribers. One fiber carrying one channel at a time, together with switching in the central office, is another method. Subscribers are not too enthusiastic about the possibility of monitoring their viewing habits. Therefore, the only good solution is one fiber per subscriber, each of which carries all channels in parallel. This can be accomplished either in the form of →wavelength-division multiplexing (WDM) or in the form of coherent transmission. The latter is explained in the paragraphs →coherent detection and →systems (coherent-).

Sunlight

For a comparison with other light sources, we give some characteristics of sunlight. On a clear day at vertical incidence, the sunlight irradiance H_0 (power density) is around 900 W/m^2. Without the absorption of the atmosphere, the irradiance would be 1330 W/m^2 (solar constant). The spectrum ranges from 300 nm up to 2000 nm with a peak at 480 nm.

The sun appears on earth at a **full** angle $\phi = 32' = 0.533°$, or 9.3×10^{-3} rad. In terms of laser →safety, the sun can be considered a **point source**, because the IEC defines a minimum full angle for an extended source of 24×10^{-3} rad. The IEC's Maximum Permissible Exposure is set to 0.01 W/m^2, at a wavelength of 480 nm. Therefore, the sun can be considered a highly dangerous Class 3B light source, and should be equipped with a key switch, beam stop, remote control switch and laser warning signs.

Superradiant LED

An LED on the border line between spontaneous and stimulated emission is called superradiant. Those LEDs are typically of the edge-emitting type. They combine characteristics of lasers and LEDs, without the problems typically associated with lasers: high threshold current and complex bias circuits. See →LED.

Systems (Coherent-)

Coherent communication systems carry light of high spectral purity. As a consequence, there is negligible chromatic dispersion on the fiber; coherent systems are purely attenuation-limited. Another advantage is due to →coherent detection: the sensitivity is improved by typically more than 10 dB$_{opt}$. In comparison to direct-detection transmission systems, these features result in much greater transmission capacity (bitrate x repeater span). In [9.4], a coherent system operating with 2 Gbit/s over 170 km of fiber was reported.

Finally, the spectral purity and the coherent detection allow an extremely narrow channel spacing in the case of →wavelength-division multiplexing (WDM). In contrast to classic-optical multiplexing and demultiplexing, the channel spacing in coherent systems is only limited by the spectral width of the modulated carrier. A factor of more than 1000 is gained this way, allowing hundreds of channels on 1 fiber.

All systems discussed here carry binary (0 and 1) data. The following types of laser modulation are used in coherent systems:
1. Amplitude-shift keying (ASK), which is modulation of the generated power
2. Frequency-shift keying (FSK), which is frequency modulation of the optical carrier
3. Phase-shift keying (PSK and DPSK), which is phase modulation of the optical carrier.

In the receiver, the electric fields from the fiber and from a local oscillator are combined on a detector. If the 2 waves are polarized in the same way, then the square-law characteristic of the detector creates an intermediate frequency (IF); see the chapter on →coherent detection. **Heterodyne** systems are those in which the 2 participating frequencies create an IF which is greater than zero; in **homodyne** systems, the average difference between the 2 frequencies is zero. A demodulation circuit must be capable of distinguishing between ASK-, FSK- or PSK-coded "ones" and "zeros". A signal which controls the frequency of the local oscillator is also derived from the demodulation circuit.

As indicated above, a fixed (linear) state of **polarization** is required at the input of a coherent receiver. Standard single-mode fibers are not capable of maintaining the state of polarization. One possible solution is →polarization-maintaining fibers; however, their higher price and higher attenuation is usually not accepted. Today, most system designers try to use **standard** single-mode fibers. The polarization problem is either solved with automatic →polarization control [6.4], or with a polarization-independent optical receiver, an example of which is given in [9.1]. In such a receiver, the incoming wave is split between to 2 possible orientations of the electric field, with the help of a polarizing →beam splitter. Then the 2 signals are independently processed and later recombined to a final output signal.

Here, we want to discuss the characteristics of typical coherent systems. **Heterodyne ASK** detection offers around 10 dB better sensitivity than direct detection. However, FSK detection is 3 dB more sensitive and PSK/DPSK detection is 6 dB more sensitive. The first example shall be a heterodyne FSK system.

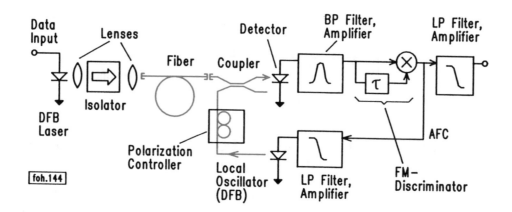

HETERODYNE FSK SYSTEM
(not shown is the decision circuit)

Heterodyne FSK: Neglecting the difference between digital and analog modulation, frequency-shift keying is similar to FM radio, i.e. the information is coded in the instantaneous frequency of the (optical) carrier. The transmitter is typically based on a distributed-feedback (DFB) laser, the spectral linewidth of which is on the order of 20 MHz. FM modulation is obtained from the chirping effect, which means that standard intensity modulation generates parasitic FM modulation, see the paragraph on →spectrum (laser diode-). An isolator with 60 dB isolation prevents optical feedback to the laser. The optical signal is then carried over a standard single-mode fiber. The length of the fiber may be 100 km or more.

In the receiver, the local oscillator and the received signal are added with the help of a →coupler and a →polarization controller. The output current of the detector contains a DC component and an IF component. The latter is fed to an FM discriminator which, in this case, consists of a delay line and a microwave mixer. We now want to derive the function of the discriminator. As a first step, the input to the discriminator shall be an unmodulated sine wave, $s_0(t)$. The output shall be $s_1(t)$.

$$s_0(t) = A \cos [\omega t]$$

$$s_1(t) = A^2 \cos [\omega t] \cos [\omega(t-\tau)]$$

$$= A^2 (\cos [\omega\tau] / 2 + A^2 \cos [2\omega t - \omega\tau]) / 2$$

ω - 2π x input frequency (IF frequency)
τ - delay time

The second part of the output signal s_1 is suppressed with the LP filter. Then the output of the discriminator is time-**independent**. In the next step, the input shall be an FM signal with a time-average frequency f_c. For a symmetric function of the discriminator it is advisable to select $\omega_c\tau$ such that $s_1(\omega_c)$ is zero. We also assume that the low frequency f_{space} represents a "zero", and that the high frequency f_{mark} represents a "one".

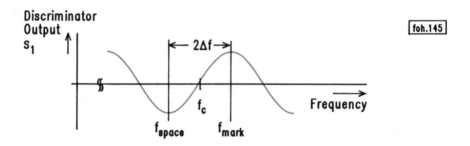

DISCRIMINATOR OUTPUT AS A FUNCTION OF THE INPUT FREQUENCY
(for the case of maximum attainable output voltage swing)

Developing the cosine function around f_c leads to a condition for the maximum useful delay time, τ_{max}:

$$2\pi\Delta f \, \tau_{max} = \pi/2 \qquad => \qquad \tau_{max} = \frac{1}{4 \, \Delta f}$$

Δf - maximum frequency deviation from the center frequency f_c

Another popular type of discriminator is based on **filtering**: the detector signal is passed through 2 parallel bandpass filters which are centered at f_{space} and f_{mark}. Both outputs are then rectified (envelope detection). If, for example, a mark signal is present, then the "mark" circuit delivers a pulse, which is then delivered to the decision circuit.

The discriminator not only drives the decision circuit, but also feeds another LP filter and the local-oscillator laser (LO). This effectively forms an automatic frequency control **(AFC)** for the LO, such that the time-average mixing frequency is the desired center frequency f_c.

Another question arises: What is the optimum frequency deviation Δf ? A large deviation is desirable for a clear distinction between marks and spaces. On the other hand, a large deviation will cause a wide spectrum; this requires a receiver with a large bandwidth. In order to avoid the calculation of complex FM spectra, we only want to present a result obtained from [9.2] : the most compact spectrum is obtained for a modulation index of m = 0.5, where the **modulation index** is defined as:

$$m = |f_{mark} - f_{space}| / bitrate$$

Typically, the required receiver bandwidth is 2 to 3 times the bitrate.

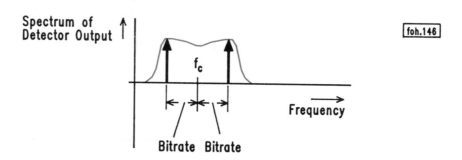

THE DETECTOR's OUTPUT DEFINES THE BANDWIDTH OF THE RECEIVER

The most difficult problem in coherent communications is the spectral purity requirement. For FSK systems, the required linewidth depends on the bitrate and the modulation index. The usual linewidth is 1 to 10 % of the bitrate; the 1% number is advisable in the case of a small modulation index. Generally, distributed feedback →laser diodes with a linewidth of 20 MHz are acceptable for both the transmitter and the local oscillator. In any case, an →isolator with at least 60 dB isolation is necessary in order to protect the laser diode from reflections and back-scatter from the fiber. A thorough analysis of the linewidth problem is given in [9.3]. Here is a summary of the most important characteristics of FSK systems:

Parameter	Typical Number	Example
Bitrate	BR	560 MBit/s
Frequency Deviation	0.5 to 2 x BR	800 MHz = $(f_{mark} - f_{space})$
IF Center Frequency	1.5 to 3 x BR	1.5 GHz
Receiver Bandwidth	2 to 3 x BR	1.5 GHz
Linewidth	1 to 10% of BR	20 MHz
Gain in Sensitivity	3 dB against heterodyne ASK	

TYPICAL FSK SYSTEM PARAMETERS

Heterodyne PSK: In fiber optics, phase shift keying (PSK) is a technique in which the information is coded in the phase of the optical carrier: e.g. zero phase for a space, 180° phase for a mark. This is usually accomplished with external →phase modulators. In the receiver, it is necessary to generate an IF carrier. The transmitted information can then be retrieved by comparing it with this carrier. Another complication is the requirement for very high spectral purity: unwanted phase modulation of the participating optical carriers causes excessive bit errors. A typical linewidth requirement is 0.2 % of the bitrate. Such performance is only obtained from external-cavity lasers. Typically, the required receiver bandwidth is 2 to 3 times the bitrate. The typical gain in sensitivity against ASK systems is 6 dB. Easier to implement is:

Heterodyne DPSK: In systems with differential phase-shift keying (DPSK), there is no direct correspondence between bit content and phase. Instead, the bit content is coded with the help of a differential: a mark is represented by a 180° phase shift against the preceding bit, whereas a space means no phase shift. Again, this can be done with a →phase modulator which follows the transmitting laser. In the receiver, the optical signal is mixed down to an intermediate frequency. It is easy to show that the IF signal also exhibits 180° phase shifts.

In principle, the FSK receiver outlined above can also demodulate DPSK signals: the main difference is that the delay time τ must be equal to the bit period. As demonstrated in the signal diagram, the multiplied sequences result in a signal from which the bit sequence can be easily detected. In agreement with published systems, the instantaneous IF frequency was chosen to be 1.5 times the bitrate.

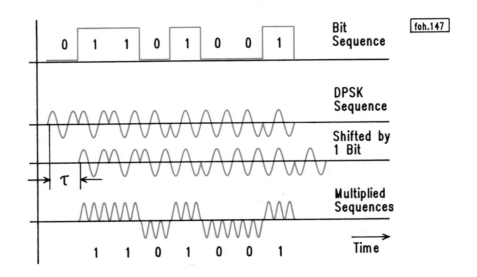

IDEALIZED DPSK SIGNALS IN THE IF REGIME
(Note that the demodulator function does not depend on a precisetiming of the phase jumps)

The advantage of the system is that no IF carrier must be generated. Also, both participating optical carriers need only be stable for one bit period. This results in a less stringent linewidth requirement: typically, DPSK systems require a linewidth of 0.5 % of the bitrate. There is some indication that in systems with high bitrate, advanced DFB lasers may be sufficient in the future. Again, the required receiver bandwidth is 2 to 3 times the bitrate, and the typical gain in sensitivity against ASK systems is 6 dB. DSPK experimental systems are described in [9.4] and [9.5].

Homodyne PSK: Ultimate performance is expected from homodyne PSK systems. In this case, the local oscillator must be locked to the received carrier so that an intermediate frequency of zero is generated; this requires a phase-lock loop (PLL). The advantage of such systems is that the receiver bandwidth is only **half** of the one in FSK and PSK/DPSK systems. This should improve the sensitivity by another 3 dB, resulting in a 9 dB improvement against heterodyne ASK. The necessary linewidths of the 2 participating lasers is very demanding; published numbers are on the order of 0.05 % of the bitrate. Until now, this does not seem practical.

For a comparison of the transmission capacities of direct-detection systems and coherent systems, see the next paragraph.

Systems (Direct Detection-)

Classic fiber optic communication systems carry intensity-modulated optical power. A "one" (mark) is coded as high power, and a "zero" (space) is coded as low or zero power. This is convenient because in both LEDs and laser diodes the output power is nearly linearly dependent on the input current. At the receiving end, the optical power modulation is reconverted to electric current pulses, again with the help of linear power-to-current conversion. The latter is often called **direct detection**, in contrast to →coherent detection. In this context, it is important to mention that virtually all fiber optic transmission systems carry digital data in pulse-coded (PCM) form.

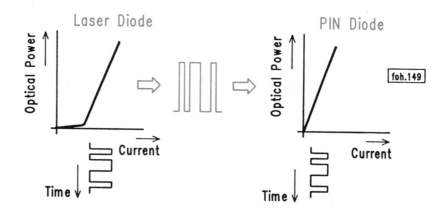

INTENSITY MODULATION AND DIRECT DETECTION

A typical point-to-point connection consists of transmitter module which comprises an amplifier and a light source (LED or laser). The modulated optical power is fed into a multimode (step-index / graded-index) or single-mode fiber. The receiver basically consists of a detector (PIN-diode or APD), an amplifier and a decider circuit which regenerates the PCM data. The proper choice of source, fiber, detector and optical wavelength depends on how demanding the transmission capacity is. The transmission capacity of a communication system shall be defined as the product of the bitrate and the unrepeatered fiber span, under the condition that the bit error rate (BER) stays below a certain borderline, e.g. 10^{-9}

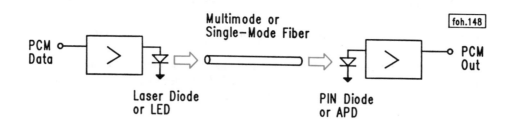

INTENSITY-MODULATED, DIRECT-DETECTION FIBER SYSTEM

Fiber optic system design started around 1975 with the "short" wavelength of 850 nm, because AlGaAs LEDs / laser diodes and silicon PIN-detectors were the only active components available. At 850 nm, the attenuation of glass fibers is more than 3 dB/km. This number decreases to 0.4 dB/km at 1300 nm and to 0.2 dB/km at 1550 nm. Accordingly, there was a strong motivation to switch to longer wavelength. InGaAsP sources and detectors for these wavelength became available in the early 1980s. The latest additions were InGaAsP avalanche photodiodes (for improved receiver sensitivity) and InGaAsP distributed feedback (DFB) laser diodes (for low pulse broadening on the fiber). Today, the telecommunication industry exclusively uses the long wavelengths. The short wavelengths remain in the field of lower capacity systems, because short-wavelength components are still more economic.

In the field of fibers, graded-index and step-index fibers were most popular before 1980. Because of their extreme bandwidth capabilities, combined with a relatively simple manufacturing process, single-mode fibers have an estimated market share of 90 % today, with a negligible fraction of special single-mode fibers such as →polarization-maintaining fibers and →dispersion-shifted fibers.

The table gives an overview over the most important applications and the typical components. System prices rise from the upper left corner to the lower right corner:

Wavelength: 850 nm	Wavelength: 1300 nm	Wavelength: 1550 nm
Computer Links & Buses: 1 Mbit/s, 500 meters Step-Index Fiber, LED, PIN		
	Local Area Networks: 100 Mbit/s, 2 km Graded-Index Fiber, LED & PIN	
Presently	Telecommunications: ⩾ 565 Mbit/s, 50 km SMF, Laser, PIN/APD	Telecommunications: ⩾ 565 Mbit/s, 100 km SMF, DFB Laser, PIN/APD
Later	Subscriber Systems: Wavelength-Division Multiplexing 1300 to 1550 nm maybe 565 Mbit/s, 10 km Single-Mode Fiber (SMF), Laser, PIN	

MOST ECONOMIC SYSTEM CHOICES LISTED BY APPLICATIONS

The transmission capacity is usually limited by one of the following mechanisms:

1. Marginal average power (and signal amplitude as a consequence) at the output of the fiber: in this case, the receiver will generate a too high BER because of a too small signal-to-noise ratio. This is called an **attenuation-limited system**. See the paragraphs on →sensitivity and →bit error rate.

2. Marginal bandwidth of the fiber: this leads to pulse broadening and a reduction of the power amplitude (while the average power is still acceptable). This is called a **dispersion-limited system**. →Chromatic and/or →multimode dispersion are the cause for the loss of bandwidth. Chromatic pulse broadening is proportional to the spectral bandwidth of the source; in this respect, single-mode lasers are preferred before multimode lasers and LEDs. Multimode dispersion is observed in multimode fibers; therefore single-mode fibers are advisable. Mathematically, the bandwidth is usually calculated from the achievable output

pulse width, with the assumption that a non-return-to-zero (NRZ) format is most effective. For further information, see →bandwidth (fiber-) and [8.3].

3. Mode partition noise: the total power output from laser diodes is usually distributed among different (longitudinal) modes. There is always a random exchange of power between these modes; only the sum of these modes is nearly constant. The chromatic dispersion of a fiber is capable of separating the laser modes in time, and the effect will be unwanted (noisy) amplitude modulation. This is called a **mode-partition-limited system**. See the paragraph on →modal noise.

4. Marginal modulation bandwidth: LEDs are usually limited to a bitrate of a few hundred Mbit/s. With today's laser diodes, several Gbit/s can be achieved.

Note that an attenuation-limited system **is not** limited by dispersion, i.e. the signal amplitude is not affected by the bandwidth of the system in this case. Conversely, a dispersion-limited system is not limited by attenuation.

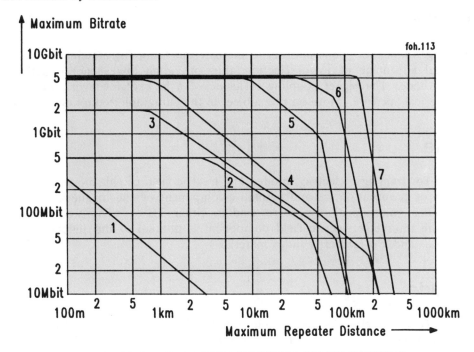

TRANSMISSION CAPACITY OF FIBER OPTIC SYSTEMS

The diagram was compiled from various publications on actually achieved transmission capacities. Only the most economic system choices are drawn. In all curves, the moderate slopes are defined by dispersion- or mode-partition limitation. The steep slopes are defined by attenuation limitation. The upper borderline is set by the modulation capability of the source. The numbers in the diagram denote the following systems:

1: 850 nm LED and step-index fiber: limited by multimode dispersion, chromatic dispersion, and possibly by mode-partition noise.
2: 1300 nm LED and single-mode fiber: limited by chromatic dispersion.
3: 1300 nm laser diode (LD) and graded-index fiber: limited by multimode dispersion.
4: 1550 nm standard LD and single-mode fiber: limited by chromatic dispersion and possibly by mode-partition noise.

5: 1300 nm standard LD and single-mode fiber: limited by moderate chromatic dispersion.

6: 1550 nm DFB-LD and single-mode fiber: attenuation-limited, with negligible dispersion-limitation due to narrow linewidth.

7: 1550 nm coherent system, external-cavity laser and single-mode fiber: purely attenuation-limited.

An example of the state of the art in direct detection is given in [8.3] : 100 km at 565 Mbit/s with a 1550 nm DFB laser. A record in coherent transmission was published in [9.4] : 170 km at 2 Gbit/s with a heterodyne-DPSK system.

Tap

A tap is a device which is capable of coupling a fraction of the optical power from a fiber to a receiver or monitor. See →coupler.

Tapered Fiber

Fiber tapering is sometimes done in order to increase the →coupling efficiency to a laser. It has the additional advantage of low reflection, thus providing lower backreflection noise, see →noise: laser diode. The higher coupling efficiency can be explained with an increase of the fiber's →numerical aperture. More on this subject in the paragraph →coupling (source to fiber).

TE Mode

Abbreviation for transverse electric →mode. The electric field of this mode is perpendicular to the direction of propagation (z), and a small z-component of the magnetic field exists. In a multimode fiber, →meridional rays correspond to either TE or →TM modes. In a dielectric waveguide, the transverse electric field component is **parallel to the junction** between high-refractive-index and low-refractive-index material.

TEM Mode

Abbreviation for transverse electromagnetic →mode. Both the electric and the magnetic field vectors are perpendicular to the direction of propagation, with negligible field components into the direction of propagation. This assumption is usually applied to the fundamental →mode of a single-mode fiber.

Threshold Current

Lasing operation in a semiconductor laser requires an operating current larger than the threshold current. Compare the laser diode with a conventional (electrical) oscillator: in this case, oscillation starts when the loop gain is larger than one. In a laser diode, the gain is proportional to the injected current. Lasing starts when the current is large enough to produce a gain that exceeds the losses in the cavity. See →laser diode.

TM Mode

Abbreviation for transverse magnetic →mode. The magnetic field of this mode is perpendicular to the direction of propagation (z), and a small z-component of the electric field exists. In a fiber, →meridional rays correspond to either TM or →TE modes. The TM mode in a dielectric waveguide is characterized by a magnetic field which is parallel to the junction between high-refractive-index and low refractive index materials; i.e. the electric field is **perpendicular to the junction**.

Transimpedance Amplifier

Transimpedance amplifiers help enhancing the bandwidth and the noise of receivers. See →receiver.

Transmission Capacity

The transmission capacity of a communication system can be defined as the product of the bitrate and the unrepeatered fiber span, under the condition that the bit error rate (BER) stays below a certain borderline, e.g. 10^{-9}. On the parameters which influence the transmission capacity, see →systems (coherent-) and →systems (direct detection-).

Waveguide Dispersion

Waveguide dispersion is part of the →chromatic dispersion, which determines the pulse broadening on a fiber. Waveguide dispersion is caused by the wavelength-dependence of the modal characteristics of a fiber. The reason is that the geometry of the fiber causes the propagation constant of each mode to change if the wavelength changes. This effect would be observed even when the fiber's refractive indices are assumed to be wavelength-independent.

In multimode fibers, this effect can be neglected because it is washed out by the presence of many modes. In single mode fibers, waveguide dispersion can be explained this way: in a typical operating condition, the light spot extends into the cladding. This yields an effective refractive index somewhere in between the index of the core and that of the cladding. A change of wavelength changes the spot diameter (even if the refractive indices were constant), which, in turn, changes the effective refractive index. For a more detailed analysis, see →chromatic dispersion.

Waveguide dispersion is defined as change of group velocity per length of fiber per change of wavelength. A typical number for a single mode fiber is -2 ps/km nm at 1300 nm. A practical consequence from this is a shift of the zero dispersion point of a single mode fiber: if the fiber shows zero material dispersion at a wavelength of 1300 nm, the net chromatic dispersion will be zero at a wavelength of around 1330 nm.

Don't confuse this term with →multimode dispersion.

Wavelength

The wavelength λ_m of light travelling in a dielectric material is given by:

$$\lambda_m = \lambda/n = v/f$$

λ - wavelength in vacuum
v → phase velocity, $v = c / n$
c - speed of light in vacuum
n - refractive index of the dielectric material
f - optical frequency

Wavelength Division Multiplexing (WDM)

The information capacity of a fiber system can be increased by transmitting more than one colour (wavelength) on the same fiber. Suitable couplers must be utilized at the input: the usual fused-fiber coupler is not recommended because it introduces too high losses. Therefore multiplexers based on diffraction →gratings are more advisable. Wavelength-filtering is required at the output: again, diffraction gratings can be used for this purpose. The proper function of a diffraction grating depends on the input state of polarization. Therefore, an unpolarized state or a fixed state of polarisation is required at the end of the fiber. These conditions can either be met with a multimode fiber or a polarization-maintaining single-mode fiber. The standard single-mode fiber is not recommended because it produces a changing state of polarization; see →birefringence.

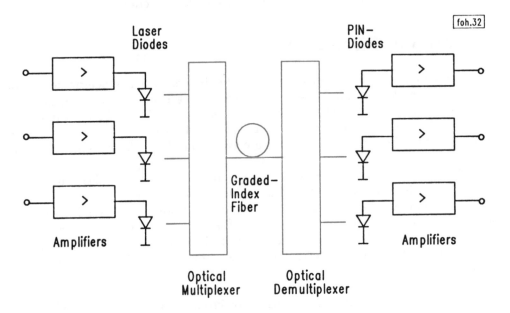

WDM TRANSMISSION SYSTEM

A simple multiplexer (MUX) / demultiplexer (DEMUX) is shown in the next figure. In the **MUX** case, each input fiber carries one wavelength. The beams from the fiber ends are collimated with the help of a SELFOC® lens. The →diffraction grating refracts the beams at an angle which differs from the incident angle; the angle depends on the wavelength. This way, all beams are combined to a single output fiber, which is usually a 50 μm graded-index fiber. In the **DEMUX** case, all wavelengths enter the device on one fiber. The grating then separates the different wavelengths towards the appropriate output fibers. In this case, the output fiber can be of the 100 μm step-index type; therefore, the demux usually exhibits a lower insertion loss.

In contrast to the "classic" multiplexer structure which contains bulk lenses, the system depicted here is compact and contains no refecting surfaces [8.2].

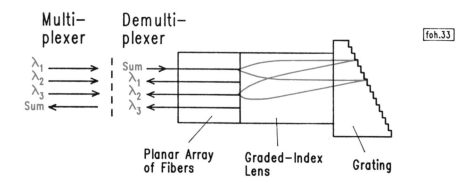

OPTICAL MULTIPLEXER / DEMULTIPLEXER

WDM-systems employing up to 10 colours with a channel spacing of 30 nm have been published [8.1, 8.2]. Much narrower channel spacing is offered by →coherent communications. Often one colour is used for the transmission into one direction and a second colour for transmission into the opposite direction. Typical wavelength sets are 850 nm plus 1300 nm, or 1300 nm plus 1550 nm.

WDM

See →wavelength division multiplexing.

5. LITERATURE

[0] BOOKS ON CLASSIC OPTICS AND FIBER OPTICS

[0.1]   Driscoll, Vaughan
           Handbook of Optics, McGraw Hill
[0.2]   Jenkins, White
           Fundamentals of Optics, McGraw-Hill
[0.3]   M.K. Barnoski
           Fundamentals of Optical Fiber Communications
           Academic Press, New York 1981
[0.4]   W.S. Gornall
           The World of Fabry-Perots, Laser & Applications, July 1983, 47-52
[0.5]   G. Keiser
           Optical Fiber Communications, McGraw-Hill 1985
[0.6]   W.A. Shurcliff
           Polarized Light, Harvard University Press, Cambridge MA, 1962
[0.7]   S. Geckeler
           Lichtwellenleiter für optische Nachrichtenübertragung, Springer-Verlag 1986
[0.8]   G. Grau
           Optische Nachrichtentechnik, Springer Verlag, 1981
[0.9]   D.A. Ross
           Optoelectronic Devices and Optical Imaging Techniques, The Macmillan Press, London, 1979
[0.10]   D. Marcuse
           Light Transmission Optics, Second Edition, Van Nostrand Reinhold Company, New York 1982
[0.11]   M. Born, E. Wolf
           Principles of Optics, Pergamon Press, 1980
[0.12]   A. Yariv, P. Yeh
           Optical Waves in Crystals, John Wiley & Sons, 1983
[0.13]   A. Yariv
           Quantum Electronics, 2. Edition, John Wiley & Sons, 1975
[0.14]   D. Marcuse
           Principles of Optical Fiber Measurements, Academic Press, 1981

[1] FIBER OPTIC STANDARDS AND MEASUREMENTS

[1.1]   IEC Technical Committee No. 76 (Laser Products):
           825:        Radiation Safety of Laser Products, Equipment Classification, Requirements and User's Guide (1984)
           76(Sec)12: Power and Energy Measuring Instruments for Laser Radiation

[1.2]   IEC Technical Committee No. 86 (Fibre Optics):

           793-1:   Optical Fibres, Part 1: Generic Specification
           794-1:   Optical Fibre Cables, Part 1: Generic Specification
           874-1:   Connectors for Optical Fibres and Cables, Part 1: Generic Specification

875-1:	Fibre Optic Branching Devices, Part 1: Generic Specification
875-2:	Part 2: Sectional Specification: Transmission Star Coupler
876-1:	Fibre Optic Switches, Part 1: Generic Specification

[1.3]   Electronic Industries Association (EIA), Fiber Optic Test Procedures (FOTP)

10:	Acceptance Pattern Measurement of Fiber Optic Devices
30:	Frequency Domain Measurement of Multimode Optical Fiber Information Transmission Capacity
34:	Interconnection Device Insertion Loss Test
43:	Output Near-Field Radiation Pattern Measurement of Optical Waveguide Fibers
44:	Refractive Index Profile, Refracted Ray Method
46:	Spectral Attenuation Measurement for Long-Length, Graded-Index Optical Fibers
47:	Output Far-Field Radiation Pattern Measurement
50:	Light Launch Conditions for Long Length Graded-Index Optical Fiber Spectral Attenuation Measurements
51:	Pulse Distortion Measurement of Multimode Glass Optical Fiber Information Tansmission Capacity
53:	Attenuation by Substitution Measurement (Graded-Index Fiber)
54:	Mode Scrambler Launch Requirements for Information Transmission Capacity Measurements
58:	Core Diameter Measurement of Graded Index Optical Fibers
59:	Optical Time Domain Reflectometry
68:	Microbend Test Procedure
78:	Spectral Attenuation Cutback Measurement for Single-Mode Optical Fibers
107:	Return Loss
164:	Mode Field Diameter Measurement of Single-Mode Optical Fibers (Far-Field Scan Method)
165:	Mode Field Diameter Measurement of Single-Mode Optical Fibers (Near-Field Method)
166:	Mode Field Diameter Measurement of Single-Mode Optical Fibers (Transverse Offset Method)
167:	Mode Field Diameter Measurement of Single-Mode Optical Fibers (Variable Aperture Method in the Far Field)
168:	Chromatic Dispersion Measurement of Multimode Graded Index and Single Mode Optical Fibers by Spectral Group Delay
169:	Chromatic Dispersion Measurement of Single Mode Optical Fibers by the Phase-Shift Method
170:	Cutoff Wavelength of Single-Mode Fiber Cable by Transmitted Power
171:	Attenuation by Substitution Measurement for Short-Length Multimode Graded-Index and Single-Mode Optical Fiber Assemblies
174:	Mode Field Diameter of Single-Mode Optical Fiber by Knife-Edge Scanning in the Far Field

[1.4]   Electronic Industries Association, EIA Standards:

          RS-440:   Fiber Optic Connector Terminology
          RS-455:   Standard Test Procedures of Fiber Optic Fiber, Cables, Transducers,
                      Connecting and Terminating Devices
          RS-475:   Generic Specification for Fiber Optic Connectors

[1.5]   CCITT, Volume III, Fascicle III.2, Recommendation G.651:
          Characteristics of 50/125 μm Multimode Graded Index Optical Fibre Cables, Geneva
          1985

          CCITT, Volume III, Fascicle III.2, Recommendation G.652:
          Characteristics of a Single-Mode Optical Fibre Cable, Geneva 1985

[1.6]   Food and Drugs Administration (FDA, United States Government)
          Performance Standards for Light Emitting Products, Publication 21, Part 1040.10
          Laser Products (Safety)

[1.7]   IEEE Standard 812-1984
          IEEE Standard Definitions of Terms Relating to Fiber Optics, Published by The
          Institute of Electrical and Electronics Engineers, New York

[1.8]   IEC Standard 793-1: Optical Fibres
          (most important sections: measuring methods for dimensions, mechanical characteris-
          tics, transmission and optical characteristics)

[1.9]   IEC Standard 874-1: Connectors for Optical Fibres and Cables
          (most important sections: measuring methods for optical and mechanical
          characteristics)

[2] MULTIMODE FIBER

[2.1]   Kleekamp, Metcalf
          Designer's Guide to Fiber Optics, Cohners Publishing Company, 1978
[2.2]   Kim, Franzen
          Measurement of Far-Field and Near-Field Radiation Patterns from Optical Fibers,
          National Bureau of Standards, Technical Note 1032, Feb. 1981, USA
[2.3]   Epworth
          Modal Noise - Causes and Cures, Laser Focus, September 1981, 109-115
[2.4]   L.G. Cohen, C. Lin
          Pulse Delay Measurements in the Zero Material Dispersion Wavelength Region for
          Optical Fibers, Applied Optics, Vol. 16, No. 12, December 1977, 3136-3139
[2.5]   E.M. Kim, D.L. Franzen
          Measurement of the Core Diameter of Graded-Index Optical Fibers: an Interlabora-
          tory Comparison, Applied Optics, Oct. 1982, Vol.21, No.19, 3443-3450
[2.6]   C.M. Miller, S.C. Mettler
          A Loss Model for Parabolic-Profile Fiber Splices, Bell System Technical Journal,
          Vol.57, No.9, Nov.1978, 3167-3180

[2.7]   P. DiVita, U. Rossi
Theory of Power Coupling Between Multimode Optical Fibers, Optical and Quantum Electronics 10 (1978), 107-117

[2.8]   Personick
Time Dispersion in Dielectric Waveguides, Bell System Technical Journal 50 (1971), 843-859

[2.9]   P. Kaiser
Loss Measurements of Graded-Index Fibers: Accuracy versus Convenience, NBS Special Publication 597, Symposium on Optical Fiber Measurements, 1980, 11-14

[2.10]   N.K. Cheung, P. Kaiser
Modal Noise in Single-Mode Fiber Transmission Systems, ECOC 1984, Stuttgart

[2.11]   D.L. Franzen
Measurement of Propagation Constants Related to Material Properties in High-Bandwidth Optical Fibers, IEEE Journal of Quantum Electronics, Vol. QE-15, No. 12, Dec. 1979, 1409-1414

[3] SINGLE MODE FIBER

[3.1]   A.W. Snyder
Understanding Monomode Optical Fibers, Proc. IEEE, Jan. 1981, Vol. 1, 6-13

[3.2]   D.L. Franzen
Determining the Effective Cutoff Wavelength of Single-Mode Fibers: an Interlaboratory Comparison, Journal of Lightwave Technology, LT-3, No. 1, Feb. 1985, 128-134

[3.3]   L.G. Cohen
Comparison of Single-Mode Fiber Dispersion Measurement Techniques, Journal of Lightwave Technology, Vol. LT-3, No. 5, Oct. 1985, 958-966

[3.4]   G. Coppa et al.
A New Technique for Chromatic Dispersion Measurement in Monomode Fibres, 9. ECOC Conference, Genf 1983, 189-192

[3.5]   M. Saruwatari, K. Nawata
Semiconductor Laser to Single-Mode Fiber Coupler, Applied Optics, June 1979, Vol.18, No.11, 1847-1856

[3.6]   B. Hillerich
Theory of Light Emitting Diode to Single-Mode fiber Coupling, Optical Fiber Communication Conference 1987, Reno, MD5

[3.7]   G. Garlichs
Temporal Birefringence Fluctuations Observed in Some Single-Mode Fibers, SPIE Vol. 478, Fiber Optic and Laser Sensors II (1984), 68-74

[3.8]   A. Simon, R. Ulrich
Evolution of Polarization Along a Single-Mode Fiber, Applied Physics Letters, vol.31, 1977, 517-520

[3.9]   J. Noda, K. Okamoto, Y.Sasaki
Polarization-Maintaining Fibers and Their Applicatons, J. of Lightwave Technology, Vol. LT-4, No. 8, August 1986, 1071-1089

[3.10]   D. Marcuse
Loss Analysis of Single-Mode Fiber Splices, Bell Systems Technical Journal 56 (1977), 703-718

[3.11]   W.T. Anderson, D.L. Philen
Spot Size Measurements for Single-Mode Fibers - A comparison of Four Techniques, Journal of Lightwave Technology, Vol. LT-1, No. 1, Narch 1983, 20-26

[3.12]   W. Lieber et al.
Three-Step Index Strictly Single-Mode, Only F-Doped Silica Fibers for Broad-Band Low Dispersion, Journal of Lightwave Technology, Vol. LT-4, No. 7, July 1986, 715-719

[3.13]   R.H.Stolen
Nonlinearity in Fiber Transmission, Proceedings of the IEEE, Vol. 68, No. 10, October 1980, 1232-1236

[3.14]   D. Cotter
Optical Nonlinearity in Fibers: A New Factor in System Design, British Telecom Technology Journal, Vol. 1, No. 2, October 1983, 17-19

[4] FIBER OPTIC SOURCES

[4.1]   C.A. Burrus, B.I. Miller
Small-Area DH AlGaAs Electroluminescent Diode Sources for Optical Fiber Transmission Lines, Opt. Communication, Vol. 4, No. 4, Dec. 1971, 307-309

[4.3]   M. Kitamura et al.
High-Power Single-Longitudinal-Mode Operation of 1.3 μm DFB-PBH LD, Electronics Letters, Sep. 83, Vol.19, No. 20, 840-841

[4.4]   M. Yamaguchi
Highly Efficient Single-Longitudinal Mode Operation of Antireflection-Coated 1.3 μm DFB-DC-PBH LD, Electronics Letters, March 1984, Vol. 20, No. 6, 233-235

[4.5]   G. Arnold et al.
Edge-Emitting LEDs at 1.3 μm Wavelength of Different Active Length
ECOC 1984 Stuttgart, Conference Proceedings, 154-155

[4.6]   R.E. Epworth
The Temporal Coherence of Various Semiconductor Light Sources Used in Optical Fibre Sensors, Standard Telecommunication Laboratories Publication, 1981

[4.7]   W.T. Tsang, N.A. Olson, R.A. Logan
High-Speed Direct Single-Frequency Modulation with Large Tuning Rate and Frequency Excursion in Cleaved-Coupled-Cavity Semiconductor Lasers, Applied Phys. Letters, 42 (8), 15. April 1983, 650-652

[5] FIBER OPTIC DETECTORS, RECEIVERS

[5.1]   Smith, Personick
Receiver Design for Optical Fiber Communication Systems, Topics in Applied Physics Vol. 39, Springer Verlag 1982

[5.2]   M. Kobayashi et al.
Optimized GaInAs Avanlanche Photodiode with Low Noise and Large Gain-Bandwidth Product OFC 87, Reno, Conference Proceedings MJ3

[5.3]   E.F. Zalewski, J. Geist
Silicon Photodiode Absolute Spectral Response Self-Calibration, Applied Optics, Vol. 19, No. 8, April 1980, 1214-1216

[5.4]   C. Hentschel
How to Make Accurate Fiber Optic Power Measurements, Hewlett-Packard Application Note 1034, Dec. 1987

[6] FIBER OPTIC COMPONENTS

[6.1] Botez, Herskowitz
Components for Optical Communication Systems, a Review, Proc IEEE, Vol. 68, No. 6, 1980, 689-731

[6.2] L.F. Stokes et al.
All-Single-Mode Fiber Resonator, Optics Letters, June 1982, Vol. 7, No. 6, 288-290

[6.3] H.C. Lefevre
Single-Mode Fibre Fractional Wave Devices and Polarization Controllers, Electronics Letters, 25th Sep. 1980, Vol. 16, No. 20, 778-780

[6.4] N.G. Walker, G.R. Walker
Polarisation Control for Coherent Optical Fibre Systems, British Telecom Technology Journal, Vol. 5, No. 2, April 1987

[6.5] R.E. Tench et al.
Performance Evaluation of Waveguide Phase Modulators for Coherent Systems at 1.3 and 1.5 μm, Journal of Lightwave Technology, Vol. LT-5, No. 4, April 1987, 492-501

[6.6] R.C. Alferness
Waveguide Electrooptic Modulators, IEEE Transactions on Microwave Theory and Techniques, Vol. MTT-30, No. 8, August 1982, 1121-1137

[7] OPTICAL TIME DOMAIN REFLECTOMETERS

[7.1] D.L. Danielson
Backscatter Measurements on Optical Fibers, NBS Technical Note 1034, US Department of Commerce 1981

[7.2] D. Schickedanz
Theorie der Rückstreumessung bei Glasfasern, Siemens Forschungs- und Entwicklungs-Berichte, Springer-Verlag, Bd. 9 (1980) No. 4, 242-248

[7.3] S.A. Newton
A New Technique in Optical Time Domain Reflectometry, Hewlett-Packard Publication 5952-9641, B100, 8/87

[8] CONVENTIONAL TRANSMISSION

[8.1] B. Hillerich
Grating Multiplexers with Wide Passband, ECOC 84 (Stuttgart), Conference Proceedings, 168-169

[8.2] L. Bersiner
Wellenlängenmultiplex hoher Kanalzahl für den optischen Langwellenbereich (Wavelength-Division Multiplexing for the Long Wavelength Range)
Nachrichtentechnische Zeitschrift (NTZ) Bd. 40 (1987) Heft 3, 174-183

[8.3] A.P. Mozer
Optical Fiber Communication Systems and their Physical Limitation Effects, Journal of Opt. Communications, 7 (1986) 2, 42-48

[8.4] S. Whitt et al.
Long-Wavelength DFB Lasers Extend Repeaterless Distances in British Telecom Demonstration, Laser Focus, November 1987, 126-131

[9] COHERENT TRANSMISSION

[9.1]   B. Glance
          Polarization Independent Coherent Optical Receiver, Journal of Lightwave Technology, Vol. LT-5, No. 2, Feb. 1987, 274-176

[9.2]   R.S. Vodhanel et al.
          FSK Heterodyne Transmission Experiments at 560 Mbit/s and 1 Gbit/s, Journal of Lightwave Technology, Vol. LT-5, No. 4, April 1987, 461-468

[9.3]   L.G. Kazovsky
          Impact of Laser Phase Noise on Optical Heterodyne Communication Systems, Journal of Optical Communications, 7 (1986) 2, 66-78

[9.4]   A.H. Gnauck et al.
          Coherent Lightwave Transmission at 2 Gb/s Over 170 km of Optical Fiber Using Phase Modulation (DPSK), OFC '87, PDP10, 40-43

[9.5]   S. Yamazaki
          1.2 Gbit/s Optical DPSK Heterodyne Detection Transmission System Using Monolitic External-Cavity DFB LDs, Electronics Letters, 30. July 1987, Vol. 23, No. 16, 860-862

[9.6]   S.B. Alexander
          Design of Wide-Band Optical Heterodyne Balanced Mixer Receivers, Journal of Lightwave Technology, Vol. LT-5, No. 4, April 1987, 523-537

6. INDEX OF TERMS

7. UNITS AND CONSTANTS

Physical Units

Length	1 Å (Angstroem)	$= 10^{-10}$ m
	1 pm	$= 10^{-12}$ m
	1 nm	$= 10^{-9}$ m
	1 μm	$= 10^{-6}$ m
	1 mm	$= 0.001$ m
	1 cm	$= 0.01$ m
	1 inch	$= 25.4$ mm
	1 foot	$= 0.305$ m
	1 terrestrial mile	$= 1.6093$ km
	1 nautical mile	$= 1.852$ km
Force	1 newton	$= 0.102$ kp
	1 dyn	$= 1.02 \times 10^{-2}$ kp
Energy	1 erg	$= 10^{-7}$ joule
	1 J (joule)	$= 10.2 \times 10^{-2}$ kp m
	1 J (joule)	$= 1$ Ws
Mass	1 pound	$= 0.4536$ kg
Temperature	°C (Celsius)	$= (F - 32) \times 5/9$
	F (fahrenheit)	$= (°C \times 9/5) + 32$
	K (kelvin)	$= °C + 273.16$

Electrical Units

Capacitance	1 F (farad)	$= 1$ s/Ω
Resistance	1 Ω (ohm)	$= 1$ V/A
Charge	1 C (coulomb)	$= 1$ As
Inductance	1 H (henry)	$= 1$ Ωs
Power	1 W (watt)	$= 1$ VA

Radiometric Units

The fiber-optics community prefers wavelength-independent radiometric units, in contrast to the wavelength-dependent photometric units. Some LEDs are still specified in photometric units. All symbols used in this paragraph refer to the illustration below. Note that the optical literature often uses the term "intensity" instead of the correct term irradiance.

Area in far field	ΔA	m^2
Area in near field = Area of the source	ΔA_s	m^2
Emittance (near field -)	$M = \dfrac{\Delta P}{\Delta A_s} = L\Delta\Omega$	W/m^2
Electric field (amplitude)	E	V/m
Irradiance (far field -)	$H = \dfrac{\Delta P}{\Delta A} = E^2/2Z$	W/m^2
Intensity	$I = \Delta P/\Delta\Omega = H\,d^2$	W/sr
Power, total radiated	P	W, watt
Power, fraction from ΔA_s	ΔP	W, watt
Radiance	$L = \dfrac{\Delta P}{\Delta\Omega\Delta A_s} = H\,d^2/\Delta A_s$	$W/(sr\ m^2)$
Solid angle	$\Delta\Omega = \Delta A/d^2 \simeq \pi\Delta\phi^2$	sr, steradian
Linear half angle	$\Delta\phi$	rad
Characteristic impedance, see →constants	Z	Ω (ohm)

foh.09

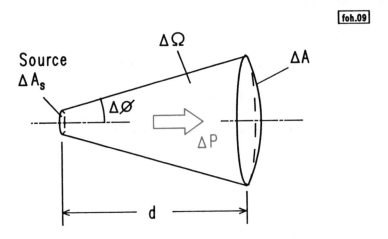

EXPLANATION OF RADIOMETRIC AND PHOTOMETRIC UNITS

In the above graph, ΔA_s represents a part of the radiating area (source). ΔP is the fractional power from that part of the source, radiated into the solid angle $\Delta\Omega$.

Photometric Units

These units use the wavelength-dependent sensitivity of the human eye as measurement standard. For explanation, refer to the paragraph →radiometric units.

Brightness *

Exitance, luminous	$M = P/\Delta A_s$	lumen/m^2
Flux	ΔP	lumen
Flux density = Luminous incidance	$E = \Delta P/\Delta A$	lumen/m^2 = lux
Intensity	$I = \Delta P/\Delta \Omega$	lumen/sr = candela = cd
Luminance = Sterance	$L = I/\Delta A_s$	cd/m^2

* The obsolete term **brightness** was formerly used instead of sterance or luminance.

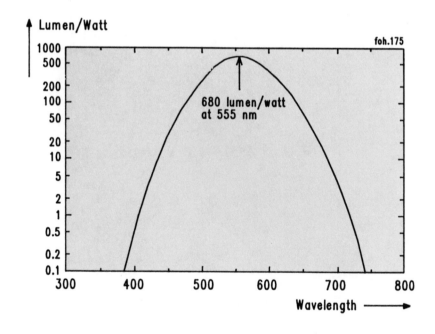

SPECTRAL SENSITIVITY OF THE HUMAN EYE FOR DAY VISION

On the basis of the above curve, photometric units can be converted to radiometric units. The curve is called "standard observer curve for day vision" or "photopic curve". It was suggested by the Commision Internationale de l'Eclairage (CIE).

Constants

These are the most important physical constants in conjunction with fiber optics:

$h = 6.62 \times 10^{-34}$ Ws^2 Planck's constant

$e = 1.6 \times 10^{-19}$ As   electron charge

$c = 2.998 \times 10^{8}$ m/s   speed of light in vacuum

$k = 1.38 \times 10^{-23}$ Ws/K   Boltzmann's constant

$\mu_0 = 1.257 \times 10^{-6}$ Vs/Am   permeability of vacuum

$\epsilon_0 = 8.85 \times 10^{-12}$ s/(Ωm)   dielectric constant of vacuum

$Z_0 = 376.7 \; \Omega$ characteristic impedance of vacuum

About the Author

Christian Hentschel (45) is a technology consultant at Hewlett Packard's Böblingen Instruments Division in the FRG. He studied communications engineering at the University of Aachen and graduated with a Dr.-Ing. degree in 1971. He worked for Hewlett-Packard in various R&D positions since 1972: He was project leader of HP's 1 GHz pulse generator. Later, he was project manager for a line of bipolar integrated circuits and for HP's first generation of fiber optics instruments. Currently, he is responsible for the development of fiber optic instrument technology and for fiber optic measurement standardization.

Acknowledgment: For many fruitful discussions, the author wishes to thank his colleagues, in particular: Steve Newton, Moshe Nazarathy and Dave Dolfi (HP Laboratories), Rory van Tuyl (HP Rohnert Park), Wilhelm Radermacher, Franz Sischka and Michael Fleischer-Reumann (HP Böblingen).